ENTRIES FROM OXFORD

Thad Stem, Jr.

Moore Publishing Company
Durham, North Carolina

Library of Congress Catalog Card Number: 78-171456

ISBN 0-87716-033-3

This book is dedicated to

Virginia Owens Mitchell.

Books by Thad Stem, Jr.

Picture Poems

The Jacknife Horse

The Perennial Almanac

The Animal Fair

Penny Whistles and Wild Plums

Light and Rest

Spur Line

A Flagstone Walk

Journey Proud

Entries From Oxford

ENTRIES FROM OXFORD

Oxford, November 3, 1959:

My father was buried two days ago. It is hard to write about him, but it is much harder not to write about him. I feel that I have to make this entry about my father, about his time of life. What I write will not be a success story, not in conventional terms. He was success infinitely more than he ever attained success.

Right now the woodlands around Oxford are flushed with a poignant fever called Indian Summer, or Second Summer. The earth is so lovely I feel a strange compulsion to walk on tiptoe, almost, to speak in low whispers, for fear any extraneous sounds will break the spell.

My father's old friend, Wallace Wade, the great football coach at Alabama and at Duke, drove over for the service. Coach Wade and I stood in our front lawn. He looked around at the trees that seemed to be burning from fires of red and yellow leaves.

I followed Coach Wade's swift, tender kaleidoscope. I half expected to hear the crackle of flames, to smell smoke, because the woodlands seemed engulfed in a glorious red and yellow conflagration.

Coach Wade is not an emotional gentleman, but he said to me, softly, clearly, "It's a nice day for the Major, a very nice day."

I ·nodded. I understood precisely what Coach Wade was saying. Later on in the afternoon, when we were returning from the cemetery, the smell of first frost was in the air. A large flight of wild geese, flying in a perfect inverted V, was heading south. I lowered the car window. The air was quick with the wild cries of these ebullient transients.

In another part of the sky some tatters of reddish clouds seemed to be old-fashioned post-riders. The fast way these tatters went down the skyland's turnpike, taking fences here and there, made me think they were cantering, post-haste, to spread the news of imminent falling weather.

If my father saw these scampering clouds, these rough weather portents, he would say: "The weather is about to fall, the way the Roman Empire fell." Or, he might look, with his sharp, gentle blue eyes, sniff all around, and say, "The weather is about to fall the way Old Man Rufe Duncan will fall when he tries to get up his front walk tonight."

The minister had read from the burial service all the words and phrases about resurrection and rebirth. While my father was not a religious man, certainly not in the ortho-dox sense, he would have said, "The minister's entitled to be heard."

Two days prior to his death, my father had said to me, knowing he was about to die, surely, "Well, what do you think is going to happen to me?"

I said I didn't know. He cocked his eye: "You've never been timorous about expressing your opinions up to now. So, what do you think?"

I told him I didn't think anything would happen to him, one way or the other. He nodded, readily, and he smiled. Then he quoted some of the once-famous lines of the conclusion to Tennyson's poem, "Ulysses," which he had learned by heart long ago when he was a student at Trinity College, now Duke:

It may be we shall touch the Happy Isles
And see the Great Achilles, whom we knew.

Then he smiled again. He waved his huge right hand the way a judge does when he says, "Call your next case."

I think my father enabled me to have the best of two worlds, although this may not be in the exact sense that

Joseph Wood Krutch wrote "The Best Of Two Worlds."

One world is the best of homogeneity as this endures in the time of the bomb. The other world was the lusty one before "image" became the big dog in the meat-house, when rustic humanism thumbed its nose at political and social expediency. (By "rustic humanism" I mean, succinctly, the perpetuation of three great traditions: Judeo-Christian ethics, Greek aesthetics, and Roman law.)

Before it is too late, before my faded photographs crumble and are scattered by impersonal winds across Time's Potter's Field, I have acute, if vain, urgency to share those puppydog days when children were two-legged centaurs and not self-appointed Napoleans.

As bizarre as it sounds, there was a time when a house was big enough for parents and their children. There was a time when honorable parents were not the permissive captives of their children's whims and caprices and peeves.

I tried to please my father. His approbation was always the supreme accolade. We loved each other deeply, but he never tried to curry favor with me. He always leveled with me as much as a mature adult male can be completely frank with an impressionable boy.

When he whipped me, he never said the whipping hurt him more than it hurt me. Obviously, I was aware of that aphorism, and once, when he whipped me, I asked him if the thrashing hurt him more than it hurt me.

He looked at me as if I were the village idiot: "That's hookum. It didn't hurt me a damned bit, boy."

To attain one's majority, to receive all of the cherished privileges of manhood, was worthy of lengthy apprenticeship. But when a boy grew up, finally, to deserve long trousers, to be trusted with his full share of local moral and intellectual responsibilities, his blood raced as if he were a possum with the only keys to the henhouse. I know my blood raced that way.

3

Today when so many intellectual red-necks wear button-down collars, when cost harasses merit, to paraphrase Oscar Wilde, I find myself seeking succor and sustenance in an insular world that was bounded by Wake County on the south and by the state line border on the north. Yet, if my geographical domain was highly restricted, if my physical sorties hardly ever carried me beyond the sight and the smell of the smoke from my father's chimney, I managed to cross many continents of love and excitement.

When I seem to be ensnared by today's expediencies and social flap-doodles, I think tenderly of many folks who are dead and buried but who remain preciously quick to me. For instance, my father, an old-time lawyer, exuded more excitement over a spelling bee, an old ham, the first snow of winter, or from chanting Whitman's "I Hear America Singing" than his current counterpart would get from a week-end visit to the White House.

Perhaps, memory wants to use a blue pencil on the past, but I am positive everything Papa did was pitched to a distinctive tune, even when the music was as silent as the phantom fragrance of lilacs.

I remember those scented, buried summer nights when I went out to catch lightning-bugs in a bottle, just for temporary captivity, mind you. I'd pretend the bottle was the tower of the Old North Church, or that I was a flagman, waving my lantern, as I used the front porch banisters for a long line of careening box-cars.

I can still hear Papa's booming voice when he waved me out to the evening's wonderland, as he quoted the last of Whitman's poem:

At night the party of young fellows, robust, friendly,
Singing with open mouths their strong melodious songs.

There was a sampler on our parlor wall, just above the piano. The state motto was stitched there, *Esse Quam Videri*. It meant "To be rather than to seem."

I still translate the phrase that way, but there are those times when I feel I am in a minority almost as short as the one old Noah was in on a celebrated occasion. For, aside from the fact that Latin fetches no green stamps, the ancient and honorable motto is currently construed: "To seem rather than to be."

Hence, you may plumb my desire to share with you a time in local history when life was intensely personal, and much less standardized, mechanized, and by-the-numbers. You see, I remember when buttons were something mothers sewed on the britches and shirts of little boys. Back then one didn't push buttons the way Aladdin rubbed his lamp.

As Emily Dickinson had said about her own father, "Our whole house was filled when Papa was on the sofa." Of course, we called it a "settee," and not a sofa. In that era, when Papa's personality was a benevolent flood, the arms on our settee were decorated by "antimacassars." There was no wall-to-wall carpeting. Indeed, the word "carpet" was hardly ever used in Oxford. Our settee rested on a "drugget."

We had no electrical vacuum cleaners, and each spring we carried the "drugget" to the backyard to beat it. This was man's work, and Papa pretended that the "drugget" was Judge Erasmus Booker, who, Papa said, thought he was the Old Testament God and every poor white and Negro defendant was Job.

Many times I imagined that the "drugget" was Jo-Jo Tulgin, who won my marbles at school, and who beat my tail regularly just to keep in practice.

5

Papa would swing his flail against the "drugget" and then exclaim, "Take that, you polecat." I'd swing my flail and yell, "Zooks," even if I didn't know what it meant. But "Zooks" seemed eminently pertinent as I imagined Jo-Jo's being knocked on his "keester", or tail.

When I was big enough to smell myself a little, I imagined that the "drugget" was Brailsford Entwhistle, who stole my girl, in the seventh grade, because he slicked his hair with "Stay-Comb." Even worse, he put me down in a big spelling bee by getting Constantinople correctly . . . My revenge was hearty, if deferred, when Constantinople was changed to Istanbul, and old Brailsford's laurel became as rusty as a tool left in the rain, all winter.

(If my father had never read Freud, we engaged in the most active sort of psychiatric therapy everytime we walloped that drugget. It was the receptacle for our hostilities. Therefore, my father didn't emulate our neighbor and friend, Mr. Lester, who always mumbled aloud as he walked home from a mean day downtown: "If supper ain't ready, I'm go raise pluperfect hell. If supper is ready, I ain't go eat er damned bite.")

Man was a free agent in Oxford, when this century was a gangling colt, and for a short while afterwards. To be sure, God made the world, in seven days. (Papa said God forgot to make Texas while He was fashioning the other states and territories. Papa said God made Texas late Saturday night when he was tired and His mind wasn't on His business fully.)

But God made the world the way Mr. Elgin made a watch. He handed it over to you, fee simple, and you had the complete running of it. This freedom, if full-throated and open-handed, was a matter of utmost gravity. It was never an abstraction, even when it was outrageously faithless or funny. The pursuit of freedom, happiness, and labor

6

was a sort of pantry, a larder, as well as an inspiration.

I heard a stanza from Shelley quoted many times. Most of the men who quoted it hadn't been off to college, but they respected learning, for the beauty and joy of learning, as if learning were the last dab of fire on earth and a hard sleet was falling:

For the laborer thou art bread,
And a comely table spread.
Thou art clothes, and fire and food,
For the trampled multitude.

Shelley was talking about freedom, and his stanza is gallingly pertinent right now as I look around and admit the depressing fact that Oxford is merely an extension of the mores of some Metropolitan place. For, the image, the status-symbol, and things (just "things") are everywhere.

It used to be different. People were turned on differently. I remember one day Papa left a hard-cash client in his office to walk rapidly across the Square to climb the long steps to Mr. Ben Parham's law office to tell his friend that Shelley's father had been born in Newark, N. J. (They both knew about Garibaldi's residence in this nation. Mr. Parham didn't know the odd fact Papa had gleaned, God knows where, about Shelley's father, although Mr. Parham got a law degree from Harvard in 1907, or "ought seven," as Papa put it.

Shelley's stanza is balefully germane today when virtually every family in town, including the ones that have artificial grass, seems to be bucking so hard for "Yard of the Month." Almost every lawn in Oxford stands posed as if it is waiting for a photographer from *Life* to come and take its picture.

One wily, sneaky-pete of a wild onion in a lawn brings

more embarrassment today than a shotgun wedding did back when yards were for human enjoyment, when they were paeans to love, to sunshine, and to rain. If Blind Pew came to town, he'd know these lawns aren't for leap-frog, marbles, stick horses, one-eyed-cat, treehouses, or Prisoner's Base. For, a grass-sticky void stands where the resounding hosannas of "Bum, Bum Here I come," once erupted from games of Pretty Girls' Station.

Chickens don't run and scratch or leave a raucous cackle for a calling-card when they lay an egg almost surreptitiously in the shrubbery. If a passing dog uses a tree for a rest-station, you'd think the honor of the town has been sullied. And, God knows, if a bitch in heat and her boy-friend dog used such a lawn for a trysting place, a lot of modern people would expect J. Edgar Hoover to come down and handle the heinous offense, personally.

The last rooster in town is crowing in the dawn in some other place, and the last goat must be butting with Mr. Scratch somewhere south of Suez. But we had a wonderful goat. His name was Miltiades, but we called him Milt since we all voted a Woodrow Wilson ticket, whether or not we were all old enough to vote. Milt mowed the lawn, and he could tell an honest hobo from a free-loading tramp a block away, against the wind. He never butted Mr. Farris, the postman, who read all the cards and told you what they said as he handed them over. He never "wet" or "grunted" when ladies were visiting Mother on the front porch; and when he was ailing, he always cried a little when we comforted him, to show his gratitude.

Papa taught Milt to count to five, with his right front foot. Papa said, many times, that Milt could have been elected president of the Rotary Club if he had a place to put his tail. But, then again, Papa said he didn't think Milt liked green peas and calf liver enough to walk down to the hotel to the weekly meeting of the Rotary. But you have to know that Papa never joined anything but the Methodist Church and the Democratic Party and he said anybody could join these . . .

When Milt was as old for goats as Methuselah was for folks, Papa sat up with him three straight nights, so I could sleep and be fresh for school. When Milt died, we buried him in the far, right hand corner of the vegetable garden, and our friend, "Old Dan" Tucker, put a little picket fence around the grave.

At the services, Papa made a sizzling anti-sheep speech. I guess, now, he did this to dry our tears with anger at foolish sheep. He compared Milt to Tom Paine, Thomas Jefferson, Andy Jackson, Mark Twain, and Vachel Lindsay, whoever he was. He said sheep reminded him of the Bloomer Girls' baseball team, baaing in the field and drinking Lydia E. Pinkham's between innings.

If there was anything incongruous about Milt's long, intimate association with our family, there wasn't a man between Richmond and Atlanta who had grown enough to say so to Papa.

But, I know, too, that one really can't return from the grave. This month my sister, who lives at our old place, won the "Yard of the Month" award from the local Beautification Committee. The sign, "Yard of the Month," will stand in our old lawn for a month. If angels can cuss, I'll bet Papa hasn't raised such hell since Harding was elected. And if one could "come back," you can bet your bottom dollar Papa would have tattooed Sister's bottom with that sign, before he threw it to hell and away.

Again, I must push on and tell you about Oxford when it was much more fig leaf than white dinner jacket, so that you will know there was such a minister as Mr. Thompson, A.B., D.D.

His successor, two or three times removed, sits on his emotions as if he were trying to hatch out a nest of golf balls. The way this fellow talks one would think he is giving mouth-to-mouth tranquilizing pills. He uses "however" and "on the other hand" the way Floyd Collins used that cave.

He sounds as if Billy Graham, Norman Vincent Peale, "Dial A Prayer," and "Popular Psychiatry" had been condensed into a capsule by *Reader's Digest*. The only way he could ever get his hands dirty is from holding one of the avant-garde novels he reads to show how open-minded he is . . . Papa used to say to me: "A damned fishnet is open-minded, Sandy, my boy."

But I have to admit this fellow has done a neat job of keeping Jesus locked up in the church, tightly, except for the hours each Sunday morning when people visit Him there. Everyone praises His name from eleven to twelve on Sunday morning. Then, this minister locks up, and during the week Jesus doesn't get out and get into anyone's hair or conscience or cause any trouble.

Now, it's difficult for me to say what kind of church-preacher Mr. Thompson really was, because I associate him with the town, not with his church. I suppose he was ambivalent.

He talked about love a lot but when he did, his face wasn't so long a barber would charge two dollars to shave it. Shaves cost only 25 cents back then. He talked about love and life. He loved life and he hated suffering and death.

Other people talked, sometimes, about suffering through something if it was God's will. Mr. Thompson (everyone called him "Brother" or "Brer") said God never made you suffer. Hell no. God wasn't a bloody idiot. But God might help you through your suffering.

10

About his ambivalence: Papa said "Brer" Thompson was a great Greek scholar. Very quietly, he talked about eros, philos, and agapē. He didn't use any scholastic blackjack. He just told about the difference.

He and Papa used to write letters regularly, even if they saw each other on the street two or three times each day. I have in possession, at this moment, a letter, and the paper is quite jaundiced, Mr. Thompson wrote to Papa, dated "11-20-24".

Apparently, the two had talked, earlier in the day, about the phrase, "On (and "in") the lap of the Gods." In a bold, uphill script, as if his letters are marching men, Mr. Thompson says:

"I write from Tom Stewart's where I wait with Dr. Henley until the pneumonia crisis is done. Anent our discussion, at the P. O. earlier this morning: The phrase, of course, is from our ancient friends, the Greeks. It means that everything has been done that can be done. The result awaits a power beyond known human control. Betimes, I checked. The phrase is found in the 17th book of the 'Illiad': 'Yet verily these issues lie on the lap of the gods'. Likely, reference is to the pagan custom of placing prayers written in wax tablets at the knees of the statues of the Gods. I fear the custom still persists. Will see you at the oyster 'bilin'' if all goes well here. O, yes. A thoughtful Christian has promised me the loan of a big snake for the evening. Surely, a snake-bitten servant of the Lord is entitled to a stiff dram before a 'bilin''."

Despite his learning and all the quiet conversations he had with Papa, and many others, about Aristotle, Aristophanes, Aristides, Homer, and Sophocles, "Brer" Thompson was as outgoing as a gate that swung toward the big road. He was always joking about his huge appetite. He said when people invited him to supper, their children started cutting turnip greens without being prompted, and the children used a mowing machine. He said all the chickens and hogs ran off and hid in the woods when they heard his steps.

I remember this joke he told on himself: He was (he said) visiting an old lady who lived on the other side of a foot-log. In mid-stream, "Brer" Thompson had a sneezing spell and lost his false teeth in the creek. The water was more than belly deep, he said, but he went on to the old lady's house and returned with a drumstick of a chicken.

He waved the drumstick over the water, and the false teeth jumped up from the bottom of the creek and bit into the meat. "Brer" Thompson put his "Roebuckers" back in and went on his way.

At the time of which I write, he was about fifty, but his muscles were like those on the baking soda box. His lean face looked as if it had been cut from whitleather, but his eyes laughed and sparkled the way smooth stones at the bottom of a clear brook laugh and sparkle.

He was the chaplain of the local volunteer fire company, but such a sinecure was not for "Brer" Thompson. He acted as Captain of Number One Nozzle Unit. He was always "in the middle of the fire," with his "boys".

Papa said there never was a fire unless Mr. Thompson was preaching, on Sunday morning or night, or at Wednesday prayer meeting, or unless he was getting a shave at the barber shop.

The bell would ring and we boys thought the whole sky was made of iron and clappers and it was falling. Mr. Thompson would yell, "Play the Doxology," and he'd run down the aisle, leaping past pews in tremendous strides.

The barber shop was right up the street from the fire house. When the telephone bell, the small alarm, sounded, all the firemen who worked or loafed up town would run to catch the wagon, or the truck, after we got a truck.

Many times I have seen Mr. Thompson running from the barber shop to catch the tail-gate of the fire truck. He would bound from the door, throwing the apron back over his left shoulder. As he ran to catch the truck, he would blow the lather from his face, and from his lips, as if the sweetest, fleetest hound of heaven were frothing at the mouth.

If the fire was a big one, Matt Venable, who was our fire chief as well as our High Sheriff, would yell up and down the street: "Dammit, pour it 'em, boys. Dammit, give 'em hell, boys."

And "Brer" Thompson would nod his head and thunder in his great baritone: "That's right, boys. That's exactly right, boys. You do precisely as the chief says."

Not just incidentally, the fire company in Oxford was integrated for almost fifty years, although I never heard anyone make a point about the fact, one way or the other. No issue ever precipitated any schism. The Negroes began dropping out when the new-style red-neck came to town with his button-down collar, his golf sticks, and his asperities for political liberals such as "Old Lady Ruse-se-velt," "them Kennedy boys" and so on.

Now, don't get me wrong. I'm not trying any soft-soap. We were as wrong about Negroes as David was when he sent Uriah off to be killed. We are all damned to hell on that terrible score. But there was much love between individuals. I know that sociologists call this "Uncle Tom," but it was more "Uncle Remus," really.

If there was a long-lasting fire, ladies brought coffee, or

lemonade, and all sorts of sandwiches (everyone called them "samitches") to the firemen. And after the fire, when all the "boys" were on the truck, en route to the fire house, the ladies along the street clapped to them, and many of the men on the sidewalk yelled nice words and took off their hats.

Boot Ransome, our blacksmith and champion chrysanthemum grower, was foreman of the white firemen and Cap'n Dave Johnson was foreman of the Negroes, but white and black firemen usually worked the same hoses together.

Cap'n Dave was big, strong, black, and prudent. He was dignified and intelligent. His occupation was straw-boss of the hanging-line at a local tobacco redrying plant. He worked his men hard, on the job and at fires, but his sense of command and his austerity on the jobs were leavened with a surpassing compassion for human frailty.

The Dave Johnsons were Episcopalians. We were Methodists, more or less, and Papa was always telling Cap'n Dave we would go to heaven in a grimy daycoach while the Johnsons would go in a Pullman.

People were always making jokes about the high-toned Episcopalians. Papa said the Episcopalians worshipped a remote God in billowing raiments while the other denominations tried to catch Jesus's bloody robe.

If the fire bell rang when I was at school, and if the commotion on the street indicated it was a big fire, I'd hold up one finger with my right hand and two fingers with my left hand, signifying to the teacher, always a female, that I had to be excused to do "number one" and "number two," also.

If the fire occurred after school, or in summer, I'd usually reach the scene almost as soon as the firemen. If there was a fire at night, I'd beat Papa to the car and hide on the back seat.

Gradually, I was accepted around the fire house, via a process similar to osmosis. Several times, after fires, when the "boys" were lounging around the firehouse and drinking their "re-wards," the confiscated whiskey supplied during Prohibition by Sheriff Matt Venable, Cap'n Dave asked "Brer" Thompson if one of the thieves crucified with Jesus might have been a black man.

"Brer" Thompson didn't know but he always pondered the question seriously.

There was a song Negroes used to sing about the crucifixion. It was about Jesus's lack of response when one of the thieves asked Him to speak up and save them. The song was called, "And He Never Said A Mumbling Word." Cap'n Dave sang and hummed it often, more as an oblique question than as a searing indictment, I guess.

Papa and "Brer" Thompson said Cap'n Dave had every right to raise the question.

There was a public toilet between the firehouse and the courthouse, a brick privy built before the Revolutionary War. The smelliest sort of plumbing had been installed by my time. The walls of this toilet caused me deep consternation. The walls were littered with words that I could not find in any dictionaries or reference books.

I couldn't find any of the words in any of the books we read at school, or in any of the books on the shelves in the parlor at home. Finally, I concluded that these words were entirely local, a sort of sacrosanct graffito restricted to Oxford.

I ask permission to amend this entry, slightly: In 1969 the new "Heritage" dictionaries came to Oxford. There is some wry consolation in learning that all the words written on the walls of that old public toilet, long dismantled, are for real, are in the new dictionaries.

15

Oxford, April 15, 1970:

There is much revulsion and shock relative to newspaper and TV stories about the senseless slaughter of redwood trees in Wisconsin. People were not so concerned a few years ago when the Allegheny County commissioners cut down two-thirds of the trees that surrounded the Joyce Kilmer Memorial, in South Park. These trees were cut because they obscured the tourist's view of the memorial, prevented the visitor's reading Joyce Kilmer's ditty, "Trees."

Many of us who are eloquent, indignant, and vociferous since ecology became a vital topic were mute, indifferent, and unknowing in all the years in which trees were casualties in man's incessant inhumanity to himself and to his environment.

One trouble is that few of us are tied to trees intimately. In many of our new housing developments trees come with the house the way the wrapper comes with chewing gum, the way the hydrant comes with the street. Just the same, every young couple should plant one tree of their very own, regardless of how many have been transplanted by the real estate people. Every couple should plant at least one tree, nurture the sapling, help it grow, and measure their children against the trunk.

This tree will become especially beautiful because it grows from love, because it serves as a living measurement for time and event. Of course, it will always represent most tangibly the dreams of the glorious time when it was planted, when two hearts were beautiful hounds clamoring for everything precious in and out of sight.

As this tree grabs skyward in ecstatic grandeur, the mind will notch on its buds, blossoms, and leaves, and upon its nudity, too, the daily events that aren't spectacular within themselves but blend to make truly memorable music.

For as the wise Greeks, Dr. Johnson, and Ben Franklin all said, in substance, you are happy only when you know you are happy.

When this specially endowed tree is talked about, by the couple who planted it, a stranger will assume the health of a cherished friend is being discussed. They will speak a thousand tree-phrases:

"The third spring, when the petals were pink kisses or pink poems, we had chimney trouble, remember? And the fifth year, when we were snowed silly in January, our tree was a wooly lamb, knocking and bleating at the window· and asking to be taken inside to warm by the fire. Yes, and the tenth year, we watched November turn its greenbacks into gold and we stood by the window and hummed our special love song."

And after much toil and sharing, when the good days come, and come they must or what's a heaven, a love-song, or a tree for, great limbs will publish a variorum edition of all that love and labor have sought. That's what a special tree is all about, an integral part of a highly intimate procession, a journey to the stars, especially when none is shining.

When I was a boy, Mr. Ed Settle preached the gospel of trees. This was at the time when conservation was a drunken truant, when many local farmers burned over stands of pines to make new grounds in which to plant tobacco.

I never saw Mr. Settle without a gunny sack of pine seedlings in his buggy. This was far into the automobile era, and Mr. Ed kept cars for members of his family. But he always rode around in a buggy. He wasn't six feet tall and he weighed about 475, and he had to go to the railroad freight depot everytime he wanted to see what he weighed.

His buggy was a two-seated carriage with the front seat removed. Even so, his improvised buggy was a tight squeeze. For a petrified fact, his sons and I used to make tents of his old shirts. I swear a small boy could play Hiding in one of his old shirt sleeves.

His belly and his knees weren't even on speaking terms. His stout young assistant, a boy named Aleck, always went with him, to help Mr. Ed in and out the buggy, and to help Mr. Ed make water. Mr. Ed not only couldn't see that far down below his bail of cotton of a belly. He couldn't unbutton his fly or find his hammer. When nature called, and she never seemed to have laryngitis, Aleck reached under the seat for a pail. Then Aleck placed the pail between Mr. Ed's legs and he unbuttoned the fly and found the hammer.

One day on College Street, in front of the music store, Mr. Ed had a terrible call from nature. But Aleck couldn't seem to find Mr. Ed's hammer.

"Hurry up, hurry up, I'm dying," the old man screamed.

"I'm sorry. I'm sorry as hell, Mr. Ed, but I can't find it nowhere."

Sweat was flooding the old man's agonized face. "Well, Aye God, boy, you better find it. You're the last man to have his hands on it."

But if he took his bathroom along in his make-shift buggy, he carried his own piped-in music, too. He always carried a big chromatic mouth-organ, or harp, as the instrument was called in Oxford. The harp was in his right hand coat pocket, summer and winter. It looked big enough to fell an ox, but the music was sufficient to sweeten all the coffee in town.

We boys used to walk beside the buggy to be serenaded by "Ora Lee," "On The Banks of the Wabash," "Wait Til The Sun Shines Nellie," and other sentimental tunes. Then he would switch to such "salty dogs" as "Didn't He Ramble," "Too Much Mustard," "Everybody's Doing It," and "The Lady Stooped Down To Tie Her Shoe" ("The wind blew up the avenue ").

The Settles lived a block from us, and sometimes when I had gone to bed, Mr. Ed would be driving home from one of his farms. The whole street would be as quiet as a child spent from play. Suddenly, the deep, purple stillness of the night would be annointed by the sounds of the big harp. I'd lie there in bed as the room filled with the sounds of "Let The Rest Of The World Go By," "Let Me Call You Sweetheart," or "A Kiss In the Dark."

Then I'd hear Mamma and Papa, downstairs, singing softly, or humming, along with the floating serenade. Sometimes, Papa would yell, "Encore, Ed, encore, please, Ed."

I never heard Mr. Ed speak any reply, but in a few minutes the horse and buggy would be coming up Front Street again. I remember one night his first encore was "A Hot Time In The Old Town Tonight," the fence-rattler that was associated with Teddy Roosevelt and the "Rough Riders," the irresistibly infectious tune that percolated a-round Teddy Roosevelt his entire political life.

I grabbed a walking-stick that Papa never carried. I used it for a sword and for a rifle, too, as I went charging up San Juan Hill with Teddy, Bucky O'Neil and the other swashbuckling "Rough Riders." I ran through several Spaniards with my sword. Others I clubbed with the rifle butt. Before we routed the enemy I was knocked down several times, but despite the shock and pain I had the bounceability of an especially resilient tennis ball.

When we reached to the top of San Juan Hill, Teddy clasped me in both of his strong arms. He almost rattled my teeth out when he hugged me and yelled, "Bully, Sandy, Bully."

19

I must have made quite a ruckus. Just about the time Teddy was giving me the accolade, Papa yelled upstairs: "That's enough, Sandy. That damned war is over. Leave enough Spaniards for seed corn." (I never was sure just how Papa knew what I was doing, acting out, but, then again, Papa had been a boy, too.)

That same night Mr. Ed's second encore was "Pretty Baby," one of Papa's favorites, and he sang the words to Mother, along with Mr. Ed's harp music. The Entwhistle's house was dark, but the lights came on, like a trail of fireflies, in a few minutes, and someone over there played "Pretty Baby" on the fabulous Steinway piano that Mr. Entwhistle had ordered all the way from Baltimore.

For his last encore, Mr. Ed played "Be My Little Baby Bumble Bee." I heard Papa buzzing around Mamma downstairs. Then some courting couple on a porch near by took it up on a mandolin.

The way Mr. Ed played the tune made me think every bee extant was buzzing around, sipping clover. One part of the lyrics say:

> *Hon-ney keep a-buzzing please,*
> *I've got a dozen cousin bees,*
> *But I wantchu to be my baby bumble bee.*

Many years later I wrote a short story which I had not given a title. Near the end I remembered that wonderful night. I called my story "A Dozen Cousin Bees." I don't know that the title really came across, but the story did about as well as anything I have ever written.

As I said, one of Mr. Ed's coat pockets held his harp, when he wasn't playing it. The other pocket, which seemed as big as a bushel basket, was always crammed with candy "Mary Janes," "Downey's Taffy," and a wide assortment of jaw-breakers and all-day suckers.

God knows how many different pieces of candy he gave each day to us black and white urchins.

I see him now giving out candy with one hand and pine seedlings to adults with the other hand. As he handed out his packages of seedlings, he made about a one-minute speech, along the line, "The Forest Is The Future." Anyway, he explained that growing pines were money in the bank, drawing whopping interest. If a young farmer had small children, Mr. Ed told him: "Plant pines and educate your chillun in a show-nuff college."

When he was not playing his chromatic harp or giving away candy and seedlings, Mr. Ed was reading a book. Some of them were kiddie books, things such as *Billy and the Major* and *Miss Minerva And William Green Hill.* And he read so many "Westerns," I think he acted some out in his mind.

One day he told Papa the Sioux — he pronounced it "Sow-ex" — had attacked him and his buggy. He said he had been gut-shot by ten Sow-ex arrows. However, none did more than penetrate the first fold of fat on his belly.

One summer he got hold of a copy of *Gentlemen Prefer Blondes.* He would see Papa on the sidewalk, park the buggy parallel to the sidewalk, and ask Papa all sorts of questions about Paris.

Papa had been in the First World War. Naturally, Mr. Ed considered Papa an authority on Gay Paree, and the old gentleman related Papa's information to the peregrinations of Lorelai Lee.

As he read, a fat dictionary lay in his huge lap. When he saw a word he didn't know he looked it up, then and there. Finding a new word was more nearly a new world than a new thrill or a gem. One such world was the word "probity," and another was "peradventure."

I remember, this very moment, the gentle way that

Papa, "Brer" Thompson, and Doc Henley made it easy for Mr. Ed to insert his glittering new worlds, his words, into conversations.

One time Papa said, "Ed Settle is the most omnivorous reader in town." Mr. Ed "looked her up." Then he beamed as if God Almighty had given him His best milk cow. He said the word over and over, smacking his lips as if he were tasting the finest brandy.

Everytime Mr. Ed passed Papa for a week the old gentleman doffed his tremendous straw hat and said "Om-niv-O-rus," adding a soft "t" to the "rus". Instead of saying "howdy", he said "Om-niv-O-rus, Major, Om-niv-O-rus."

He liked the narrative poetry of Scott. His favorite passage was from *The Lady of the Lake*:

> *The stag at eve had drunk his fill,*
> *Where danced the moon on Monan's rill,*
> *And deep his midnight lair had made*
> *In lone Glenartney's hazel shade.*

A man in town, Dougald Cameron, had moved from Scotland. He came to Oxford to work for the local branch of the Imperial Tobacco Co., a British concern. Dougald knew all about Monan's rill, as well as other places described by Sir Walter Scott.

Mr. Ed would fix enough lunch to arrest an Old Testament famine. Then he'd take Dougald Cameron fishing. He had a super-reinforced canvas chair for fishing. Then Aleck got the whiskey, the best local brandy during Prohibition and the best Scotch when North Carolina voted in the package stores.

Mr. Ed would sit enthroned until the sun knocked off for the day listening to Dougald tell about Monan's rill, about Scott's home, Abbotsford, and about the Highlands.

The triumphant, exultant look of discovery in Mr. Ed's eyes made the astronauts seem as if they had discovered their big toes instead of having landed on the moon.

Until FDR called in all the gold Mr. Ed gave an annual award of a twenty dollar gold piece, a "double-eagle," to any local student ("scholar" was the old designation) who learned by heart a long poem. The teacher had to say the poem was rendered before the class, and Mr. Ed always asked, humbly, for a private recitation.

After FDR called in the gold, Mr. Ed upped the prize to thirty dollars in greenbacks during the few more years he lived. But I doubt that extra ten dollars compensated for the gold pieces.

Each gold piece was more than a glorious diadem. It was a passport. It meant distinction rather than status.

I won one of the last gold pieces awarded. I had it put on my watch chain for a job. Papa told me not to be ostentatious. So, the "double-eagle" usually rested in a vest pocket, from my watch chain, but I could hardly wait for someone to ask me the time of day or night. When I whipped out the Elgin Papa gave me for my 16th birthday, Mr. Ed's gold piece managed to expose itself. It was as if I toted the moon in my vest pocket. And the Lord knows how many hours I spent twirling the chain when no one was looking.

When FDR called in the gold, I took my glorious fob to the bank, to exchange it for greenbacks. I gave it to Mr. Kennon Taylor, an officer in the bank. My heart was as heavy as the gloom of those grim Depression days. Mr. Taylor fondled the "double-eagle:" "The new President seems to be a fine man, a good man, but he can put your gold medal where the monkey puts the nuts."

I didn't tell Papa, not for a while. I knew he would say I was breaking the law, and I knew, also, he would say that

23

if I got arrested for hoarding gold, I would have to represent myself. Lawyers said when a man represented himself he had a damned fool for a client. I knew Papa would think I qualified, all around.

My "double-eagle" was awarded for learning the "Rounding the Horn" section of John Masefield's "Dauber." The section I memorized must have been at least sixty lines.

Mr. Ed invited me to his house to say the lines to him. He sat on his side front porch, in a swing that had double chains to hold his incredible girth. He filled the swing the way two people always seem to fill a hammock, or the way May grass seems to fill a lawn.

He asked for, and got, a synopsis of the long narrative poem, up to the point where my recitation took over. He nodded his big head as if he had just seen some parallel lines that crossed and criss-crossed. From the way the old gentleman sniffed I am sure the rose arbor was emitting the twang of salt spray.

His eyes scanned the horizon the way the master of a sailing ship would see everything in and out of sight. I was, I am, reasonably sure Mr. Ed was acting out the role of ship's captain.

But about the time I reached the part of the poem that says,

Up! yelled the bos'un, Up and clear the wreck,
The Dauber followed where he led.

it was I who got an urgent call from nature. Mr. Ed perceived my distress. "Jess go there to the banisters, boy, and make water over them. Don't lose time going inside to the water-closet. By God, I want to know how she turns out."

24

So, I cut loose over the banisters. Mr. Ed rubbed his hands as he waited for me to continue the narrative. I knew Mother would have an old-fashioned Methodist fit and fall into the middle of it if she heard I had done "number one" on the Settle's porch, and right in broad daylight, too.

Mr. Ed probably detected my consternation. For, just as I finished he said, firmly: "There ain't a gal in nine counties who can stand flat-footed and do what you just did."

We had a copy of Masefield's *Salt Water Ballads* at home. Papa lent the copy to Mr. Ed. He read it in his buggy, off and on, the remainder of that spring and summer.

He took his family to Morehead ("Mo-haid") City, N. C. or to Virginia ("Foreginger") Beach for two weeks each summer. He said he "never really saw" the ocean until he read Masefield's book.

When he died in 1939, he left an estate of about one million dollars, mostly in good property and land. God knows what his holdings would be worth in the currency of 1970. However, I am sure his proudest attainment, his most choice possession, was reading Masefield's famous poem "Sea-Fever" over and over, and aloud to himself, in the buggy until he got the whole twelve lines letter perfect.

He never told his family about this accomplishment. He said the poem to his cronies, to Papa, "Brer" Thompson, and Dr. Henley. Papa made him an honorary Doctor of Letters, at Oxford. But the "degree" was not bruited a-bout. It never became cheap by dint of talk-talk.

Dr. Henley said Mr. Ed had the "Chair of Poetry, at Oxford." The old gentleman's eyes danced merrily as April showers, as he laughed and said: "Doctor, you better make that 'settee' or 'davenport'. A cheer wouldn't be big enough for me."

On the western edge of town, beyond the old corporate limits, he owned a lovely grove. Everyone used to call it "Settle's Lane." A private road, maintained by Mr. Ed, ran through this magnificent stand of pines and oak trees. (Papa told me "Settle's Lane" contained 82.5 acres, more or less.)

Weekdays a chain barred the entrance to the road, but it was down on Sundays so people could ride, slowly, or walk through the gorgeous woodland. And he let respectable people in for picnics, for "Gypsy Teas," as they used to be called. But "Settle's Lane" was posted against all hunters.

Even back then real estate hustlers were trying to get "Settle's Lane" for housing developments. They might as well have tried to buy the Washington Monument to make room for a filling station. Albeit, Mr. Ed didn't waste his breath trying to explain his refusal to sell the lovely acres to those who couldn't understand.

His explanation was the same, to anyone who asked: "What'd become of the fire horses?"

When Oxford had bought motorized fire equipment, Mr. Ed had bought the two horses that had pulled the fire wagon. They were two wondrous bays, Matt and Bertha. Matt was named for Matt Venable, the fire chief and High Sheriff, and Bertha was named for Miss Bertha Hornbuckle, the telephone central who gave the fire alarms.

Without being at all fulsome, Mr. Ed said the two fire horses deserved a pension, the same as other faithful employees. So he paid the town $1000.00 for the pair. He built a fence around a big grassy field he owned, just off the lovely woodland.

Aleck, the young man who held the pail between Mr. Ed's legs, fed, watered, and groomed the retired fire horses. I visited these beautiful horses many times, with Mr. Ed and Aleck and alone. They'd eat lumps of sugar out of my hand; but when the fire bell rang, they tore around and around the pasture, just as if they were pulling the wagon again. Their eyes blazed like headlights on a locomotive, and their neighings rolled up and down "Settle's Lane" as if rapid bursts of small thunder were announcing a freshet.

Whenever there was a local parade, or some big wing-ding, the Chamber of Commerce or the Kiwanis would say it would be a fine idea to put Matt and Bertha into the parade, to let a new generation see horses pulling a fire wagon. But Mr. Ed sucked his breath and said: "The circus is fer freaks." (Papa said the first civic club member was the first poppinjay who ever called John the Baptist "Jack." I'm not sure if this was original, but it was insofar as Papa was concerned. He also said if one of the television talk-show fellows had interviewed Leonardo di Vinci, the guy on TV would call him "Lee" within five minutes.)

Matt and Bertha have been in heaven, or wherever it is that good and faithful horses go, for many years, and about five years ago Mr. Ed's lovely lane lost out to the bull-dozer. Most of the trees were used for building timber. The housing development is called "Shamrock Drive," but I haven't seen a shamrock out there since old man McDuffie passed out about 25 years ago walking home from a three-man St. Patrick's Day celebration in Oxford.

Architecture isn't my bag, but most of the homes in Shamrock Drive seem to be identical twins, to me. I hope this bland sameness doesn't attach to the folks who live in these look-alive houses, but I certainly wouldn't make book on it. One thing is for damned sure:

The election results show that they vote alike. Nixon walked off with the vote in Shamrock in 1968. I find this mildly sardonic because the fathers and grandfathers of the ones who live in Shamrock were broke as hell when FDR was elected.

Mr. Ed Settle's granddaughter lives in Shamrock, and her house doesn't resemble the others. It is a replica of Tryon's Palace, at New Bern, N. C., but bigger. The house crowns a slight knoll, smack in the middle of the luscious pasture where Matt and Bertha sported in light-leafed breezes. The estate, called "Brigadoon," covers the 82.5 acres that the lady's grandfather set aside for beauty.

My wife and I just attended a swanky bash at the home, at Brigadoon. It was one of these deluxe parties at which everyone is a guest and no one is company. Everyone was given a guided tour of the elegant premises. The tour started with one of the six opulent bathrooms and it ended with one of the six bathrooms.

Just about everyone was deeply impressed and no one seemed to think it incongruous that he had to visit six bathrooms, whether he needed to or not. It was almost as if the Big Rock Candy Mountain had materialized, with gold faucets.

These bathrooms have harmonic chimes, portable TV's, health vibrators, health drinks, piped-in music, sunken tubs big enough to accomodate an old-fashioned August Meeting's baptizings, and, I was told, walk-through showers that wet, soap, clean, dry, and scent the body with a series of swift, deft motions.

I really got the impression that it would be a social breech to use one of these lavish Xanadus to make water. Anyway, I figured if a kid entered one when he was six, he wouldn't have to leave it until he was 21 and wished to get out and vote.

When the Canterbury pilgrims were entering the third bathroom, I slipped away into the luxuriantly paneled library, much as a player would steal home when the catcher is at the hot dog stand.

Aside from the four-in-one condensed versions of

Reader's Digest novels, the book shelves were filled with expensive-looking works on flower arranging, landscaping, interior decorating, personality analyses, and treatises on diets and the raising of children.

A special table held some statuettes Mr. Ed's granddaughter had won for prizes at local golf tournaments, and there was a handsome Revere bowl she had won for "Civic Contributions" in 1967. On another table there was a handsome copy of *War and Peace*. It rested in a manner that reminded me of poor Poe's story, "The Purloined Letter." I opened *War and Peace*, and the pages were as clean and as untouched as a child's innocence. It was balanced, on a hassock, by Norman Vincent Peale's *Guide To Confident Living*.

I had heard our hostess make some furtive allusion to *All You Need To Know About Sex*. I couldn't locate this book, and while I was looking around I heard the entourage going into yet another bathroom.

I thought about Mr. Ed Settle, about Aleck and the pail, and about his insisting that I wee-wee over the banisters the time I was reciting from "Dauber." I knew he made all the money for this paean to plumbing.

It was easy to imagine the horror and consternation a visit from him would cause his granddaughter. And I already knew what Mr. Ed would think of this mansion. But it hurt too much to speculate on what the old gentleman would think of the brutal demolition of his lovely grove.

Oxford, October 22, 1968:

Today, profanity, in all phases of society and conversation, is almost as axiomatic as ants at a picnic. The chaste dash ("---g") is gone from literature, and profanity in mixed company, with or without mixed drinks, is as commonplace as chiggers around blackberry bushes.

Hardly anyone whispers swear words, uses pantomine, or says "h," "d," or "g.d." I suppose this trend was inevitable when books, the theater, the movies, and TV relaxed the old strictures relative to graphic language.

This doesn't bother me, personally, but it annoys me, somewhat, that so many people swear because they seem to think free-swinging talk makes them cool or groovy, per se. What I do object to is the fact, the sad fact, that much current swearing resembles the worst of modern poetry, cubist art, and rock music.

It's a jumble of sounds devoid of verve, spontaneity, purpose, and passion. Much of modern swearing is shorn even of that therapeutic relief which appealed so much to Mark Twain and to his alter-ego, Pudd'nhead Wilson.

I remember long ago Papa's telling me that in Chaucer's time swearing was a privilege, a badge. All the top cats during Chaucer's time had distinguishing oaths, the same way big-name American dance bands used to have definitive theme signatures.

During this same conversation, "Brer" Thompson said that several British monarchs – William the Conqueror, King John, and King Edward I – all had special, identifying oaths.

However, as I understood it, swearing was not a divine right in the New World. Swearing was the prerogative, if not the privilege, of the eloquent, of the fervent. For a long time each community had some champion cussers, men who could swear for an hour and never repeat the same expletive.

The community used such men the way many of their grandfathers hired substitutes during the Civil War. They sort of took a verbal last strike for someone. If something occurred that demanded profane redress, someone sent for a champ, for a real pro, to do the cussing.

Papa combined the magic of Mark Twain and the bravado of Wagner's overtures. Without preamble or research, Papa exuded righteous indignation, social protest, moral outrage, frustration, or the hellishness of some hurt or offense.

What I object to today is the fact that swearing has been usurped by arrant amateurs, by effete poseurs, by rank dilettantes. Hence, many of the surviving old-time experts are mute for the same reason that Buffalo Bill wouldn't mount a merry-go-round horse and shoot a water-pistol.

Swearing today, with most of the cult, is as vacuous and as incongruous as giving a Stradivarius to one of the fiddlers in one of the ersatz hillbilly bands on television.

About 1928, long before civil rights was ever spoken about locally, before the phrase was ever used, within my hearing, I was uptown one day, barefooted, when I ran into Papa.

He invited me into Hill's Drug Store for a cool drink. While we were sipping our lemonades, Ramsay Davis, a college senior, came into the drug store.

Ramsay was all the rage, with what Papa called the "jawbone set." A "jawboner" was someone, who, in Papa's judgement, had more brains in his jawbone than in his head.

Anyway, Ramsay had won national acclaim for swallowing a fantastically large number of live goldfish. He had won a Charleston dancing contest, a marathon dancing contest, and he had been so successful as chief cheerleader at football games that one of the cough drop companies had given him free sample of small boxes of cough drops to hand out to his yellers at the Saturday games.

He greeted Papa with "Put her there, Major, old boy," but Papa pretended not to see Ramsay's hand extended. With mock solemnity, Papa asked Ramsay about the great honors he had won at the university, and Ramsay went into profuse details about swallowing the live goldfish, winning the marathon dancing contest, and attracting the attention of the cough drop company.

He winked at Papa and gave this yell, one he had perfected, he said, when he was chief cheerleader at the university:

Zim, zam, zee,
Hit 'em on the knee,
Zin, zam, zazz,
Hit 'em on the other knee.

Ramsay doubled up laughing. "You get it?" he asked Papa.

"I get it, Ramsay," Papa replied. Then, turning to Mr. Tasker Davis, Ramsay's father, who had followed his son into Hill's, Papa said, with terrible anguish: "Tasker, it must have been for this blessed moment, for these cherished honors, for this exalted hour, that Homer recorded his journeys, that Erasmas sequestered himself at Oxford, that Columbus put out to sea, that Whitman wrote *Leaves of Grass*, that Edison made illumination a way of life."

Mr. Davis nodded assent, as if he were conceding he had a frightful, terminal illness: "Yes, sir, I am reasonably sure Gutenberg pointed to this hour when he invented printing, and, beyond peradventure, Major, Hannibal anticipated Ramsay's triumphs, or, otherwise, he would not have troubled to invade Rome."

Another time Papa encountered me on the street and took me into Hill's for a "repast." When we were leaving the drug store, Mrs. R. C. Shaw was walking along the sidewalk.

Her husband was the principal of the Negro high school

and the preacher at the Negro Presbyterian Church. Papa tipped the brim of his hat and said, evenly: "Good afternoon, Mrs. Shaw."

Just Plain Snake Imboden was slouching under the awning, holding onto the awning rope. Just Plain Snake was a blockader. People said his blockade whiskey must be all right since he drank so much of it himself. He was called "Just Plain Snake" to distinguish him from his brother, "King of the Green Snakes" Imboden, who raised such wonderful Green Snake watermelons and other luscious produce.

Just Plain Snake dropped the awning rope. He siddled up to Papa, his eyes sizzling like fresh spittle on a red hot stove. "How come you call at damned nigger um-man 'Mrs. Shaw'?"

Papa said, softly, unemotionally: "Well, Mrs. Shaw's older than I am. She's better educated than I am, and she has more money."

Then, thrusting Just Plain Snake away as if he were afraid he would get his hand dirty, Papa boomed out: "But more to the point, none of your business, you damned low-life miscreant, you two-for-a-nickel jackal, you son of a bitch, net."

Tom Day, the soda water clerk at Hill's, told Papa: "I think Just Plain Snake understands the last part of what you said, Major."

It's been a long time since I've heard anyone append "net" to son of a bitch. Yesterday, "net" meant a real son of a bitch, doubled, and in spades.

A lot of people in town sent for Old Man Rufe Duncan to cuss for them, the same way they sent for Mr. Erk Mayberry to do the main out-loud praying at a meeting held to pray for rain. (Old man Erk was usually the only person to take an umbrella to meetings held to pray for rain. One time there was a terrible storm before he even finished his thirty minute prayer for rain. The severe rain, and the wind and the hail that followed almost destroyed all the crops.)

(Miss Bertha Hornbuckle, the telephone central, said: "Huh, folks ought to have more sense than to keep asking old man Erk to pray for rain. He always does overdo everything he does.")

Old Man Rufe Duncan was best at cussing things that people referred to as "a sin and a shame." His epithets were "vile uv the vilest," "fiend incarnate," "pot-likker hound uv hell," "not worth a dried apple dam in trade," and he said of people whom he didn't like, "I could whittle a better specimen uv humanity with a piece uv bark and a Barlow knife."

One of his pet words was "egregious." He called it "E-gree-juice." In fact I learned to spell several fifty cent words from the way Old Man Rufe pronounced, or mispronounced, them:

Virtually all politicians, living or dead, except William Jennings Bryan and Al Smith, were "in-come-pete-unt swine." Lazy folks were "non-shall-unt hobbledehoys." Old Man Rufe got the jake-leg from the yellow-jack, when he was in the Spanish-American War, or so he said, and he was forced to spend the remainder of his life "con-val-sing."

I never had any trouble spelling incompetent, nonchalant, or convalescing.

When Al Smith was running for President, several of the local ministers opposed him because they said he was a "wet." Papa said this was a "loathsome deception." The preachers who opposed Al Smith were against him because he was a Catholic, but they didn't have the guts to say so. Hence, they preached against him because he favored moderation of the 18th Amendment.

But being against Smith was sufficient to send anybody "to the bottom cellar in hell," in Old Man Rufe's opinion. One day during the 1928 campaign, Old Man Rufe was making a speech for Al Smith in front of the "Ivanhoe," the local candy store.

There were three or four adults, Albert, the "town dog," and me. Silas, Mr. Virginius Purvis's old horse, was at the curb. Then this minister came up and started putting Smith down. The minister had flaming red hair.

Papa saw me, and he walked up about the time Old Man Rufe denounced the preacher: "You lying, red-headed, knock-kneed, fiend incarnate, you psalm-singing, lily-livered imp uv Satan, you double-dealing, whore-hopping enemy uv mankind, you Judas I. Scariot son of a bitch, net, you."

The preacher turned to Papa for refutation. Papa said, "Let us examine the evidence, good sir." Then Papa repeated every word and phrase in Old Man Rufe's diatribe. When he had finished quoting Old Man Rufe, Papa said, blandly enough: "Well, your hair is red, isn't it?"

Old Man Rufe Duncan was what was known as a "town farmer." He and his wife, Miss Texanna, did own a lot of rural property, but Old Man Rufe was too busy "con-val-sing" to visit his farms. However, Miss Texanna was an excellent manager, and the Duncan's were "good livers." (They had one child, Pansy Alice, or "P. A.," as she called herself, and P. A. was Oxford's first fully liberated woman. I have an entry about her.)

Old Man Rufe reminded me, exactly, of the description of Ichabod Crane. Dr. Henley said if he cut open Old Man Rufe there wouldn't be any more blood in him than there is in a fishing worm.

He was so thin his bones rattled like a shackly wagon when he walked around. He carried a handsome blackthorn cane, on account of the jake-leg he got fighting the Spanish

35

down in "Cuby." The cane had a hard point, and I could hear Old Man Rufe three blocks away as the cane went rat-ta-ta-tat on the sidewalk.

Sometimes he used the cane for a pointer. About five o'clock in the afternoon, when he was always plastered, he used it for a baton to sort of direct his own singing and whistling.

He always walked, no matter the weather, and Miss Texanna could hear him singing two streets away, when he started lurching, stumbling, strutting, and wobbling homeward.

His piece de resistance was "Amazing Grace." When Miss Texanna heard the sounds, she'd say to Pansy Alice: "Go open the gate, honey. Your Pa'll be along directly."

When he sang the part that says, "A-maz-ing grace, how sweet the sound/That saved a wretch like me-ah," he'd always shout, "Hurrah fer Williams Jennings Bryan."

Other housewives, along the route, knew it was time to get supper ready when they heard Old Man Rufe's yelling out, "Hurrah fer Williams Jennings Bryan."

His second tune was "Heaven Will Protect The Working Girl," and I think he projected himself as some kind of knight-errant, some avenging force. For, his cane became a sword, or "swore-wurd," while he sang "Heaven Will Protect The Working Girl."

Many times I saw him stop, lurch, and strike out in all directions with his cane, with his "swore-wurd."

Papa would say: "Hold your trousers up when you walk down Front Street. Old Man Rufe, I mean D'Artagan, has the sidewalk strewn with the corpses of the malefactors of the working girl."

Except on Sunday, when he wore a straw or a felt, he always wore a huge tin hat, shaped like the helmets the American soliders wore in World War I, but much bigger in

36

the brim. (It was almost a larger replica of the hard-hats construction workers wear today.) Of course, no one had ever seen such hats back then, not around Oxford, anyway.

It was never told, for certain, where he got his tin hat, but he wore it all of the years I knew him, and Papa, and others, said he wore it long before I was born.

He said he had a tinsmith make it when he enlisted for the Spanish-American War, but by my time, he probably forgot where he found his hat. But his cronies tapped on it for good luck, in lieu of wood, I suppose, and others said it kept birds from roosting in his hair. He hated barbers and he never went into a barber shop in all the years I knew him. His hair was almost as long as many young men wear theirs today. Miss Texanna gave it a few whacks with her scissors, occasionally, when she got him to sit still long enough.

He said he promised his mother, on her death-bed, never to enter a barber shop. When he told of this pledge, his eyes filled with tears. Then he would say, to anyone or to no one: "By God, sah, Rufus Duncan, E-sick (that meant "Esq.") is a man uv his word, sah."

I have seen him look at the sky, towards heaven I guessed, and say, sonorously: "Ma, to my pledged word I'm true. The bastards can't tempt me with gold, ner seduce me with promises uv high office. I spit on them and they bribes and tempertations, dear, dead lady in hebben."

When FDR was elected, people said things would get better. Old Man Rufe demurred: "Lemme tell you somep'n, boy. There won't be no cot ding peace or prosperity in this nashion untwil every egg-sucking barba is putt to the swore-wurd."

The Lord only knows why he disliked, or pretended to dislike, barbers so fiercely. I did hear, once, that some barber had beat his time with a girl, long ago, and I heard, again, that some barber had bluffed him out of a big pot in a poker game.

In a hard rain his tin hat sounded as if two skeletons were jumping up and down in it. And in a hard sleet or a hail storm his hat was a mobile "Anvil Chorus."

He got so worked up about the theory of the world's being round he would beat his hat, on his head, with his cane. He used to argue with Papa, "Brer" Thompson, and Dr. Henley. Or, to be more precise, they listened to his tirades about the fool teachers who taught that the world is round.

He had an unimpeachable demurrer. He said every night when he went to bed Miss Texanna put eggs in a nest, and, "by Jesus H. Christ," the eggs were still in the nest the next morning.

(Invariably, Old Man Rufe said "Jesus H. Christ," rather than "Jesus Christ," for an expletive. I didn't know Jesus had a middle name. One day I asked him what the "H" stood for. He scratched his tin hat a second and said, "Hubbut," his way of saying "Herbert." Ever since I've wondered if the angels know Old Man Rufe gave Jesus a regular middle name.)

Q.E.D. If the world were round, if it turned on its axis, like the "id-jut teachers" said, why the eggs would fall out of the nest during the night. He beamed at his irrefutable logic the way I always imagined Descartes beamed when he said, "I think, hence I am."

One day when I was walking home from school, he accosted me on the street: "Sandy, on your Ma's honor, do 'em id-jut teachers rilly tell yawl the world turns round and round?"

I conceded the fact.

He tapped his tin hat, lightly with his right hand fingers. Then he smiled and he put his hand on my shoulder, gently: "If what them teachers say is so, then God, Jesus, and William Jennings Bryan would be standing on they haids half uv the time, and jess fer your own information, and because I like you, William Jennings Bryan ain't go stand on his haid in hebben half the time jess to pleze your id-jut teacher."

He patted my shoulder, briefly, gave me a nickel, and said, the same way a minister dismisses a congregation, "Now, go long wiff you. Mind your Ma and Pa, don't steal Miss Texanna's peaches withouten permission, and don't never let nobody ketch you in a barba shop."

Old Man Rufe built the first mausoleum in Oxford, insofar as I can determine. It was, is, a handsome marble structure, designed in the manner of a miniature Grecian temple. He called it his "mossy-lee," and he used it, from spring to fall, as a combination office and playhouse for several years. I think the "mossy-lee" was built at least fifteen years before Old Man Rufe died.

He said it was the coolest place in town, next to the ice plant, and each morning, in pretty weather, he took his newspaper and stumbled and jerked over to the cemetery to his "mossy-lee."

He would sit in the doorway in a rocking chair, read his paper, sing and whistle his songs, and smoke his roll-your-own cigarettes. He was the only man in town who smoked Maryland Club. This was the smallest sack of smoking tobacco and it cost a dime, twice as much as ordinary sack tobacco cost back then.

As soon as he rolled and licked his cigarette paper, he put the cigarette into the grippers of one of those clamp things that men used to wear on their right legs to keep their pants from getting caught in a bicycle chain.

The smoking ring, the clamp thing, was so big you could hardly see the roll-your-own in its metallic teeth, but billowing smoke poured from the door of the "mossy-lee."

I had never seen a French cathedral, of course, but sometimes when I rode by the cemetery on my bicycle I got the impression someone was burning incense.

I was in the "mossy-lee" a few times. I used to deliver some stuff for the "Ivanhoe," and a few times I took oddments to Old Man Rufe, in the "mossy-lee." There was a small table inside which he and his cronies used for checkers and for set-back and poker.

Old Man Rufe kept jugs of buttermilk, which he used for a chaser, and mason-jars of Just Plain Snake Imboden's homemade whiskey. On the shelves, where the coffins went, ultimately, were apples and pears, in season, and there was a huge glass jar filled with horehound candy.

Old Man Rufe dropped sticks of horehound into the white whiskey, to give it color and to soak up the fussel oil. He gave me a stick to suck on, several times.

(Women in town were always raising hell about the poker games that had gone on, without interruption, long before Lord Cornwallis marched through Oxford. Occasionally, some irate wife would charge into a game to grab her husband by the ear, but no one ever mentioned anything about raiding the poker games in Old Man Rufe's "mossy-lee.")

Although the "mossy-lee" was not used for an office or recreation center in cold weather, Old Man Rufe always ran off a batch of persimmons-and-locust beer in it along about October.

He had a large barrel, with a spigot and a dipper attached, and he filled the barrel with layers of persimmons and locusts and broom straw, alternately. Then he filled the barrel with water and let the persimmons, locusts, and broom straw "work."

Most people in town drank persimmons-and-locust beer for a soft drink, but Old Man Rufe let his get as hard as his tin hat. He and a few of his tombstone buddies slipped over along about Thanksgiving to sample the beer.

Sometimes the sampling went on for two or three days. Miss Texanna didn't worry about Old Man Rufe's being exposed to pneumonia, to any disease. As she explained: "Germs and mosquistoes jess get pickled when they bite into Rufe."

One Thanksgiving Just Plain Snake Imboden passed out in the "mossy-lee" and Old Man Rufe locked him up inside. Whether this was an accident, I can't say. Anyway, he awakened about ten o'clock at night, and he started bellowing for someone to let him out.

There was a lovers' lane, right by the cemetery, and several couples were out there in cars, courting. Ramsay Davis was there, with some girl. He bolted from the car and ran all the way to his father's house, where he hid in a closet. I don't know about the girl, but I understand that she took off in the opposite direction.

Each fall Old Man Rufe put boards on the concrete floor of the mossy-lee "to bed" Irish potatoes. He sprinkled lime all over the potatoes so they wouldn't rot or get frost-bitten.

Just Plain Snake had gone to sleep on the potatoes, and when Sheriff Matt Venable came with Old Man Rufe's keys to let him out, he was as white as any ghost.

Some other people, walking home late at night, saw Just Plain Snake as he emerged from the "mossy-lee." They were sure he was a ghost, a "hant."

The true story became garbled. The sparkers swore they heard ghostly yells from the tomb, and the pedestrians swore they had seen a "live ghost."

The whole cemetery became haunted, or "hanted." The adjacent lovers' lane became a briar patch, and for a long time, most of the people in town gave the cemetery a wide berth at night.

Tom Day, the soda water clerk at Hill's, lived just beyond the cemetery. When he walked home at night, he went half-a-mile out of his way, to avoid the cemetery. One day Papa said to him: "Tom, boy, don't you know dead folks can't hurt you?"

"Yes, sir, I know that, Major, but they show as hell can make you hurt yourself."

I was about grown when Old Man Rufe died. When he was laid out in his coffin, his tin hat was on his chest, his long, bony hands clutching the hat. I don't know if the hat was buried with his body, but I never saw it again.

The choir sang "Amazing Grace," and when they got to the right part, Papa whispered, "Hurrah fer William Jennings Bryan."

Just as we were leaving the cemetery, a terrible storm came up. I thought the salvos of thunder would break every window and glass in town. Papa looked at the black, angry sky, and he said to "Brer" Thompson: "Well, I suppose Old Man Rufe is up there by now, and he must be telling St. Peter all about the barbers on this earth."

Oxford, November 1, 1968:

About a week ago I mentioned Hill's Drug Store and Tom Day, the soda water clerk. But Tom was infinitely more than a jerker of cokes ("dopes"), a squeezer of lemons, and a landscape artist who fashioned banana-splits.

Mr. Hill's soda fountain was a bench and Tom held court behind it. Tom was a town-crier, sans bell, a psychiatrist, without a couch, and a crack reporter without a pad and pencil. He was not profound or learned, but his mind was an active filing-cabinet in which the oddments, whimsicalities, nuances, and footnotes of the town reposed.

He knew whether you wanted a cherry-smash or a dope

42

when you walked into the drug store, and he knew if you wanted lemon, lots of ice, or no ice in your dope.

He knew which men had been out late raising hell the night before, and if some customer, some man whom he knew well and liked, called him "Dr. Tom," he knew the fellow was suffering that living death known as a hang-over. So, he laced the dope copiously with Jamaica Ginger, which was known in Oxford as "jump-steady," or "stiddy." Drinking an ounce or so of Jamaica Ginger was comparable to swallowing a bolt of lightning.

The belly thought the mouth had swallowed a blow--torch. As soon as the customer swallowed the potion, Dr. Tom said, "Walk her down, walk her down." So, the customer stumbled around the tile floor until "the fire was under control."

Men who had to have help to get into the drug store strutted out almost as royally as drum-majors if they were able to get Dr. Tom's "jump-steady" to stick.

Dr. Henley said he couldn't recommend Jamaica Ginger as a steady diet. Too much of it impeded locomotion, brought permanent impairment, but the doctor said it was all right as a desperate remedy. Dr. Henley said Dr. Tom saved more lost souls than Billy Sunday and Sister Amiee Semple McPherson combined. The doctor quoted a proverb written by John Heywood (1497-1580):

> *I pray thee let me and my fellow have*
> *A haire of the dog that bit us last night.*

And, in that connection, Papa quoted Ben Jonson: "I do honor the very flea of his dog."

Late in the afternoon, those whom Dr. Tom had saved in the morning, lifted their glasses to "the very flea of Dr. Tom's dog." Dr. Tom's dog was "man's best friend." Indeed, toasts to "man's best friend" endured long after Dr. Tom and Jamaica Ginger departed the local scene. I have heard such poignant toasts in the swanky new country club by men who never heard of Dr. Tom and his magic potion.

The original allusion was completely unknown to the next generation, some of whom even inquired after the name, nature, and deeds of the celebrated Oxford dog that was the object of emotional verbiage. Several immortal dogs were contrived, to satisfy morbid curiosity. A few times it was Albert, the town dog of my youth, owned by no one and loved by virtually everyone. Finally, the mythical dog became Argus, Homer's faithful companion.

Newcomers were told they were toasting Argus because he had sounded the alarm, barked to hail the fire company, and had saved the business section from flames. Again, Argus had swum into Sweetgum Creek to retrieve, by the nap of the neck, some toddler who had fallen into the stream.

Ramsay Davis, to the wonderment of many, went to law school, graduated, passed the bar, and practiced law in Oxford. Somewhere, after he abandoned live goldfish and cheerleading, he stumbled across Lord Byron's words, inscribed upon the monument of Boatswain, Byron's famous Newfoundland dog, at Newstead:

"Near this spot are deposited the remains of one who possessed Beauty without Vanity, Strength without Insolence, Courage without Ferocity, and all the Virtues of man, without his Vices. This Praise, which would be unmeaning Flattery if inscribed over human ashes, is but a just tribute to Boatswain."

I suppose I heard Ramsay give the exhortation five hundred times, on the stump, as a candidate for the legislature, at barbecues and fish fries, at country stores, at the bar in the country club, and at assorted parties. He always

44

substituted Argus, for Boatswain, and Argus always happened to be buried close to whatever spot Ramsay spoke from. Argus had more graves than a dozen cats have lives and tails.

But, back to Tom, the soda-water clerk. He knew who was pitching for the Yankees, where fish were biting, how to tell a mushroom from a toadstool, when Mr. Entwhistle would return from Raleigh, and why he went there, who was pregnant and when she got pregnant, and who was overdrawn at the bank.

He knew all the popular songs, word by word, and he could do all the latest dances, many of which he came around from behind the fountain to demonstrate.

A story, probably apocryphal, attested to the extent of Tom's knowledge of the minutiae of Oxford and to his nimbleness in relating these facts. Three wiseacres, who had framed-up on Tom, came into Hill's one day. Each asked Tom a question, in rapid-fire order. "What time does the train leave for Henderson and get back from Durham?" "How deep is the mud-hole in the alley by Boot Ransome's blacksmith shop?" "How much are moth balls?"

Tom didn't look up from the lemon he was squeezing: "Half-past six and a quarter of nine; up to your ass; and ten for a dime."

Today, sodawater clerks are females, "fountain assistants." Their "Floating Palaces" are succulent works of art, but, good God, they can't even tell you who is on the jury the next term of court.

Hill's, in common with many other drug stores, was never just a place to buy refreshments, to have a prescription filled, or to purchase razor blades or face cream. It was a forum, a debating society, a community center, and, above all else, an exalted trysting place.

It had as many clientelles as it had flavors of ice cream.

You could set your watch by certain foregatherings. The neo-swingers assembled at ten each morning and at four each afternoon to sip dopes, smoke cigarettes, and to talk about movies, fashions, hanky-panky and crushes. The older women, those who served on altar-guilds and did good works for the community, came in at eleven. They drank grape-juice or lemonade. They didn't smoke, certainly not in public, anyway, and they talked about sin, the P.T.A., and church suppers and bazaars.

The neo-swingers sat in booths. They yelled back and forth to each other, from one booth to another, and many hopped from one booth to another, to exchange verbal goodies. They read movie magazines, and they passed a-round a copy of the latest *Esquire* to share the cartoons.

The older ladies sat in a tight circle around a marble-top table. Unlike the neo-swingers, they never slurped their drinks with their soda straws. They never spoke loudly. Conversation seemed to be as earnest as it was subdued. The noises always seemed to simulate the varied murmurs of a summer day.

Periodically, they cast brief, oblique glances at the younger women in the booths, but everytime I saw these brief, furtive glances I got an idea of how the women in *The Scarlet Letter* looked at Hester Prynne. And their incessant murmurs sounded to me as if all the bees in the whole country were sipping clover, simultaneously.

The older women always left first. When they arose, they shrugged their shoulders. I always thought this gesture was more comprehensive than Walter Lippman's *A Preface To Morals* and Philip Wylie's *A Generation of Vipers*, put together.

With the neo-swingers and the younger courting couples Hill's was a bucolic version of cafe society. Some men used Hill's as Dr. Johnson and his coterie used the British coffee-house, and at night (Hill's stayed open until "bed-time," or around 9:30 each night except Sunday) it was a news-room and an editorial sanctum. The chief topics were politics, sports, crops, and the weather.

And I digress to say the weather was never an abstraction. Almost all our daily events were orchestrated by the weather, and whenever a good story teller told of some memorable event in the past, he always described the weather that attended the event. If a stranger had heard us discussing the weather he might assume we were talking about the health and personality of an old, intimate friend.

Other stores had definite clientelles, too, and by "clientelles" I mean people who came to a specific store regularly but not necessarily to buy something. Actually, "clientelles" were "customers," but certain people visited certain stores, just as city people might belong to social, political, or eating clubs.

Few country people came to Hill's save to shop. It was the gathering place for many town folks. And, insofar as I know, the first "radio parties" in town were at Hill's.

When I was a boy, radios were still novelties. There were only a few sets in town. The President (Mr. Quigg, president of the bank, but always called "the President") had a set, but he never had a "radio party." Papa said the President was afraid some guest might ask for a bank loan.

"Struttin' Bud" Davenport, our wealthy eccentric, had three or four sets in his huge house, but he hardly ever played them. He took them apart and tried to put them back together again. He did the same thing with his cars and his motorcycle.

He never rode anywhere. Mrs. Davenport rode. She had her own car, and she had a separate garage built for it, exclusively. She kept the door locked when the car was in the garage so that "Struttin' Bud" couldn't tear that one up, too.

Mr. Bengough, who ran the department store, had a radio in his home, but he turned it on only to hear Mr. Henderson, the fellow in Louisiana who swore to put all of the chain stores out of business. Mr. Henderson ranked chain stores below sin, Satan, and Sherman. He had his own broadcasting station. He sold "Ten O'Clock" coffee, at the stupendous price of $1.00 a pound, to pay for his broadsides against the iniquituous chain stores.

He was always telling home-town merchants to "get modern," to take down the fly-stickers, to get the cat out of the sugar barrel, to put in a water-closet, and not to keep fish more than two days unless there was plenty of ice.

But Hill's radio was for regular playing, and there was a party almost every night. The radio was on a shelf, on the wall behind the cigar counter. No one could touch the dial but Tom Day, and he had to get on a stool to reach it.

His power was greater than the F.C.C. has today, but he really tried to vary the programs to please as many people as possible. The great trick was to get K.D.K.A., in Pittsburg. Even so, many people said it was all a hoax. Old Man Rufe Duncan said someone was out behind the drug store talking, maybe throwing his voice and playing a gramaphone. And Old Man Rufe got some adherents when a duet or a quartet sang: Any damned fool knew two people couldn't sing through the same microphone, simultaneously.

However, Billy Jones and Ernie Hare — "We're the Interwoven Pair" — were great favorites, and they sang duets. If Old Man Rufe messed up the singing, with all his talk, someone always lured him down the street with the promise of a drink.

Older men wanted political speeches, and the ball scores and weather reports from the government station at Mt. Alto, outside of Washington. The younger folks wanted Rudy Vallee or Ruth Etting.

Ramsay Davis was sweet as hell on Pansy Alice Duncan, on lovely P. A., our liberated woman, our feminist movement. Once or twice he was overcome with pathos, or yearning, with some emotion, when Ruth Etting sang "The One I Love Belongs To Someone Else." He sang along with Ruth Etting. Actually, he had a pretty good voice, but people threw pennies at him to shut up his singing.

One night, I guess P. A. had been about half-way kind to him, he sang "Life Is Just A Bowl of Cherries," along with Rudy Vallee. Tom Day called Ramsay over to the soda fountain. Tom told him Miss Texanna and Old Man Rufe might think the song was appallingly suggestive. Ramsay hadn't thought of that possibility, and he didn't sing anything, along with anybody, for several weeks.

Oxford, November 7, 1968:

The other day I talked about Ramsay Davis's incessant speeches about the remarkable, non-existent dog, Argus.

There used to be a lot of litigation about dogs and other animals. Farmers were always trying to sue the railroad to recover damages for cows, mules, and horses killed by the locomotive. Mr. Moorefield, one of Papa's contemporaries, brought endless suits against the railroad. In his summations, Mr. Moorefield always pictured the railroad as a diabolical monster seeking innocent prey to slaughter, merely to satisfy its lust for blood.

I remember a particular case wherein Mr. Moorefield alleged that the locomotive had deliberately set fires, by overtly blowing coals from its smokestack, that burned a wheat field, an orchard, and a pen of pigs.

The fires had been set on a Sunday, according to Mr. Moorefield's allegation. In his preoration, Mr. Moorefield accused the locomotive of disturbing the peace of the

Sabbath. He said to the magistrate: "Here it was, Squire, a-ringing its hellish bell and blowing its infernal whistle and running around the countryside seeking something to destroy when all God-fearing people were a-worshipping the Lord."

He continued: "It could have unloaded its heathenish fires, done its brutal arson, when it passed Buzzard Swamp or when it crossed Tar River, where there's nothing to burn. But, no sir, it waited until it got to my client's wheat field. It waited for that wheat field the same malicious way General Sherman waited until he got to Columbia, South Carolina to start his fires.

"When it spied that wheat field it started to belching its fiendish destruction. Then it burnt up the wheat field, it burnt up the orchard, it burnt up the creek . . ."

At this juncture, Squire Stovall interposed: "Mr. Moorefield, you didn't mean to say the fire burnt UP the creek, did you?"

"Yes, sir, aye God, I did, indeed, sir. It burnt up the creek, and then it burnt down the creek to get at those pigs it missed coming the other way."

As I say, there was much litigation, usually about the railroad, about cows getting into somebody's corn, about stray dogs that weren't returned by the people who found them, about the sale of blind mules and the sale of horses that had the "heaves."

Sometimes, owners were indicted for keeping vicious animals that attacked people. But Old Man Rufe Duncan is the only human I ever heard of who was indicted for biting a dog.

The Entwhistles, neighbors of the Duncans, had this blooded boxer, Sir Gay. Sir Gay had such a lavish coat-of-arms he could have joined the Colonial Dames, if he had been a bitch.

50

Almost every afternoon when Old Man Rufe lumbered home to supper, he picked some kind of argument with Sir Gay. Minor altercations between the two were rudimentary, and people said Old Man Rufe came by the Entwhistle's house dragging croaker sacks on which bitches in heat had lain.

According to the story, Sir Gay got all charged up, but alas, there wasn't much he could do with a croaker sack. And I know it to be an unvarnished fact that Old Man Rufe threw Sir Gay choice cuts of meat that were saturated with black and red pepper. Sir Gay yelped as if he had swallowed sheer brimstone but he couldn't slake his thirst for paroxysms of sneezing.

One night the two had a real fight. Sir Gay snagged Old Man Rufe's trousers and coat sleeves, but Old Man Rufe bit a big chunk out of Sir Gay's left ear.

I think Mrs. Entwhistle forced the issue. Anyway, Mr. Entwhistle swore out a warrant for Old Man Rufe, for malicious injury to Sir Gay. Miss Texanna asked Papa to represent Old Man Rufe at the trial. The trial never occurred, but Old Man Rufe explained to Papa, and to others, that he didn't take advantage of Sir Gay. No, siree, bob-jackimo-tail. When the fight started, Old Man Rufe got down on all-fours, to give the dog a fighting chance, a sporting chance. And that's how he managed to get the dog's ear in his teeth.

Dr. Henley wondered if Old Man Rufe shouldn't be "put up" for three weeks, since he hadn't had any rabies shots. Old Man Rufe asked why in the hell he needed rabies shots since he wasn't a Jewish minister?

A lot of folks said if Sir Gay didn't have a hell of a case of hydrophobia he'd miss a damn good chance.

I think Papa achieved the best solution to a bona fide

51

"dog case." This man named Coon ran a battery shop. (He was called "Zip," and he accepted the nickname. When he answered the telephone he always said, "This here is Zip Coon doing of the talkin'.").

He was so stingy he wouldn't give you a stale biscuit if he owned the Red Band factory. He was so disagreeable people wouldn't believe he was telling the truth if he swore on a Bible that he was lying.

Anyway, Zip Coon owned this pointer, this bird dog, that he bragged about constantly. One day the bird dog came to the battery shop, just visiting. Three or four loafers occupied all the chairs in the place. Zip Coon looked around and said: "One a you bastards git up and give this here gennelmun a seat."

One day the dog strayed, all the way to Fairport, six miles away. People said the pointer was trying to run away from home, away from Zip Coon. A young farmer named Arch Clay found the dog. He fed and cared for the dog for six months.

When Zip Coon tried to get his dog, Arch Clay wouldn't hand the pointer over until he was paid $2.50 for boarding the dog. Zip Coon refused to pay the board bill.

Now, about this time the boy scouts were trying to raise money for a camping trip. Our scout master, Bill Hunt, went into the battery shop twice trying to solicit for the scouts. Each time Zip Coon ran him out.

I belonged to the scouts and Papa and I were passing the battery shop when Zip Coon asked Papa if he could get the bird dog back. Papa said he could. Zip asked how much it would cost.

Papa said his fee would be $15.00. Zip had been drinking, and he told Papa to get the dog and he'd give him the $15.00. Papa said: "No, I've had a lot of experience in dog cases. A lawyer has to have the cash, in advance."

52

Zip went to his cash register and he returned with the $15.00. I rode with Papa down to Fairport. He asked Arch Clay if he had the dog. He said he did, and he told about the $2.50 board bill Zip Coon wouldn't pay.

"That's not enough," Papa said. "Here's seven dollars and a half." We put the dog in the car. When we passed Bill Hunt's house, our scout master was cutting his grass.

Papa stopped the car: "Bill, here's seven dollars and a half Zip Coon has contributed to the camping trip. When you put the list of donors in the *Torchlight*, be sure to put his name at the top of the list."

Bill said, "Why, I can't believe it, Major. That devil has run me out twice, just for asking."

"He's had a change of heart," Papa explained. "He's seen the light."

We rode on to Zip Coon's house and we gave him his fabulous pointer. He was soberer by now. He scratched his head: "I bin thinkin'. I b'lief I coulda got my dawg back fer less'n fifteen dollars."

"That's correct," Papa said, "You could have got him back for two dollars and a half."

"Well, Ah entitled to know what you done with the balance of mah money."

"You're entitled to go to hell, but I'll tell you, anyway, free of charge: I gave Arch Clay seven fifty and I gave Bill Hunt seven fifty for the scouts."

He grimaced. He sizzled: "That putts a bad taste in mah mouff. Whatcha you gonna do?"

"You can kiss my damned tail and see if that puts a better taste in your mouth," Papa told him.

Oxford, February 3, 1960:

Today is Papa's birthday. I don't know where he is, but

I can't believe there are any telephones or chewing gum, wherever he is these days.

For many years, after I attained physical maturity, whether or not I was intellectually mature, Papa and I had regular informal debates arguing about who is the biggest son of a bitch in history.

We had too much material, too much subject-matter, too many diabolical inspirations, and we always ended our debates by espousing two men: Alexander Graham Bell, if he invented the telephone, and William Wrigley, if he invented chewing gum.

Papa said the devil invented the telephone because it always rang just as he was carving the supper beef, ladling out the soup, or helping us to the fish or chicken.

The supper calls, almost invariably, were from some pseudo-client who wanted street advice. Papa said street advice was free and wasn't worth a dried apple dam. But people called him, just the same.

If I answered the 'phone, Papa yelled, "Tell him I'm dead, Sandy." Mother rebuked Papa for asking me to tell Liza-Janes on the 'phone. But one night — we had oyster soup and Papa said cold oyster soup was worse than fondling a pretty girl while wearing heavy gloves — Papa told some alleged client he was dead.

The man said if Papa was dead how come he could talk on the 'phone? Papa boomed out: "We're all dead at this house, and we'll all be laid out until seven-thirty. We're all dead as King Tut until the last damned bite of supper is swallowed and digested."

Papa and I never could decide whether chewing gum was a bigger menace in blobs on the sidewalk or in a wad in someone's mouth. Whenever the phrase, "social disease," was whispered, Papa always pretended he thought the speaker was referring to gum chewing and not to venereal infections.

"It would be most salutary if the health department really could do something about this pestilence, about gum chewing. However, Walter Reed's job in fighting yellow fever was much easier."

We never had much success with chewing gum, but Papa got me to promise him I would never pull for the Chicago Cubs, not so well long as Wrigley owned the baseball team. And, as was the case with Rufus Duncan, E-Sick, I to my pledged word am true.

Today, when instant dialing is cracked up as a major miracle, I think of what Thoreau said when someone asked him what he thought of the miracle of a telegraph line's being strung from Massachusetts to Texas. Thoreau said it might be that Massachusetts and Texas had nothing to say to each other.

Thoreau also said that people didn't ride on railroads as much as railroads rode on people, and I apply that to today's instant communications, too.

To be honest, I was overawed by the telephone when I first encountered it as a boy in Oxford. And, for that matter, I still don't understand how it works. But the telephone used to be highly personalized and intimate, even if it was as mysterious to me as my attempts to read *Finnegan's Wake*.

There were several nerve-centers in town when I was a boy. If we thought these nerve-centers were vibrant, they did not conjure the frenzy and hysteria that the phrase often denotes today. For, this was at a time when all business and professional men came home at twelve noon to eat dinner and to take a short after-dinner snooze. ("Lunch" was something a workman, a school kid, or a fisherman carried in a pail or in a soda-cracker box.)

Actually, I never heard the phrase, itself, spoken, but hosts of magnetic sparks emanated from our insular nerve-

55

centers all the same. And I think the telephone exchange was the most acute and the most extensive nerve-center in Oxford. It was the Mt. Mitchell of local communications, and I say Mt. Mitchell, deliberately, rather than Pike's Peak.

Ours was a local telephone exchange. It was not a portion of some far-flung system. The line, which ran from Oxford to Henderson, ten miles to the northwest, was mystifying to me. How one frail, hump-backed line could carry such an enormous verbal cargo was completely beyond my comprehension.

There was no direct hook-up with other cities. Albeit, Miss Bertha Hornbuckle, our operator, could hook in on a "foreign" line for a long-distance call, but first she always satisfied herself that the call was of considerable magnitude. A long-distance call was consummate drama. Most men went to the telephone exchange and remained there, usually all day, while their calls were being completed. They put on their Sunday suits and they took something to read throughout the day.

I remember, precisely, the first long-distance call that involved our family. My father had urgent business with a lawyer ("fellow attorney" was Papa's phrase) in Norfolk, Virginia. He left home, our house and our "social" 'phone after breakfast, and he didn't complete the call until the shank of the evening, or late afternoon. Mother took his hot dinner to him as he waited for the call.

People said Papa "wasn't afraid of God, man or the devil," but his nervous fingers had pulled his black, string bow-tie all askew, and Mother retied it so that Papa would look his best when he talked along the line with his fellow attorney in Norfolk.

When the call was finally done, half the town really expected Papa to hand salt-water taffy, or to exhibit a big channel bass, or to have a bit of tar on his shoes.

The line from Oxford to Henderson (it extended out into the country on all sides of Oxford, into what are now the suburbs) was built and operated by a man, a foreign gentleman from Henderson, by the name of Hoffman. It was several years before this exchange became a part of today's big telephone system.

The first poles were called "Hoffman's Boulevard." Back then, a double row of trees, planted at regular intervals, was called a "boulevard," locally. Some called the poles "Hoffman's oaks." I remember that Papa said the beams across the poles, the handle-bars, were limbs, perhaps, that the lines were singing birds, eerie ones. (The first time I heard the word "cello" was one day when Papa said the lines made a fine cello for the wind to play salty tunes on.)

When I was first aware of the local telephone exchange, conscious of it as a pulsating, local entity, it was located on the top floor of a three-story building, the "Bengough Building," the tallest thing in town, not counting a couple of church spires and the bell-tower atop the courthouse.

It was so high up in the sky I thought God probably used the top of the building for a foot-stool to rest His bones when He got tired from counting fallen sparrows and from putting fainting robins back into their nests.

But hardly anyone ever used such a pretentious phrase as the "telephone exchange." It was the "central's office," or "Miss Bertha's roost," after Miss Bertha Hornbuckle, the lady who ran it and who had the whole town at her fingertips.

The telephone brought extraordinary changes in our lives, in our mores, although "customs of the country" was used in lieu of mores. Heredity had given Miss Bertha, the central, resoluteness and hardihood, at her advent, and the telephone put her strength into workable dramatic focus in our town.

The telephone, to my knowledge, was the first importation that would be classified the way an "in" thing is classified today. It came in among and upon our community "as tight as Dick's hatband." That was the phrase people used to denote the inexorable measure of the 'phone. (Papa explained to me the original phrase referred to the pathetic efforts of Richard Cromwell, old Oliver's boy, to wear the crown of England). But if wires went across the nation, the 'phone was local, local in contrast to the telegraph.

The telegraph instrument hadn't slept or even slumbered for at least three generations. It rattled on and on, like a shackly wagon. It droned on interminably, as some sort of immortal summer insect. But the big news bulletins were public coinage.

The bulletins that Mr. Thurston, the operator, pasted on the windows of the local Western Union, or "The Western and The Union," as most of us called it, belonged to the whole nation, whether they had told about the Johnstown Flood, Christy Matheson's pitching three shut-outs in five days, or about the sinking of the great ship, the *Titanic*.

People in town used it to get specific information or to say something explicitly. They asked the price of something, or they told someone when they would arrive in Washington City. I mean, of course, one couldn't lollygag, or socialize, or pass the compliments of the morning in ten words. (Some folks said the President of the local bank was so stingy he wouldn't use up his ten words. One time the President wanted to know the age of an out-of-town man who had applied for a line of credit. The President wired the man's firm: "How old George Hollingsworth stop." The reply came: "Old George fine stop. How you stop.")

You have to try to understand that the telephone was a church sociable, a quilting bee, and a visitation combined.

58

It not only knocked on virtually every door in town. It had a pass-key to virtually every home in town.

The 'phone ran over the insular communications barrier the way a Sherman tank would run through a paper fence. Women who didn't have the time or strength to dress, wash, and fix up to go calling could "talk along the line." People, especially women, could "how-d-do" everyday with folks whom they hadn't been able to talk to previously except for a few minutes right after church each Sunday.

Come to think about it, I was victimized a little bit by the telephone, even if I didn't get Papa to make a Federal case of the matter: I had picked up some nickels, some tinfoil, and a few ginger snaps from Ramsay Davis, before he could afford an office 'phone.

Before the 'phone I used to take, on foot, notes, all sealed up, from Ramsay Davis to Pansy Alice Duncan, whom he was trying to court. However, Pansy Alice, or "P. A." as she preferred to be called, hardly ever sent a written answer back to Ramsay Davis.

Sometimes her answer to Ramsay Davis' fat mash notes was an inelegant sound with her lovely lips. If she was in the mood for Ramsay Davis, she would say, over her shoulder, usually: "What the hell, kid. I guess so." One message involved my first full brush with the truly emancipated woman. It happened that Miss P. A. had been thrown, a minute or two earlier, by a horse, and she was the best horsewoman for nine counties around. She was rubbing her backsides as I ran up with Ramsay Davis' note. Tearing the note into ten pieces she sizzled: "Tell that shyster to go out and screw himself."

The electric shock of my incredulity would have knocked out every 'phone in town, and the lights, too. For, I would have bet my Barlow knife, my baseball cigarette cards, and my twenty dollar gold piece against a cymling seed that the only woman in town who ever heard the word "screw," in that sense, was Miss Opal, the boss-lady of the whorehouse.

I tried to write the message down for Ramsay Davis, in my own hand, but even the pencil point seemed to blush. Papa acted as my intermediary. He told Ramsay Davis: "Miss Duncan declines, with the stipulation that you go out and have criminal conversation with yourself, my boy."

Actually few people, save for rank strangers, or for some local galoot who had one year of "star courses" at a hard-drinking "gentleman's" college, ever asked Miss Bertha for a specific number, even when Miss Bertha's booming, "Num-bah, pleze," flooded the "hearer," the end of the 'phone that went to the ear.

Someone picked up the receiver and said: "Miss Bertha, will you fix me up along with Katie, pleze?" After the two passed the compliments of the morning, or the afternoon, Miss Bertha might reply: "I just saw Katie going into the drug store. She'll be in the asylum if she doesn't stop taking that headache medicine all the time. Why don't you try her at Mary Helen's about four o'clock. That's where the altar-guild is meeting." If Miss Bertha forgot something, she called back: "I forgot that Katie's going to Jo's to look at some patterns after the altar-guild, about five. Call her then. She can talk a heap sight better at Jo's than with all those grapejuice sisters a-buzzing around."

Again Miss Bertha would say: "Katie has gone downstairs (meaning Bengough's) to the shoe sale and you better hurry, Gladys, if you expect to get anything in your size. They didn't have but a few five and a half B's a little while ago."

Or she might tell Gladys: "Don't call Katie now. The Sheriff took Clem home from Miss Opal's last night, drunker than a goat, Clem was, and they are bound to be fighting to beat the band this morning."

If someone called for Dr. Henley, and if Miss Bertha diagnosed the call as being somewhat trivial or superficial, she would say, firmly: "Doc Henley stayed with Miz Turner, way out at Old Goshen, all night long while she was having twin baby gals. He's over at Thorne's Funeral Parlor grabbing some sleep in that special coffin. You just take some baking-soda and call Doc Henley this afternoon." I remember that "special" coffin well. It had a big, fluffy pillow in it, for the good Doctor to put his tired head on. Actually, few people knew that Dr. Henley used Mr. Thorne's Funeral Parlor for a hide-away when he was completely bushed. But, Papa knew, and he told me, but I had to promise not to tell, and I never have, until now. If Dr. Henley could get by with a furtive cat-nap, he used the extra chair in the barber shop. There were four barbers, invariably, and there were always five chairs. I don't know if that fifth chair was put in as an added attraction, but it endured, as a local cat-bird's seat, long before the phrase entered American literature.

Of course, if the doctor was needed urgently, Miss Bertha got him, P. D. Q. If she couldn't locate him by 'phone, she'd run to the window and yell to men along College Street: "Some a yawl run this way and some run that," she indicated the directions with her hands, "Until you find Dr. Henley. Tell him the little Ragland gal is scalded half to death."

The same courtesies were extended to Dr. Marks and the four other physicians. She never called Dr. Peabody unless there was an earthquake. Miss Bertha didn't like Dr. Peabody. He was a physician and a lawyer. He had two offices, straight across the hall from each other, on the second, or top, floor of the drug store. The sign on one door read:

> *Littleton H. Peabody, M.D.*
> *General Practice of Medicine*
> *Specializing in Diseases of Infants*

The other sign read:

> *L. Hinsdale Peabody, B.S., LL.D.*
> *Atty-At-Law — General Practice*
> *The Settlement Of Estates*
> *Is A Speciality*

Papa said Miss Bertha hated Doctor-Lawyer Peabody because he was always belittling Carrie Jacobs Bond and Ella Wheeler Wilcox. But Papa said those two asperities were Doctor-Mister Peabody's principal recommendations as man, physician, and attorney.

Miss Bertha's real animosity was probably due to the fact that "Mr. Hypenated" Peabody, as "Brer" Thompson called him, pronounced vegetables as "vege-tubbles," tomatoes as "tee-mar-toes," and said "this noon" instead of dinner-time. Then, when he vaccinated some kid, he always said, about somebody's arm: "Hark. Don't exercise the 'member' for two days."

Papa said "Mr. Hypenated" picked up "this noon" when he was reading medicine in Baltimore. Papa said the "switch-hitter," as the baseball fans called him, was really from Virginia — hence "veg-e-tubbles" — and that he studied law in barber college at Norfolk and "transferred" to North Carolina during the night, a snowy winter night. Back then, some lawyers were derided, mercilessly, as "barber college graduates," just as some physicians were said to have studied medicine at "Lynn, Massachusetts," the home base of Lydia Pinkham's "Vegetable Compound," introduced in 1876 "to relieve the horrors of women brutalized by perfidious males."

Mothers were always calling Miss Bertha to see if she could spot a stray or a tardy boy. If a housewife had a special delicacy she wanted to serve steaming hot, she called Miss Bertha to see if her husband was walking straight home to supper or if he was loitering around the candy store, "The Ivanhoe," hearing the pianola at Piano Hutchins' music store, or standing around the depot waiting for the "six somep'n train" to spew in amid a black hail storm of cinders and soot.

If Miss Bertha spotted a temporary truant she would yell at someone to yell at the truant. Or she might telephone the music store or the depot to get the word to the man. (There never was a 'phone at the Ivanhoe. I am sure of that).

As a boy I knew, as everyone knew, that Miss Bertha had as many eyes as a starry night in June. Our town, with all of its energies, tears, secrets, and minor intrigues, was her charge, her ward.

On her shirt-waist, just above the spot where it was assumed that a maiden lady's left bosom reposed, was a solid gold watch, with 21 jewels, and a golden case. This watch was there on her shirt-waist as if time had not hitched up until the day Miss Bertha pinned it there. When the golden case was closed, time was under a bushel, like the lights and the talents in the Sunday school lesson, but, in reality, I knew that inside the case was the real time of every single day in town.

Miss Bertha's time was the official time in town, and it didn't matter what some interloper at the Naval Observatory or at Greenwich said on the subject. Almost anybody could rig a box-supper box for a sucker, but Miss Bertha was the only person in town who could rig the time.

For instance, the same devilish boys (I guess I was one) who were always putting alum in the school picnic lemonade, and taking field mice to the "fill-ums" to turn loose to torment girls and ladies, had a sly way of turning the schoolhouse clock ahead.

When this happened, the principal, Miss Jennie, called Miss Bertha to get the correct time. (We couldn't keep our eyes off the clock once we had turned it ahead.) If Miss Bertha was suffering from the "fresh sausage complaint," or from the "Lydia E. Pinkhams," she might salt the time back by as much as thirty minutes, to keep us two-legged wiggle-worms squirming on our hard benches that much longer. On such occasions if we didn't get to play but five innings after school, we said the baseball game was "called on account of Miss Bertha."

On the other hand, if she was happy, if she had a treat, such as Alma Gluck's victrola record of Carrie Jacobs Bond's "End of a Perfect Day," she might salt the time ahead, maybe as much as fifteen minutes. We boys thought Miss Bertha did that so that Miss Jennie's "little ladies" would have a longer spell of "Pretty Girls' Station." Albeit, we weren't so sure she was being deferential to us young Babe Ruths who needed extra time to exercise squatters' rights on some bit of unused real estate.

For a long time, for three or four years, as I recall it, Miss Bertha stayed at her perch from eight in the morning until nine at night, on all week days. Of course, she got an hour off for dinner and another hour off for supper.

Frequently, she got her friend and fellow spinster, Miss Daisy O'Dell, our local artist, to spell her from twelve to one and from six to seven. Some folks, with tricks up their sleeves, tried to utilize Miss Bertha's off-hours to get a lot of clandestine stuff along the line. The trouble was that Miss Daisy usually brought her easel and her paints, especially her water-colors.

Miss Daisy couldn't be expected to see anything so

64

pedestrian as a light flashing on the board when she was absorbed totally in capturing the eternal wonder of a pine cone, a robin, or Albert, the town dog, that had a delicate constitution and couldn't eat juicy bones but loved ladyfingers. To be fair, Miss Daisy was, all things considered, the first local painter to go in for realism, for indigenous color and themes, instead of copies of things she hadn't ever seen.

She painted many pastorals. I remember one showed some cows grazing in luscious grass along the banks of Sweetgum Creek. The stream was so real-looking you almost thought you could drink from it. However, realism didn't allow any of the cows to have udders, not any udders that showed. So, they might as well have been bulls, in Miss Daisy's painting.

A boy, or a series of boys, came on at nine at night. There was a cot in the office, and the boy usually went to sleep. But someone might awaken him by yelling about a fire. If so, he called the firehouse, if the news hadn't been carried down there already.

When someone 'phoned in to report a fire, the number of the house or building might not be mentioned at all, if, indeed, there was a number.

The person would yell: "Miss Bertha, there's a fire at the old Cameron place." Or, "Miss Bertha, I see a lot of smoke in Egypt Land (the Negro residential section). It looks like the smoke is on that street that Cap'n Dave lives on."

Then Miss Bertha rang the firehouse and she told Pete Wood, who drove the fire truck, what she knew about the fire. When the 'phone rang, the alarm bell sounded. This attracted the attention of near-by firemen, before the big fire bell in the belfry started booming and bonging.

Pete had started as driver in the days when the horses,

Matt and Bertha, pulled the fire wagon. He always said, and our Chief, Matt Venable, and Papa agreed, that he could get out of the fire house quicker with the horses than he could with the fire truck, especially in cold weather.

I still regret that I was too young to see, just once, those horses swinging out of the fire house. But I heard about it so often sometimes I really think I witnessed this spectacular feat.

A cord was attached to the telephone box. Pete pulled the cord as he was taking the message from Miss Bertha, and the cord released the chain-gate to the stalls. The horses backed themselves under the harness, which was suspended above the tongue to the fire wagon. The harness dropped onto the backs of the two horses.

The two collars were split, and the hames were already on the collars. The collars dropped over the horses's necks, rather than the normal upside-down way of putting a collar on a horse. The bridles, save for the bits, stayed on the horses at all times. It took Pete only a second to put the bits into their mouths. Thus, the horses were practically ready to go, from the moment Pete pulled the cord, save for the snapping of the buckles.

The traces stayed fastened to the double-trees, and the lines were already run through the harness rings. Pete, and the others, estimated the wagon was on the street within twelve seconds of the time Miss Bertha called.

Bertha died when I was in the seventh grade. Matt died within two months. Mr. Ed Settle said Matt grieved himself to death, but he was getting old and feeble.

When Matt and Bertha died, the flag on the courthouse was lowered to half-mast. There was black crepe on the front door of the Town Hall, and old man Poe Peters, generally called "Po-Mouth" Peters, put some crepe on his RFD wagon. (This was a wagon, painted red, white, and blue, including the wheels and spokes, with the words "U. S. Mail" in big letters on each side.)

The *Torchlight*, our newspaper, carried a front page story, with photographs of the horses and with accounts of their accomplishments. Captain Wade, the editor, explained something that everyone didn't know: Once the horses were hitched to the wagon they ran the show. It wasn't enough that Matt and Bertha were strong and brave and fast. For, few local streets were uniformly level, and many corners were short and as mean as Old Scratch.

The wagon could crush unwary horses, as it went down a sharp incline. Matt and Bertha knew the nuances of local contours. They knew how to swing dangerous corners and not lose their speed, and they knew how to arrest the force of the heavy wagon when it went downgrade. I remember, vividly, that Captain Wade, in his newspaper piece, referred to Matt and Bertha as "four-legged topographical engineers." I asked Papa what "topographical" meant, and, of course, he made me look it up and then use it in a sentence.

The *Torchlight* also carried remarks made by "Brer" Thompson and others at the memorial service held in the fire house. But the paper didn't quote Mr. Settle. He said one good stud-horse and one good bull were worth more to the state of North Carolina than ten sessions of the General Assembly.

As I look back down the years, I think the ultimate rapport between local folks and their government probably came during the era of Matt and Bertha. These fire horses were the antithesis of political theories, promises, and abstractions. The horses were not oratory. Their eight flashing legs took our local government out for a public ride, to help someone who needed help in a hell of a damned hurry.

Naturally, virtually every patron of the telephone company dingled Miss Bertha to express sympathy when the beautiful gray mare died. And as kookie as it sounds to today's hippie generation, a few folks even took pies and cakes to the central's office and to Miss Bertha's house.

Nonetheless, I really can't say what Miss Bertha's reaction was to the death of her name-sake. She probably didn't confide in anyone but her friend, our artist, Miss Daisy O'Dell. However, she did her duty at the switchboard, just as if there were an epidemic of typhoid and she was working around the clock.

There was a sampler above the cot in the exchange that said: "Duty Is The Sublimest Word In The Language." Under the statement there were the words: "Robert E. Lee."

Miss Bertha knew her duty, all right, as well as her duties. She had spent a while in Richmond at a school learning to become an operator. Some said she studied as long as a month. Her official duties were written out on parchment, in Miss Daisy's hand, and the paper was under a piece of glass on her arm-rest:

"Rules And Duties Of A Telephone Girl"

1. She must possess health, and excellent sight, hearing, and reading ability.
2. Her first duty is to learn the language of the telephone.
3. She must know the intricate techniques of the switchboard.
4. Her fingers must be as well-trained as her mind.
5. Good posture is an essential for a successful operator.
6. An operator must know her high degree of impor-

tance to her company.

7. A pretty floral center-piece on a table adds to the attractiveness of the office.
8. She must be discreet in the manner in which she handles 'Information' calls.
9. The telephone operator is never treated like a machine, as so many working girls are.
10. She must be thoroughly familiar with every detail of her switchboard map, as she must be prepared to handle from 80 to 100 calls each day."

Evidently, Miss Bertha imparted some of the sacrosanct language of telephony to Miss Daisy O'Dell. When the two walked along the street, Miss Bertha spoke obliquely, almost sotto voco, such words as "jack," "trunk," "plug," "magneto," "relay," "induction coil," and "A-Board."

The conversations were as frustrating to us as those head-to-head ones held between Professor Max Schmidt, the music teacher, and "Governor Poly," who spoke Latin and Greek and everything else.

The High Sheriff said Miss Bertha was the "eyes" of the law, and he said this without jest. However, Papa sometimes called Miss Bertha "William J.," after William J. Burns who had the national detective agency. Papa said Miss Bertha's ears were key-holes bigger than the Grand Canyon. He said she knew more about the town than a 100 year old sparrow knew about fresh horse manure, "dos," as animal excrement was called in polite circles when I was a boy.

She could spot a suspicious character from the legitimate drummers who came to town on the train, in their derby hats, spats, and carrying their sample cases. She would 'phone the day policeman, or the night policeman, or Sheriff Venable, if a stranger looked as if he weren't up to something good.

For instance, I remember one sidewinder who came to town toting a huge sample case. Miss Bertha was suspicious before she actually saw this fellow. He put down his bag when he got off the train, and Bruce Jackson, who met all the trains with a dray from his mother's big boarding-house, the "Waverly Inn," had a hard job picking up the case.

Somebody said the fellow must be an anvil salesman, but the man said he sold all kinds of big wrenches, monkey-wrenches and so forth. During the next couple of days, Miss Bertha didn't like the way this wrench-salesman kept watching the bank. But she restricted her suspicions to Matt Venable.

On the third night the High Sheriff caught the stranger. The man had sawed some of the bars in a window at the back of the bank and he had jimmied the window.

Albert, our gourmet town dog, had been tailing the fake drummer around town, and Albert had bitten the man on his left leg just before Matt Venable jerked him from the window to the rear of the bank.

The next day was Albert's day in Oxford. Perhaps, we proved Cervantes's dictum: "Every dog has his day." "Brer" Thompson gave Albert a handsome collar, the first one Albert ever had. When "Brer" Thompson put the collar around Albert's neck, he quoted from Ecclesiastes, 9:4: "A living dog is better than a dead lion."

Several people gave Albert fresh lady-fingers, and the President was so overcome with gratitude he bought Albert a five-cent chocolate-eclair. But Mr. Ed Settle roared: "The devil and Tom Walker. Man's best friend can't live by bread and chocolate alone." Mr. Ed put Albert in his buggy. He drove Albert out to his dog-pen and turned him loose in a special pen with three bitches in heat, or with thee "lady dogs having a season," as old maid dog owners put it.

Papa said Albert's reward was "properly commensurate with his valorous deed, and then some." We heard that after two days in the special pen poor Albert tried to tunnel his way out, and when he was reprieved he was too weak for any nourishment except lady-fingers crumbled up in milk.

Miss Bertha and Matt Venable didn't mind at all that Albert copped top honors in thwarting the robbery.

Miss Bertha knew a thousand "secrets," such as who was sleeping off a drunk, and where. She knew which drunks to ignore until they were sober enough to go home. She knew which ones had to be at certain jobs at certain times, and she knew which were more likely to catch cold. She knew which ones were married to women who wanted them home, drunk or not. She knew which ones were more susceptible to colds and to severe rheumatism. She knew which ones saw lions and tigers.

She'd get word to the sheriff, or to Mr. Matson or Mr. Hasbrook, down at the "Ivanhoe" candy store, to see to the needs of the special cases. Miss Bertha's perceptiveness was really singular, when it came to the male animal, because she had never been married, had never courted, insofar as anyone knew, had never had a brother, and she lived alone. Instinctively, though, as her steel-rimmed eyes, the first radar in town, ranged the back alley and doorways, she knew which men were pleasure-drunk, which ones were mean-drunk, which ones were crying-and-worrying drunk, and which ones were just drunk-drunk because it was the time for them to get drunk again.

As she watched the lost sheep, she cracked more intricate codes and ciphers than Edgar Allan Poe and the F. B. I. combined. Some courting couples spent hours devising flawless codes. This amalgamation of word-symbols, dog-latin, balderdash, dramatic stresses on certain syllables, and literary allusions was known in Oxford as "Greek."

But all of the verbal subterfuges were wasted fiascoes. Miss Bertha could have cracked the puzzle in "The Gold Bug" if someone said it over the 'phone a couple of times. And if she approved of a particular clandestine meeting, and if she got tired of the endless gibberish, she would break in: "Mercy sakes, Helen. He wants you to pretend you are going to Gertrude's to read the *Delineator* and to see her new hat and coat. He'll meet you at the gate when it's dark enough."

It could work out the other way around. She would tell a girl: "Stop making these sly dates with Herman Rivers at the Orpheum. I know what you do. You and Mollie sit in the balcony. Then he slips up there and Mollie comes on downstairs. You little dumb-bell, don't you know he's got three bad checks out now and that he goes to Miss Opal's when he takes you home."

Normally, she saved such terse warnings for head-to-head conversations, but once when Francis Tice, a nice but not too smart boy, was telephoning a fast-stepper, in Greek, Miss Bertha didn't wait until she saw Francis. She called him back, as soon as his coded conversation with the fast-stepper was done:

"Look here, Francis. I'm going to give it to you with the bark on. Don't you know that gal has given herself, and I mean all of herself, to every young man in town?"

Francis replied: "Maybe so, Miss Bertha, but Oxford ain't but so damned big, anyhow."

Beyond any question, the telephone changed the format of the *Torchlight*, our weekly newspaper. For a long time Captain Wade had run a two-column feature on the front page of every issue of the *Torchlight*. It was called "Running The Gamut," and it told all the juicy items in local mores. It was, from the provincial perspective, a forerunner

72

of the syndicated gossip and cafe society columns that would sweep the nation later on.

It didn't take Captain Wade long to know that the people on the 'phone were scooping him regularly. At best the material in "Running The Gamut" merely corroborated what had been told endlessly along the line.

The column became almost devoid of local names as Captain Wade switched to nature, memorabilia, vignettes about history and literature, and countless other charming bits and pieces.

Papa said the telephone was a left-handed, blab-mouthed inspiration that made Captain Wade a thoroughly good writer, a creative writer. Indeed, dailies began to reprint stuff from "Running The Gamut." Occasionally, some magazine or Sunday newspaper asked the Captain for a piece on April in Oxford, or some facet of Christmas celebration, or something on the medicines used by the Tuscaroras in the old days.

Along with the change in the column, the Captain put in a regular obituary section, with a black border. Deaths were no longer strewn across the front page with stories of ice cream parties, large catches of fish, news of sick rooms, and local politics.

Simultaneously, Miss Daisy O'Dell became the first society editor, although her page was called "Hearth And Hall." Henceforth, social notes always appeared on a separate page, too. I suppose one would say Miss Daisy was a sort of in-depth society reporter. She put into literary focus the oddments previously spoken on the 'phone. And if anyone ever questioned her accuracy, she always smiled modestly and said in soft voice: "Don't forget, honey, I'm in a position to know." When she said that, everybody shut up because everyone knew what good friends Miss Daisy and Miss Bertha were.

Apparently, Captain Wade never read Miss Daisy's copy, and she did get carried away, now and then, by what she called the Muse. I have, at hand, three seer clippings I got from Papa's special file when he died.

One is a write-up of a wedding: "There was an allurious and lascivious wedding-cake, of five layers. After partaking of the cake and homemade blackberry wine, all the wedding guests departed in a merry and a licentious mood."

Another time the Greensboro College's "Madrigal Singers," all girls, were to give a concert at the Woman's Club. Miss Daisy learned that the group would sing some fugues. Her headline went: "Lovely Girls To Do Fugging Music."

The best one I will write down verbatim: "Last night the young ladies at Miss Jennie's school put on a performance of 'Peter Pan.' Next week this charming group of lesbians will entertain the ladies of the Geneva Presbyteria."

Actually, Miss Daisy's confusion of "lesbian" and "thespian" didn't cause much yammering or snickering. The subject of homosexuality just didn't come up in Oxford often at that time. Of course, Papa, Dr. Henley and a few other men slapped their sides, but they were careful not to offend Miss Daisy. The reason that "Peter Pan" was done by an all-girl cast was the inability of the boys to learn their lines. I know I failed deliberately, for fear someone would call me a sissy, and I am sure the other male scholars at Miss Jennie's felt the same way.

Captain Wade accused Miss Bertha of unfair advertising practices, but his charge really didn't come to much. Miss Bertha cut in frequently on the conversations of friends to tell them of bargains she had noted as she walked to work.

She let it out when doughnuts, with enough sugar to give diabetes to the whole modern A. M. A., were just from the oven at the bakery and were hanging so delectably on

74

their sticks in the window.

She passed out the news, too, when Otho Greeley, who ran the best cafe in town, had his specialities for sale. Otho, a sinewy, middle-aged Negro, looked remarkably like Satchel Paige, as I look back on him. Everything he cooked was good enough for the angels and St. Peter, but his specialities were candied sweet potatoes, clogged with brandy, strawberry ice cream, made with fresh strawberries and pure cream, and steamed oysters.

Because of poor refrigeration, oysters were a seasonal bonus. Otho put them in a pie pan, a dozen or so fat, juicy ones, and he covered the top with smooth biscuit crust. The crust made the dish a scrumptious pie, but it was really there to keep the oysters hot because most men carried the treat home to share it with their families. Otho always handed out an extra pie plate to cover the other one, upside down, for warmth.

But I always thought his supreme special was his oyster-roll. He baked long loaves of bread, with hard, thick crusts. The outside was like the streets of heaven and the soft inside was like an angel's pillow. He cut off one end of the loaf, pulled out the white clouds and stuffed in oysters richer than the President. Then he put some of the white fleecy stuff back in and he jammed the cut off end tightly into the loaf.

Workmen and hunters and little boys who found a quarter could tote hot oysters a long time. The oysters were buttered, salted, and peppered when Otho put them into the hollowed out loaf. What most folks did was to slice the loaf and eat chunks of buttered bread and oysters at the same mouthful.

Otho made specialities of herring and shad roe, but he never had any success with sturgeon roe. Interestingly enough, local rivers were quick with sturgeon, the fish whose roe is the source of caviar. But I never heard the word "caviar" mentioned. Sturgeon were so numerous and so large they were a glut in the rivers and upon the fish market, too.

They were, almost literally, as cheap as gulley dirt, selling for two cents a pound, for garden fertilizer, chiefly. During the season, great quantities of sturgeon were piled up along the gutters in the local alleys and side streets. We bought them for our garden, and I carted them home in a little red wagon, behind Milt, our family goat. I remember several times when Miss Bertha asked me to haul her "garden fertilizer" to her place.

I said Captain Wade complained about Miss Bertha's "free" advertising, but his complaint was only half-hearted. She wasn't showing favoritism to any specific merchants. And it was unthinkable that she got any sort of commission. The plain truth was that she became excited when pretty clothing was displayed, when Otho Greeley's succulent wares were available, when baskets of peaches and strawberries perfumed the sidewalk, and when "King of the Green Snakes" Imboden brought his first two-horse wagon load of luscious watermelons to town each summer.

Otho Greeley's cafe, the "Booker T.," was in the basement of the Bengough Building. Entry was made from the right-hand side of the building, as one faced it from College Street. There was a handrail, made of lead pipes, for ladies and elderly gentlemen to hold to, and there were eleven steps leading from the first floor level down to the cafe.

The steps were worn down until they were almost slick at the ends, and each one was filled with scars and abrasions. A saloon had been in the basement, before my time. The chipped and cracked places in the steps were said to be the result of barrels of whiskey being rolled down them.

The first floor of the building was used by Mr. Bengough for his store. Bengough's was divided into three large, separate divisions, with connecting open doors. One part was for ladies' clothing; another part was for men's clothing; and the third part was for "heavy and fancy groceries." There were three big show windows, and on each one there was painted, in big, sort of Old English gold letters, by the hand of Miss O'Dell: "Quality Spells What Joe Bengough Sells."

The second floor was used as a sort of club and meeting room by the Masons. I didn't know much about the Masons because Papa didn't belong to the organization. The President told Papa his law practice would be "more spot cash and less white trash and nigger" if he joined the Masons. Papa told the President: "When I take to pimping, it will be for Miss Opal." Then Papa jabbed the President in the ribs with his long right finger: "For your damned information, I wouldn't piss in a mason-jar if I got caught short at a watermelon slicing." Of course, Papa took that dig at the Masons just because the President irritated him. Actually, he said the Masons did many fine things, especially for orphans.

Of course, the third floor was all Miss Bertha's, just as the Model T was all Mr. Ford's. I rubber-necked the top floor each morning as I walked to school, and I rubber-necked it again each afternoon. I knew the town had a long, active history before Miss Bertha was born, before the telephone came along, and I am sure I recognized the fact that she was mortal. Yet I thought she was as immutable as the giant oak trees on the courthouse lawn, and everybody knew God made those oaks early on the first morning of creation week, when His beard was only a moustache and a small goatee.

As she sat there at her switchboard plugging in and out the love songs, furies, minor heroics, and caprices of an

77

entire town, I saw Miss Bertha's dominion much as I saw the ministrations of the yard-master at the big depot in heaven. In lieu of yard-master's cap, she had a growth of hair that was really fulsome. Without pins it could have been William Jennings Bryan's oratory.

But this enormous growth of hair was piled up on her head like a well-stacked load of hay, into which two pencils were always stuck.

During the week-days she wore shirt-waists and skirts. The shirt-waists usually buttoned up to her neck, and, usually, they had little pleats. Some were voile. Others were batiste or nansook. Once a month, she wore a shirt-waist of pongee. When she wore the pongee to work men along the street swung out their hats when they tipped them to Miss Bertha.

Her skirts were so low a snake with a spy-glass couldn't see her ankles. Many times when I saw her coming, "Stepping high, which was of her walk, the way," I closed my eyes and the swish-swish of her skirt along the sidewalk reminded me of lake waters gently lapping the shore. When she walked fast Miss Bertha's hemline changed from swish-swish to an urgent sort of hiss-hiss.

Just about everyone in town gave Miss Bertha the same deference I did. Almost everyone, grown folks and kids like me, "gave her the sidewalk." Physically, she wasn't any bigger than the average woman, but she "took up half the street," as people used to say.

She could have been anywhere from 40 to 70, in my eyes, as she swept down the streets of Oxford. In her right hand there was an umbrella, always, not an elegant, effete parasol, but a stout umbrella, the heavy kind that opened up with a masculine "swush." She tapped the point on the sidewalk as if she were scattering coded messages to anyone who could decipher them.

The umbrella was a staff. Too, it protected her from the elements and from the officious males. No male ever attacked her, but one Saturday night Just Plain Snake Imboden, the block-aider, got tanked on his own juice and passed some slight remark to Miss Bertha. She beat him to his knees the way Dempsey tattoed big Jess Willard at Toledo, Ohio.

I thought the umbrella was a part of Miss Bertha's right hand, the same as her thumb and her fingers. I could hear it around the corner, tap-tapping the sidewalk, before I could see her. Papa said the sounds of that umbrella reminded him of a floating crap game on Saturday night.

Insofar as I know, Doctor-Lawyer Peabody (frequently, Papa appended "Indian Chief") was the only person ever to question Miss Bertha about her umbrella. One cloudless day when the sun had complete charge of the world, "Mister Hypenated" Peabody asked: "Why do you carry an umbrella when the sun is shining?"

Miss Bertha answered, back over her shoulder: "Any blamed fool can carry an umbrella when it's raining."

Her cottage was on Spring Street, originally Gum Spring, up on the corner a block from our house. (To be realistic, the "block" was one other house, two large persimmon trees, and a vacant lot.)

She bought and paid for the house by herself and she ran and she kept it alone, too. She carried her own provisions home from Bengough's. She split her own kindling, and she toted in her stove wood and she toted out her ashes.

I can't count the times I offered to help her with woodpile and ashes chores. That is, I can't begin to remember all the times that Papa or Mother said to me: "Scoot up to Miss Bertha's and offer to lend her a hand." She'd thank me, but she'd go right on piling up a turn of wood in her bent left arm.

The cottage was green, what was known later as "Williamsburg green." There was a white, paling fence all around the house, but kids never swung on her gate, the way they swung from Spring Street to Bagdad and back on other gates, and they didn't run sticks along her palings to make whack-whack music. I don't believe that she ever forbade it. We just didn't mess with her things, despite the fact that she wasn't at home to run us away.

She had an ice pond, a small one, beyond her house, and she was the only "old" lady in town who skated. I know because she used to ask Miss Jennie's scholars to a skating party each winter. While she didn't go in for funny sayings very often, she told me one day I could break Ty Cobb's base stealing record if baseball were played on ice. Miss Bertha didn't cut fancy figures. She skated in front and we tried to follow her. After the skating we toasted marshmallows by an outdoors fire. We always brought the refreshments. Miss Bertha said: "The good Lord and I will provide the recreation."

My grown son thinks I'm a liar or a square, or both, when I tell about old-time ice ponds. Once, my son quoted a lot of former thermometer readings, or whatever they're called now, to prove that the winters were no colder back then than they are now.

Ponds don't freeze now, he tells me. So, what is all the jazz about ponds freezing over fifty years ago and more? The difference was that certain ponds were made specifically to freeze over solidly. The water was low, never more than navel deep. It was as still as a good woman's conscience, and it had lots of grass and weeds in it to aid the freezing process.

Miss Bertha sawed her ice into blocks, usually with the help of two of us boys on the other end of her cross-cut saw. We put the ice on a cart and hauled it to her ice-house — sort of like a World War I dug-out, with a single window making it a squat Cyclops — and packed it with dirt and sawdust.

Some folks said Miss Bertha kept her ice-pond, after the days of the ice-plant and the ice-wagon, just to be different. Some saw it in terms of today's status-symbol. I don't know what the impulse was, but Miss Bertha liked her ice-pond and that was sufficient reason for sensible folks.

She said ice-plant ice had dangerous chemicals in it. Perhaps, she said this so often she really believed it. Anyway, the ice-pond was her own thing, her bag.

Each summer she had a super-duper ice-cream and lemonade party for the kids who helped her cut and haul the chunks of ice to her ice-house in the winter. And she had Boot Ransome, our blacksmith, champion flower grower, and the world's greatest maker of lemonade over to take charge for the party.

And poor people from the country used to come to Miss Bertha to get chunks of ice for sick relatives and friends, especially for those who had typhoid. This was long before antibiotics and magic medications, and ice gave blessed relief. The trouble usually seemed to be that those who had the most sickness never had any ice during the summer, although they had more than they wanted during winter, when there was no typhoid. Papa said, on this subject, that there was a natural affinity among all animals because the wolf and the stork seemed to work so many of the same homes.

I remember Miss Bertha as a strong woman who was eminently capable of handling her own affairs in an insular world that was run by men. The first time I read Oliver Goldsmith's lines, about the village vicar, "And still they gazed and still their wonder grew, That one small head could carry all he knew," I thought of Miss Bertha, the first crack out of the box. When I recall her today, I think of a strong, independent woman.

When I think of Miss Bertha in the present tense, I see her up yonder, the center of a gregarious knot of angels from Oxford. The angels from Oxford hardly notice the fellow who walks in space. They bend low to feast on choice tidbits Miss Bertha gleaned along the line, but ones which she promised herself, and Miss Daisy, she would never reveal until the great getting up day in the sky.

There is one lingering footnote to the early telephone. It came out first in a debate, one of the regular debates sponsored by the old "Oxford Dialetic Society." This debate was on progress. The President took the affirmative side of the telephone issue and Papa took the negative or "hell no" side.

Obviously, a man of Papa's intelligence recognized the value of the 'phone even if someone always called every-time we sat down to supper.

And Papa never bought stock in the 'phone company. He said getting dividends from a 'phone company was equal to making money by renting out chiggers and mosquitoes during "Dog Days," July 15 to September 1, roughly.

The President won the debate because Papa was too theoretical for the audience and the judges. He said: "You want faster communications. Well, that's fine, but you must prepare to sacrifice much freedom, much privacy."

"Ladies, you say you like to vote and to come down and work. That's all right with me, but you will have to learn to put up with terrible fumes, with such sounds as ignorant armies make when they clash by night."

Then in a manner that was jocular but still on the level, Papa said the telephone had turned local people into such blamed liars they made Ananias and Munchausen look like two little boys in the "Bright Jewels," the Methodist organization for youngsters.

A man could call home and say he had to take a sick friend home when all the time he was going to the creek to shoot crap and get drunk. He said the new wrinkle was that the man's wife really knew her husband was lying, but she couldn't prove it because she couldn't see the lie in his eyes and on his face.

To augment his argument about the new breed of liars, Papa quoted some lines from one of the first telephone songs, one called "I'm Afraid To Go Home In The Dark," by Egbert Van Alstyne and Henry Williams.

Two or three wisenheimers in the audience started chortling: "Sing her, Sandy. Line her out, Alexander." And Papa said, "All right. By God, I will."

I can see mother hiding and blushing behind her fan now, but Papa didn't sing as badly as she thought:

Baby dear, listen here,
I'm afraid to go home in the dark;
Everyday the papers say
There's robbery in the park;
So I sit alone in the Y. M. C. A.
Just singing like a lark:
'There's no place like home, sweet, home,'
But I'm afraid to go home in the dark.

But the big point Papa made has never left me: He said O. Henry liked that song and that O. Henry was thinking about it when he died in 1910. Papa said it was all mishmash that O. Henry got religion at the last minute when he said: "Let up the shade. I don't want to go home in the dark." He said that was a cheap trick of the preachers and the cheap-jack big city reporters.

The President was indignant. He said it took a true Christian to write the "Gift of the Magi," but Papa convinced me, especially when I had a chance to think on it seriously, and he convinced the ones who hung around the "Ivanhoe." And I don't think Mr. Matson and Mr. Hasbrook agreed with Papa just because they hated the President's guts.

As fantastic as it seems, I got to know the second Mrs. Porter, O. Henry's second wife.* I asked her about the song, in connection with O. Henry's last words, and the way she denied it confirmed for me, forevermore, what Papa said that night when he and the President debated on progress.

*She lived in Weaverville, and she didn't die until 1965.

Oxford, March 22, 1955:

Today it's rare for a man to admit that he has told a lie about something. No, he says he was misquoted or that something was taken out of context. And other men aren't called liars very often, either. Instead, they "manage" or "slant" the facts.

Yesterday, Oxford had four distinct types of liars: Nice Liars, D-Liars, Double-D-Liars, and Munchausens. Nice Liars told plain girls they were pretty. They told feeble people they looked just fine. Frequently, if someone told an ugly truth, the Nice Liar swore it wasn't true.

D-Liars told untruths for their own benefit or profit. They used the truth as if it were a piece of goods and they were tailors using scissors to make a suit. Sometimes, D-Liars ran for office and, quite often, they concealed the real facts of a sale, the same as Ananias did, if not with the

84

same end result.

Double-D-Liars were really pernicious. Their base slanders damaged other people. They supped on vile rumors, but many Double-D-Liars ended up choking on their own virulence.

Munchausens improved upon drab and phlegmatic truths by appending wings, glamor, romance, sparkle, and excitement. Every town had its champion, a real professional. In some places he held court from a bench on a mall bench, and people crowded about as the young Greeks sat before Plato at the Academy.

He had been everywhere. He had seen everything. He knew everyone. He could top any known tale, in spades. Actually, he was a story-teller. He was as refreshing as a cold shower when July blows its stack. He was axed when international travel became instantaneous and available to almost everyone, when TV came along to dominate the home. The chief difference is that he charged nothing, sold no tickets, and he never interrupted a delightful yarn for a commercial.

Such a man was Mr. Oliphant Matson, Mr. Ollie Matson, who "stayed" in the "Ivanhoe," the local candy store operated by Mr. Amos Hasbrook.

At night, Mr. Matson came perilously close to emulating the hare and the fox. He laid his weary bones in precarious places. When I was a boy, at the time of which I write, when he must have been 75, he lived in the alley owned by Boot Ransome. His abode was a wierd arrangement of piano boxes, gifts from Piano Hutchins, who ran the local music store.

If he went underground, almost literally, at bedtime, by day he reigned at the "Ivanhoe," and Mr. Hasbrook, the owner of the candy store, was his Prince of Wales.

I never thought of Mr. Matson as a liar, per se. There

probably just wasn't enough truth extant to accomodate his insatiable urge for words. But, in a way that really annoyed certain members of the Oxford Establishment, some of Mr. Matson's extravagant yarns had devastating elements of unimpeachable historical fact.

For instance, the story he told about Paul Dresser and the background of the composition of "My Gal Sal" is true enough. And, of course, Dresser and Theodore Dreiser were brothers, just as Mr. Matson said.

I'm sure the old "Ivanhoe" is worthy of recapitulation, even if there had been no Mr. Matson. Similarly, the New York Yankees are eminently deserving of memoirization, had there been no Babe Ruth. But, fortunately for the Yankees, and fortunately for me, Babe Ruth and Mr. Matson lived and breathed and left their own indelible imprints.

The "Ivanhoe," which many folks called "Oxford's sweet tooth," was across College Street from Bengough's. It was an old wooden building, of one story, and it resembled a piece of ratty cheese in a sandwich with two huge pieces of brown bread.

But the candy store didn't touch either of the buildings next to it. There was an alley on either side. The alley next to the bank was not more than two feet wide. The alley next to Piano Hutchins' place was big enough for a boy or a lean man to walk through. The weeds next to the bank were high enough to obscure Albert, the town dog, when he sought a cool place in summer. Saturday night drunks threw bottles into it, and cats used it frequently for fights and other sporting events.

In summer, especially after hard rains, the weedy alley had that nauseating sweet smell that people used to associate with cancer. Then when the sun flailed down on the wet density the alley smelled like socks that hadn't been

86

changed since McKinley. The back end of the alley was cut off with a fence made of boarded oddments. The fence was nailed to the back of the "Ivanhoe," and to a long pole that almost touched the side of the bank but hardly ever did more than to scratch the bank's ribs.

The President always held his nose when he passed the alley, but he couldn't do anything about it. The alley was on the land of Mr. Amos Hasbrook, who owned and operated the "Ivanhoe." The bank didn't have an inch on that side, having been built plumb with the survey.

The Ladies' Cultural and Improvement Society was always threatening to take drastic action. And to illustrate the power of the Ladies' Cultural and Improvement Society, all of the local church workers and the stoutest members of the U. D. C. belonged to it.

The society always sponsored candidates for the town board and for mayor who pledged to enforce the ordinance that forbade spitting tobacco juice on the sidewalks. They sought candidates who would favor action to buy a town ladder long enough for "the proper custodian" to keep the Confederate soldier, up on his marble monument, free of bird droppings, although the word the ladies used was "unblemished."

The Society always threatened to boycott merchants who let their store cats sleep in the sugar barrels. The Society had a special committee which urged housewives to save ashes to dump on the muddy sidewalks and streets that hadn't been paved. In fact, there was a regular ceremony, at the beginning of each winter, one almost akin to the "Blessing of the Nets" in fishing places, when ladies met at appointed times to pour ashes across the street from their corner to the opposite corner.

Everybody under twenty-five despised this because a boy could carry a girl across a muddy street piggy-back, with immunity. Papa said if a girl "posted" a little bit, why it was just because she was dizzy or excited from riding at such an immense height.

But the perennial political goal was to clean up the little alley by the "Ivanhoe." And it wasn't only the weeds and the stench. No, some ladies who walked to Wednesday night prayer meeting said the "who-who-who-are you" screeches of an owl, and the horrifying, rotating eyes of an owl, down in the alley, made them lose their religion.

One night an owl really landed on Mrs. Ashton-Brown's head. She was not only rich and powerful. She was the political salt of the ladies' movement. Mrs. Ashton-Brown was extremely refined and Papa said that particular owl must have said "whom-whom" instead of "who-who."

To be honest, I was no damned fool about owls, although I always sided with Mr. Hasbrook against the Society. I always thought up some good reason for running fast whenever I saw an owl down that alley at night, his crazy eyes casting beams such as I imagined might be made by a locomotive hauling sinners to the bad place. Conversely, when winter's snow was in the alley, I thought those weeds were white birds, too chilled to sing, perhaps, but they did huddle there as if a thousand mute Chinese nightingales were dabbed in with frosty brushes.

Despite the constant pressures of the Society, nothing tangible was done about the alley during Mr. Hasbrook's lifetime. At the time of which I write, a lot of women hadn't registered to vote. Hence the women were like a she-ox across a fence, unable to gore or to kick. True, they got in some licks, but usually when the waters of reform were about to boil, public attention was diverted: Some sheer lily of a girl had a shotgun wedding, a big snow came to town, or focus was turned on Miss Opal and her soiled doves.

The women never got their feet into local politics until years later, although they followed a stringent device advocated earlier by Mrs. Ashton-Brown.

Mrs. Ashton-Brown, according to Mamma, who belonged to the Society, told the women: "You must strike against your husbands." Mrs. Ashton-Brown explained that by "strike" she meant that women should sleep with both feet in a small water bucket until the men voted for reforms.

Papa said Mrs. Ashton-Brown was an impeachable witness. He spoke of her, to his pals, as "Mrs. Forked Tongue." What Papa meant, in reference to her water -bucket suggestion, was that Mrs. Ashton-Brown was a widow. He said, too, that this strike business would be another Homestead fiasco until younger and prettier women took over the Society. That happened, about ten years later.

Even so, nothing was done about spitting tobacco juice, since chewing tobacco was really an act of patriotic faith, in our economy. Albeit, a few blatant vulgarians who spat blobs of spittle and mucus were hauled into court and fined. Finally, though, a long ladder was bought to keep the Confederate soldier spruced up. The fire company never would lend its long ladder. As Chief Matt Venable explained to the men in town: "How am I go explain to some bastard on a second floor, with his nightgown on fire, that he can't get out because some jaybird has messed on the monument?"

The alley by the music store ran straight through to a big vacant lot. The big lot was for swapping livestock and for selling farm produce. There were posts for horseshoes, and three "marble yards," the places on which grownups and talented youngsters played "ring men" with toys almost as big as billiard balls. Plugs tossed underhanded, from a distance of 24 feet, and experts shot the 24 feet from the thumb.

This alley was used, generally as a shortcut and for what Papa called a "kidney oasis." If we boys got caught short, coming home from school, one fellow would stand straight up while another bent over and did "Number one." When we were certain no one was in sight, say around two in the afternoon of a mad dog day in July, we tried to write our names on the side of Piano Hutchins's wall. Some of us got to be proficient but before we could start on our last name the first name had dried, run, or smeared.

One reason we liked this unusual name writing so much was that it was one damned thing a girl couldn't do, especially the girls who did well at school when we did poorly.

Mr. Hasbrook didn't heed either alley, or the reformers. Most of the talking for the "Ivanhoe" was done by Mr. Matson, Mr. Hasbrook's tombstone companion. But now and then, when the President stomped by, holding his nose, Mr. Hasbrook might say: "If thy right hand offends thee, cut it off." Whereupon, Mr. Matson might add: "And some po widow's savings may be spared."

The building, the "Ivanhoe", didn't look so much like something the cat dragged out as it looked like something the cat didn't bother to haul in out of the rain. All of the paint on the front had turned into blisters long ago. However, a stranger, wouldn't ever learn if Mr. Hasbrook was "too poor to paint and too proud to whitewash."

The entire front of the building was covered completely with tin signs, advertising signs made of metal, but I don't ever recall any sign that advertised anything that was ever sold in the candy store. These signs were for decoration, and to keep in the heat in winter, and, perhaps to soak up some of summer's suns. The signs told about Samson Shoes, Sovereign Cigarettes, Jacob Fuller and Joseph Green

Goosegrease, Anvil Brand Overalls, Reynold's Level Best Chewing Tobacco, Stark's Dixie Plows, Lydia E. Pinkham's Vegetable Compound, Pillsbury's Flour, Oysterettes, McDonald's Buggy Robes, and Hobson's Sweet Spirits of Nitre.

The roof of the building was patched completely with a variety of tin cans that had been hammered as flat as a tin can could be hammered by hand. The cans were to keep the wind and the rain out. Everytime a leak appeared, Mr. Hasbrook climbed up a permanent ladder, on the Piano Hutchins side. Mr. Matson took the store brush-broom and hit the ceiling. Mr. Hasbrook nailed down a smashed can or two at the indicated place.

The Society said the front and roof of the "Ivanhoe" were a disgrace to Oxford, and some men who didn't know any better said Mr. Hasbrook was so stingy that he squeezed Lincoln to the hollering point. But others, especially Papa, knew Mr. Hasbrook's singular method of remodeling the store wasn't due to stinginess. When he died the property would revert to his dead wife's people in Virginia. Only a fool could expect Mr. Hasbrook to spend his good money on a pack of damned in-laws.

Mr. Matson usually entered the store each morning at eight on the dot of Miss Bertha's watch. Mr. Hasbrook already had a half-gallon spout pot of coffee on the heavy, stubby stove. The stove heated the store during winter, and Mr. Hasbrook cooked on it the year round. He slept in the back of the store, in a space partitioned off by some old velvet curtains he had bought from the Opera House when new ones were purchased.

They shook hands, every morning, and each congratulated the other on "making it through the night." Then Mr. Hasbrook paddled, like a duck with bunions, to his sleeping place. He brought two pint-sized pewter mugs, two long iced teaspoons, and a blue sugar dish with a broken handle.

The coffee table, also the eating table, and the store desk, was the large counter of one of the combination desk-counters given out by A and P Coats thread people. The little drawers above the flat portion were used for keeping money from sales and for mementoes. There was a drawer on the right in which Mr. Hasbrook put his Roebucker teeth, when he rested his gums, and Mr. Matson used a drawer on the left for the same purpose.

Mr. Hasbrook filled each mug about two-thirds full with coffee, and then most meticulously, he poured five, never four or six, ounces of local whiskey, usually whiskey made by Just Plain Snake Imboden. Each man put three teaspoons of sugar into his mug, but the sweetener wasn't stirred. On Sunday mornings, and other special occasions, they sprinkled powdered sugar on top .

There was a large framed print of a lady on the right wall, high against the ceiling — on the right as one entered the store. The picture showed a real beauty, but there was an element of aloofness about the lady's face that kept anyone from whistling and referring to her as a "pippin" or a "peach."

Each morning at 8:05 the two men lifted their cups, simultaneously, to the picture. Normally, Mr. Hasbrook said, softly, "Yer best health, Miss Lillie," and Mr. Matson said, much louder, "Here's mud in yor eye, Lillie, my love." Sometimes Mr. Matson alluded to the lady as "Coo-uh-de-mee-ah," which, he explained to Mr. Hasbrook, meant "Heart of my heart."

The print was one of Lillie Langtry (1852-1929), the celebrated actress and beauty, whom Mr. Matson said he had known.

I never knew where Mr. Hasbrook got the print. However, it was the same kind that Frank Munsey had disseminated so widely. It was done, apparently, when Miss Langtry was at the height of her beauty. It was full-length;

it was covered by glass and was so high from the floor no one could stand on tip-toe and touch the shoe-covering hemline.

They washed the glass frequently, but there was one ancient flyspeck, beneath the glass, on Miss Lillie's left cheek that looked like one of the patches worn by ladies such as Marie Antoinette.

Children, farmers, and the uninitiated in Oxford assumed the picture was Mr. Hasbrook's dead wife, or his mother, perhaps. But most of the people who frequented the shop talked about "Miss Lillie" the same familiar way they referred to old man Poe Peters, who drove the mail cart, or to Wahoo Sam Crawford, the big league ball player.

A few fancy-dans, who overheard Mr. Matson's toasts to "Coo-uh-de-mee-ah," tried to affect what is now known as swinging rapport. However, "Coo-uh-de-mee-ah," for reasons that always eluded me, came out as "Cool-ee-me," a startling likeness to a town in North Carolina.

When the coffee was near the bottom of their cups, the two friends took their long spoons and raked the sugar crystals into tiny piles. Then for a few minutes they sat sucking the sugar. Papa said they sounded as if sex-starved bees were raping a field of ripe clover. If the weather was warm, the sucking sounds were audible on the sidewalk. A stranger easily imagined someone inside using a plumber's helper. But no one disturbed them, or tried to buy anything, during the entire ritual of coffee and sugar crystals.

After the established morning ritual, Mr. Hasbrook checked his candy in the glass showcase. There were three big showcases, curved glass ones, that screwed down on a wooden counter. The wooden counter ran the whole length of the store portion of the building. There was barely room at each end for Mr. Hasbrook to slide through, sideways, or "on a bias," as people used to say.

Some of the candy was made in the back end of the store, behind the old Opera House curtain, by Mr. Hasbrook and Mr. Matson. Each morning Mr. Hasbrook sliced some homemade chocolate fudge into squares and he put the pieces in the front showcase, in tin pie plates.

There was a pecan tree behind the store, and nuts were saved to be ground up for the chocolate fudge. Sometimes, Mr. Hasbrook put a big top hat on fudge squares in the form of hickory nuts or scaly-barks that he and Mr. Matson gathered on Sunday afternoons in autumn, along creek banks, when they took their "nature constitutionals."

Seafoam was as capricious as a beautiful girl with ten eager beaux. So, the two old men usually made it at night, after the store had closed.

The "medicinal" candy, the horehound, the rock, and the peach n' honey drops, was kept in half of the front showcase. There were a few boxes of those black cough drops, Smith Brothers, with the bearded brothers re sembling the old New England poets, but virtually every man spurned cough drops, no matter how bad his laryngitis or "hickitus" might be.

Papa said that those damned black cough drops ruined the taste of good liquor and never improved the taste of bad liquor. But rock and peach n' honey "blended admirably," with good booze and they made it easier to swallow the gnats and nits in some of Just Plain Snake Imboden's "one-day-wonder" stuff.

The next showcase had a heavy border of licorice sticks. Next to this black, maddeningly odoriferous fence were pieces of homemade taffy. Papa said when Mr. Matson and Mr. Hasbrook pulled the taffy they were so greased up with lard someone would think they were about to swim the English Channel. Next to the taffy was a lovely dishevelment of striped jawbreakers, of every known flavor. Bon-bons were stuck, here and there, like decorations at a wedding, and in the center of the showcase there was a shirt box piled up with peach and lemon drops, and marshmallow-marbles.

94

These were glass marbles covered with marshmallow. The idea was that for a penny you could eat a little dab of marshmallow and have a marble left for the games at school.

I'm sure the A. M. A. hasn't done any study on the matter, but swallowing glass marbles isn't fatal. Mr. Hasbrook sold a lot of them. I bought a lot of them, and I swallowed them, when I ate as I ran, and I swallowed them at the "fill-ums" when I was completely enthralled by Hoot Gibson. One day I overheard Papa telling Mr. Hasbrook: "Amos, I wish you'd stop selling my boy so many damn marshmallow marbles. He ran up on the front porch last night and his belly sounded like two skeletons wrassling on top of a tin roof."

The third showcase had suckers that ranged in price from two for a penny to two for a nickel. Mr. Matson called this the "hobbledehoy" or the "larrikin" section, his inevitable words for boys. However, "larrikin" had precedence, as I recall it.

Some boys were pleased, at the mysterious accolade, when Mr. Matson said: "What do you want, you larrikin." Others had uneasy, grim grins, and one of two thought the old man meant that their folks hadn't gotten married until the shank of the nine months.

Strewn around the suckers was a variety of chocolate candy, drops they were called in Oxford. Some had soft centers and some had hard centers. The chocolate was a big seller on Saturday night. The "loose" candy was bought by men who were known as "good providers."

As I recall a two-pound brown, paper sack full cost forty cents. Papa bought a two-pound sack of it virtually every Saturday night. Only, he always got an extra sack, a one-pound one, from Mr. Hasbrook. He and I would eat about thirty cents worth walking around and walking home.

When we turned the corner on Front Street, where we lived, Papa dumped the remainder — about half — of the candy from the two-pound poke into the one-pound sack. He explained carefully that this wasn't fraud. He said a good lawyer knows when to put a certain witness on the stand and when to let a witness remain silent. He said he "did away with" half the candy out of deference to Sister. "You know, son, it just rots her damned teeth and makes pimples break out on her face."

On shelves, against the wall, behind the counters, and beneath Miss Lillie's picture, were big jars, with those heavy glass stoppers. These held gumdrops, stick candies, and mints. (Mr. Hasbrook and Mr. Matson made the mints).

Also on the shelves were boxes of candy, their mysterious treasures concealed by the pasted down box-tops. There were three sections of "candy-in-the-box-candy." Mr. Hasbrook referred to the three batches of box-candy as "Peace Offerings," "Bribes," and "Love Potions."

"Peace Offerings" were boxes of mixed candies, fancy stuff that cost as much as $1.50 each. These deluxe boxes were for their wedding anniversaries. "Bribes" were around $1.00 a box. A "Bribe" was given to a wife a couple of days before a man wanted to go on a hunting or a fishing trip.

The "Love Potions" were two-layer boxes of chocolate-covered cherries. They cost thirty-nine cents a box. Papa called this candy "Cupid's Crowbar." A boy might get lock-jaw when he got on his lady-love's front porch. If the weather was warm, her parents, grandparents, brothers and sisters, several uncles and aunts, and some neighbors were certain to be waiting on the porch. If the weather was cold, a crowd was certain to be in the parlor.

But the double-decker box of chocolate-covered cherries sang better than Shakespeare and Burns. The old folks ate

96

the candy, and they couldn't very well take the gift and throw out the giver. It was told that some families didn't have dessert on the nights they knew their daughter was "expecting a gentleman friend," but, of course, these were the same folks people said were so tight they give their little boy a dime to go to bed without supper and charged him fifteen cents for breakfast.

I used to look out to see Ramsay Davis walking along, or riding in a Ford, when he was calling on Pansy Alice Duncan. He always had a box of thirty-nine cents candy, and his ukulele. He really looked forearmed. And when he walked, it looked to me as if his Palm Beach shoes were eating up the sidewalk, as if it were popcorn. The way he bounced, swinging his candy and his ukulele, I always expected him to reach up and pull down a star to put into the lapel of his blue serge coat.

Some men said those cherries, in the chocolate, were saturated with Spanish Fly. Dr. Henley told Papa: "If so, aphrodisaics cause a lof of diabetes." And Papa agreed: "Before a girl could eat enough to take off her corset, she'd be vomiting her passion all over the drugget."

Early every Saturday during the summer, Mr. Hasbrook and Mr. Matson made three big freezers of homemade ice cream, in the back end of the store. There was always a big freezer of vanilla, and, during the season, there was a freezer of peach or one of strawberry. They made them when the town was glued down sweetly with dew, and then they packed them down for the first customers. But they sold "straight through" a given freezer.

And they never "cracked" the first freezer until their friend, "Old Dan" Tucker, came into the "Ivanhoe." Mr. Tucker was the best carpenter in town, or anywhere, for that matter. He worked like hell five days a week and he spent each Saturday in the "Ivanhoe." As soon as "Old

Dan" came in, (he was about forty, I guess) Mr. Hasbrook pulled out a dasher so that Mr. Tucker could "lick her down."

When someone bought ice cream, Mr. Hasbrook asked if they wanted it for "setting er walking." If they sat, he spooned it into a bowl, or a saucer. A bowl cost a nickel and a saucer cost three cents. If a customer took it with him, the ice cream was spooned into a ten-ounce pointed cup. There were never any cones at the "Ivanhoe."

Spoons were furnished, for "setters." These were the same long iced teaspoons the two men used for their morning coffee-sugar-toddy. There were six teaspoons in all, including the ones used for coffee.

If business was brisk, a customer had to wait his turn for a spoon. The "walkers," usually boys, ate and licked the ice cream down in the pointed cup. About half-way down, they bit off the point, and sucked down the remainder. I know that's what I always did, even when Mamma made me take a "walking" spoon from home.

The "walker" was three cents, or two for a nickel. If you wanted a "two-fer," Mr. Hasbrook made a mark with a red crayon on the pointed cup and you had to bring the delapidated cup back, for the second serving, to show you weren't fudging.

Mr. Matson said the teaspoons were made of silver taken from the first great strike at Virginia City, Nevada. He said the silver was mined by a relative of his, on his mother's side, Sir Maraduke Faversham. Each spoon had a figure engraved on it. Mr. Matson said the work had been done by a world-known silversmith. He always said that Mr. Hasbrook should charge a penny extra for each spoon. He said holding the spoons was the closest anyone in Oxford would ever get to "gen-you-wine" royalty.

The President said the talk about Virginia City was

another of Mr. Matson's "liza-janes," or damned lies. The President said the spoons really belonged to some of Mrs. dead Hasbrook's folks. But Papa and Dr. Henley went along with the Virginia City account.

Papa always held his spoon reverently. He said Samuel Clemens first signed in as "Mark Twain" in an article he wrote for the Virginia City *Enterprize*, in 1863. But, Papa told Dr. Henley, and Mr. Ben Parham, as a privileged communication, that Sam Clemens got "Mark Twain" from Captain Isaiah Sellers, who had used it first, writing for the New Orleans "Picayune."

The figure on the spoons, if aristocratic, was sort of monkeyish, and Dr. Henley said he thought Darwin had studied the spoons before launching his great work. Naturally, he didn't say this loud enough for Mr. Matson to hear it.

At least twice a year, the two friends ran off batches of "small beer," a brew with low alcoholic content. "Small" normally meant from four to six per cent alcohol, but Papa said Mr. Hasbrook and Mr. Matson probably thought Russia was a small country.

The small beer was made in the basement of the store. This was reached from the back room, through a trap-down door, down steps that really aped a swinging bridge. Mr. Hasbrook and Mr. Matson used a recipe which Mr. Matson said George Washington wrote down in his own hand, at Mr. Vernon, in 1757. Mr. Matson said he had copied the recipe verbatim. The local copy read:

"To Make Small Beer: Take a large Siffer full of Bran. Hops to your taste. Boil these 3 hours, then strain out 30 Gallns into a Cooler. Put in 3 Gallns Molasses while the Beer is scalding hot or rather draw the Molasses into the Cooler. Strain the Beer on it while boiling hot. Let this

stand until it is little more than Blood warm then put in a of Yeast. If the weather is very Cold cover it with a blanket. Let it work in the Cooler 24 hours then put it into the Cask-leave the Bung open until it is almost done Working. Bottle it that day week it was Brewed."

Mr. Matson's cronies had copies, and the President said it was scandalous, slanderous and libelous, "for old Ollie Matson to try to make a bootlegger and a semi-literate of the Father of our beloved nation."

Mr. Matson always answered by saying: "Aw, go pluck some innocent goose." The President, almost apoplectic, rasped: "Mark me. One day Congress will have old Ollie Matson locked up for defiling the unblemished Washington."

Papa told the President: "I don't know how many things George Washington was first or last in, President, but aside from Chaucer, he was as poor a speller as I ever read after, and that includes Joel Chandler Harris."

Each morning while Mr. Hasbrook was checking the candy, Mr. Matson stroked down the rental-library with a feather-duster, the same kind that barbers used. The rental-library was against the other wall, across the store from the candy counters.

During the mornings and early afternoons, or until school let out, such works as *Sister Carrie, Elmer Gantry*, and the *Decameron* were displayed prominently.

Papa called such volumes "bait for mud-suckers." Many men dropped in for "sample" reading, or "grazing." Few had the unmitigated temerity to stand reading for as long as ten minutes without buying some candy or a glass of molasses water or raspberry acid. (The small beer stayed in the basement. It was consumed by the Sanhedrin of the

100

"Ivanhoe", exclusively, although some of it was sold, by the gallon, to Miss Opal, the whorehouse lady. Mr. Matson said he and Mr. Hasbrook took payment for the small beer "out in trade at Miss Opal's." I guess that was why some folks thought the cherries in the chocolate candy were loaded with Spanish Fly. Whenever Mr. Matson boasted about that, Dr. Henley smiled sweetly, rubbed Mr. Matson's shoulders and replied: "My dear Ollie, we're both doomed to fly at half-mast from here out.")

After school let out for the afternoon, the "sizzlers" were put under such volumes as *Billy and the Major, Surry of Eagle's Nest*, and *Miss Minerva and William Green Hill*.

There was a copy of *Kidnapped*. I can see it now, but there was no need to rent it for home reading. Everytime I opened it, to snitch a few pages, Mr. Hasbrook and Mr. Matson started playing Allan Breck-Stuart and David Balfour.

Mr. Hasbrook was small and thin. He was as wrinkled as honeysuckle. He had a small hump on his shoulders, and his neck formed a right angle from his shoulders. He looked as if he were a turtle and had stuck his head out and couldn't get it back in again. Even so, he was an ebullient Allan Breck-Stuart, one with almost total recall.

He was also the agent for *World's Work, The Southern Planter, Delineator*, the Sunday edition of the *Baltimore American*, and *Grit*. The *Delineator* copies were kept, always, on an old green flower stool, right by the front door. They were kept on white wrapping paper, in deference to Miss Bertha and the ladies who came in to buy copies.

Mr. Matson knocked the *Delineator*. He said people should read Bob ("Barb") Ingersoll and Brand, the Iconoclast. But the more he denounced the *Delineator*, the more the ladies grabbed up the copies.

I never saw anyone, come to think of it, who looked exactly like Mr. Matson looked. Half his head was bald. On the other side there was a large queue of hair. It came down to rest upon the bottom of his neck, like a crazy sort of pigtail.

He said he had been scalped while scouting for the Seventh Cavalry, in New Mexico. Every week or so he said he just received a letter from his old side-kick, Al Seiber, also a famous Indian scout. He would tell how one day in the old West he was drinking in a saloon and winning at faro when Al Seiber would clank in and say: "Oliphant, General Crook needs you. So you know there is a terrible emergency."

His store friends called him "Ollie," but if they introduced him to an outsider they always said: "This, suh, is Mr. Ollie-fant Matson, the famous Indian scout."

The President said: "Foot-fire. He got scalped by a whore in Norfolk because he wouldn't pay her." However, soft answers turned away wrath and interesting stories sustained credulity.

I used to stand and thumb books just to hear Mr. Matson talk, even if I knew many of his stories, his personal history, by heart. He knew Robert W. Service up in the Klondike. If someone said "Service," Mr. Matson raised his hands to heaven: "Merciful Gawd. The man's name is 'Sarviss'."

Then he'd chuckle and explain, to no one in particular, that old "Barb" really didn't get mad when he took away from him the lady that was known as Lou, the one in the Malamute Saloon, in Service's poem.

He hardly ever sat or stood as he told his history. No, he walked up and down the store's boards the way a cork bobs on choppy waters, as if his feet weren't on speaking terms with his body. But I could understand his manner of

102

walking. Undoubtedly, his rolling stumble was a result of his many years on great sailing ships.

Once, he was king of some island, for four months. He was the sole survivor of a shipwreck. The service he got from the natives made old Louie the fourteenth look like a one-legged man at a public tail kicking. If someone asked why he left such a plushy existence, he looked dunce holes through the man: "I was the only man on the island. The sailors that rescued me had to cut a bamboo stretcher to tote me off, and I hadn't had any spell of sickness either."

For a fact, Papa said there had been times when Mr. Matson had been gone from town on unexplained sojourns. When he came back, he told how Bob Fitzsimmons was a capital fellow but Jim Corbett was no gentleman, just all mouth and necktie, like the President. Christy Mathewson was a nice fellow, but George Cohan acted like a tomcat that was on a diet of green lizards.

Mr. Matson claimed he had horse-collared Charles Guiteau in the waiting room of the train station in Washington City when Guiteau had shot President James A. Garfield. I saw him re-enact the drama in the "Ivanhoe" several times, with "Old Dan" Tucker playing Guiteau.

Exhausted by capturing Guiteau, or Mr. Tucker, Mr. Matson flopped into his rocking chair. No one but him ever sat in it. Then he would sing, to Miss Lillie, it almost appeared:

Charles Gee-toe, Charles Gee-toe,
Low-down common so and so;
Splattered the waiting room with blood
And laid po Garfield low.

Each morning when he finished dusting the rental-library he sat at the A and P Coats desk and scribbled in a two-for-a-nickel notebook. The notebook was so old the "Blue Horse" was completely black. I always thought the animal needed a mercy slaying.

As he scribbled, he spread out the financial section of the most recent edition of the Sunday *Baltimore American*. If he wrote rapidly, in neat columns, everyone knew Wall Street was sky high. If he wrote slowly, everyone knew the market was playing hob. If the market was doing nicely, he added his figures, computed his astonomical wealth, and snapped his notebook closed with a happy bang.

If his stocks were down, he brought the lead end of his stub pencil to his mouth several times. He wrote as if his hands hurt him acutely. And when he closed his notebook I expected to see darkness settle on Oxford at high noon.

Mr. Hasbrook didn't play the market, but when things were "ginger peachy" for Mr. Matson, the two took an extra five ounces of local whiskey, without coffee, but usually with small beer for a chaser.

Naturally, Papa, Dr. Henley, "Brer" Thompson, and Sheriff Matt Venable went along with this financier charade of Mr. Matson's. They asked for tips and regretted they lacked the capital to follow up and make a killing.

Mr. Matson was strong on railroad stocks. In fact, he had been in the private cars of Jim Hill, E. H. Harriman, and Harry Flagler many times. But he was bitterly opposed to steel. He had hated Andrew Carnegie almost as much as he hated the President. He said anyone who played "golluff," and listened to a damn organ would put sugar on sliced tomatoes and call such a delicacy as hog nuts "mountain oysters."

The President was always bully-ragging Mr. Matson, the financial wizard. The President would turn to the customers: "Wonder where he keeps his money? Wonder why such a tycoon lives in old piano boxes?"

104

Mr. Matson always broke in to say he had just heard that the bank inspector got off the "eleben somep'n train" that morning. He never said anything was wrong at the bank, but he often wondered, aloud, why the President was always the last one to leave the bank each afternoon?

None of that ever resulted in a run on the bank. However, some folks did check by the bank to look things over. And, for a fact, the President scurried back to the bank if he saw a stranger carrying a satchel, at the times when Mr. Matson bruited it around about the bank inspector's being in town.

Some of Mr. Matson's stories almost put the President to bed. One was about Coffeeville, Kansas, in the year of our Lord, 1892. The precise date was August 6. Somebody usually asked which "Kansas," and Mr. Matson explained, patiently: "Just plain ole Kansas without the 'Ark'. I bin in Ark-Kansas, many's the time. But this was in Coffeeville, in plain Kansas."

Bob Dalton had stated openly, he hadn't bragged, mind you, that he and his brothers, Emmett and Grattan, and three side-kicks would rob both of the banks in Coffeeville, in broad-open daylight.

Coffeeville was the home-town of the Dalton boys. Mr. Matson always emphasized this fact if the President was listening.

Mr. Matson happened to be in Coffeeville because he was repairing the Western and Union line there. (Once or twice he said he was a good-will man for Colt Firearms. He went around for the Colt people giving fancy-shooting exhibitions.)

From his perch atop the power pole, Mr. Matson saw the dust from the hooves of the bank-robbers' horses, two or three miles from Coffeeville. He scrambled down and spread the alarm that saved the banks and the town.

As soon as the shooting began, the local telegrapher ran off and hid under a haystack. Mr. Matson tried to reach the telegraph office, to tap out the sensational news, but he got caught in a cross-fire. Indeed, one bullet went through the calf of his right leg. He always patted the place, through his britches, as he went on to tell how he climbed a pole, dragging his wounded leg. He said he had to drag his leg as if it were a heavy wagon tongue.

But he cut in on the wire and sent out the story as it occurred on the bloody streets beneath him. People in such places as St. Louis and Baltimore knew what was happening in Coffeeville, shot by shot, death by death.

Two of the gang, Bill Powers and Dick Broadwell, died at the bottom of the pole, and Mr. Matson could spit on the board sidewalk where Gratt Dalton gave up the ghost.

When Mr. Matson completed his world-wide scoop, the pole looked as if all the woodpeckers on earth had been boring holes in it. And he had a piece of wood that was shot off by Gratt Dalton's Winchester rifle. Mr. Matson kept the small "sue-vin-yuh" folded in a big red bandana, in his hip pocket.

He let us look at the memento but we weren't allowed to touch it.

The bodies of the six robbers were lined up on the sidewalk and photographed for posterity. Mr. Matson put a pillow under Bob Dalton's head, and wiped the dust, blood, and sweat from Bob's head and face, because Bob was a big cut above such other sons of bitches as the James boys, the Youngers and John Wesley Hardin, all of whom he knew intimately.

The telegrapher didn't come back. So, Mr. Matson went into the Western and the Union to spruce up his news story, or give what we call "color" today.

He learned that Lord Tennyson died the same day. He

went across the street to a saloon, and as he sipped a glass of red-eye he said, aloud, but reverently, "Crossing the Bar."

He knew the poem, all right enough, and he always said it when told about Coffeeville. I had to grit my teeth, sometimes, because he pronounced "put" as "putt," and when he solemnly intoned: "And may there be no mourning at the bar, when I putt out to sea," some devilish boy muttered "putt, putt, putt," as if Tennyson were crossing the bar in a motorboat.

Until Mr. Matson brought Oxford in on Coffeeville, "Crossing the Bar" was read at many funerals. Afterwards, there were some motor-boat snickers among the congregation. Mr. Bennett, the Presbyterian minister, tried so hard to concentrate on "put" he slipped up and said "putt" a couple of times. Anyway, the poem was discontinued at local funerals for a long time, after the Coffeeville episode.

Frankly, I never knew if Mr. Matson was ever in Kansas, but I did learn that the Daltons were killed the same day Lord Tennyson died.

The other story that upset the President was the one about Paul Dresser. Almost everyday, Piano Hutchins played the record on which Polk Miller's famous quartet sang "On The Banks Of The Wabash, Far Away," and "My Gal Sal."

Mr. Matson said "Sal" wasn't at all like the President's daughter or my mother. No, she ran a whorehouse in Evansville, Indiana. Paul Dresser got stranded in Evansville and "Sal," whose real name was Sallie Walker, put him up, and gave him free run of all the pleasures of the house.

But Sallie kicked Paul out one day for scrounging around too much with the other gals while she was entertaining big-paying customers. Then, several years later, in New York City, Paul needed to write a hit, because he

107

hadn't had a hit in several years and he was broke.

Mr. Matson would pause long enough to get *Sister Carrie* from the rental library. Then, inhaling deeply from his cigarette, for purposes of dramatic pause, I always assumed, he slapped *Sister Carrie* and said: "Paul's brother, Thea-do, this here book-arthur, said, 'How come you don't write up at pretty whore you ust to know in Evansville?' Well, at's what Paul done, and at's what you're hearin' from Piany Hutchins right now."

The President practically frothed at the mouth. As he denounced Mr. Matson for a fraud, he vilified Dreiser and praised Dresser. "I ask you, gentlemen, how can brothers have different names. Nay more, can you, in your wildest imagination, think of a man who writes a song as sweet as "My Gal Sal" being blood brother of a fellow who would write a book that brought such shame to his own sister?"

The President always wore a high silk hat, winter and summer. One day when the President was ragging Mr. Matson about Coffeeville and Dreiser and Dresser, the old gentleman turned to Mr. Hasbrook. He talked directly to Mr. Hasbrook as if no one else were in the "Ivanhoe:"

"Amos, did jew ever study up on the history of the Devil? Naw, well in this state he lived in the 'dismals,' and he plowed all the rivers and creeks on the coast crooked to annoy the sailors.

"Fer a spell he was a foah-legged animal, but if anybody mentioned the Lord's name he tucked his tail and he scampered. Great balls of fire shot from his eyes. Then he tuck to wearing strippeddy britches, a jim-swinger coat, and high hat to race tracks and cock fights, everywhere there was drinkin' and gamblin', Amos.

"He could look at a horse's eyes and jess draw at horse first across the line. In two years he nigh bout clint up Gates County, bettin' on races. Then one day, down in

Gates, his eyes fascinated this stallion so much the horse run agin him, and when he fell down his top hat flew off and everybody saw his old horns.

"They tarred and feathered him and rode him outta the county on a rail. He ain't bin seen in Gates since. As they was nearin' the county line, some wise apple up and says: 'How jew like your ride?' The Devil, he laffs a little, and says: 'Well, if it twont fer the honor of the damned thing, I'd jess as soon walk'."

Mr. Matson stayed at the "Ivanhoe" until it closed at nine at night, Monday through Friday, and until ten on Saturday night. "Old Dan" Tucker, always left by nine on Saturday night, to see to his daughters. When the carpenter had gone, Mr. Hasbrook and Mr. Matson would fill their coffee mugs half with local whiskey and half with small beer.

Each Saturday night the two friends usually spent the last hour drinking booze and small beer and singing hymns. Few cash customers came in after nine. If one did come in, he hardly ever interrupted the singing. I remember one time Ramsay Davis' mother sent him for a spool of thread, after nine on Saturday night.

Mr. Hasbrook liked to sing hymns with his feet on the A and P Coats counter. The more involved he got in the singing, the lower he slumped in his chair. After about five minutes he finally saw Ramsay Davis.

"Whatchu want, boy?"

"A spool of thread, Mr. Hasbrook."

"All right, have a chair."

"What do you mean, Mr. Hasbrook, have a chair?"

"Have a chair until some mo come in and I'll wait on all of you at onect. You shorely don't think I'm go get up, hot as it is, jess to sell you a spool a thread, do you?"

"See here, Mr. Hasbrook, I'll have you know I am a

practicing attorney."

"All right, boy. In at case, have two chairs."

Farmers and loafers collected at the door, on the sidewalk, while the two old men sang hymns. I lolled on the edge of the crowd several times, many times, in fact. Some of their favorite hymns were "A Cross I Bear," which came off as "A Cross-eyed bear" to most kids. Another was "Jesus Loves Even Me," and Mr. Matson had a special solo chorus all of his own. I don't remember it all, but it started: "Now don't it beat hell how Jesus loves me, Jesus loves even me, Oliphant Matson."

After a while, after "Leaning On the Everlasting Arms," some of the farmers on the sidewalk testified. However, Mr. Matson always won the testifying because he had been more places, seen more people, and done more sins.

I can't remember all of the sins Mr. Matson said he had done. I do remember the night he asked forgiveness (Papa said Mr. Matson had his fingers crossed) for slipping knock-out drops in a missionary's lemonade, out in Frisco. He said he had the missionary shanghaied to Alaska, because the Chinese were gorged with Christians already. Frequently, he asked heaven to watch out over all of his children.

Someone asked: "Children?" He replied: "I got more'n five hundredt bastards, scattered from Dawson City to Port Sa-Ed," wherever that was.

Many of the farmers cried. "Bless you, God bless you, brother," they cried. But about the time Mr. Hasbrook got ready to pitch "The Prodigal Son" and "Bringing in the Sheaves," Mr. Matson would slam the front door: "This ain't no free concert er revival. Go on home now."

Before he left for the night, he and Mr. Hasbrook shook hands, solemnly. When each said to the other: "I'll see you tomorrow," I thought they had a plan to cheat death a

110

little longer. There was never any question mark after the softly-spoken statements.

When Mr. Matson started home, he picked up his trusty tobacco stick. It was long and hefty, almost as tall as he. I never saw him on the street without his stick. If he got tired, or if he had trouble maneuvering, he leaned against a tree or a power pole and stuck the stick between his legs, the same way we boys rested our mounts when we rode stick horses.

Papa called this arrangement "Ollie's Camp stool," and the former scout would sit on the stick until he got his second-wind or direction.

Sometimes I pictured the stick as a real horse. Mr. Matson, or rather bold young Oliphant, was peeking at the Indians in the valley below. In a minute, he would raise his arm, make three circles with his arm, and the Seventh Cavalry would come pounding down Main Street.

Some people gossiped about his actually riding the stick. The Society members chortled about it. Mrs. Ashton-Brown pulled in her lips as if she were about to spit a big load of tobacco juice as she rasped that Mr. Matson was an "Old He-witch."

I never saw him riding the stick but twice. The first time I could tell he did it deliberately to annoy Mrs. Ashton-Brown, the Vicar, and some Society ladies who were fifty yards up the street from him. The second time was the day when Boot Ransome bested Mrs. Ashton-Brown, the President's wife and the others who had gardeners and greenhouses to win the Grand Prize at the annual Chrysanthemum Show.

Mr. Matson rode the stick up and down College Street and across the square to Papa's office and back, whipping his own shanks with his crumpled felt hat. As he rode, or ran, he yelled such phrases as "Tippacanoe and Tyler, too,"

111

"Remember the Maine," "Sixteen to One," and "Oh, you kid." Two or three times he half-shouted, half-sang, "Praise Gawd from who all blessings flow." Then when he had cantered back to the "Ivanhoe" he stabled his mount and forgot, apparently, the entire incident.

Once on the street, homeward at night, he rattled the front door of the "Ivanhoe" to be certain it was secure. He almost shook the building down each night. Strangers were frightened when they heard all of those old boards, all of those metal signs and those tin cans shaking and rattling, "in the dead of the night."

Then he stomped along to his home, made of piano boxes, in Ransome's Alley. For a while his stick went tap-tap, knock-knock, and blam-blam against the sidewalk. I guess the sounds were to keep time with his walking-home songs. Anyway, I am sure he was as unaware of his surroundings as he was impervious to any traffic on the sidewalk or the street.

I'll never forget a stanza of one song he used to sing, as he ambled, strutted, and stumbled on home:

I've come to this fair city
To seek a brother dear,
And you wouldn't dare insult me, sir,
If Jack were only here.

When the last line went to limbo, he lashed out with his stick. I saw him brain the offensive city slicker with his stick and then kick the scoundrel into the gutter. Then the way he stood, with the stick's end resting on the sidewalk, and pointing to heaven, I knew he had his conquering foot on the fallen dastard's chest.

Of course, the ladies in the Society said Mr. Matson was a public nuisance. They said he would hurt someone with that fool stick, sooner or later.

Papa demurred, as did Dr. Henley, "Brer" Thompson and many other men: "Better a barked shin or shoulder than assault and battery upon the innocent and defenseless who walk our streets. Far better that a Sunday hat fall into the gutter than virtue be trampled upon our fair streets."

Papa would raise his glass of whiskey: "Here, then, is to Mister Oliphant Matson, protector of the feckless and guardian of virtue. Here then, my friends, is a toast to the intrepid Indian scout who bestows upon our community, in fee simple, the vigilant protective custody on which the Seventh Cavalry reposed its consummate trust."

Oxford, September 25, 1970

"Old Dan" Tucker and Mr. Virginuis Purvis were important members of the "Ivanhoe's" inner circle, although their visits were limited to Saturdays, pretty generally.

I never walk by the site of the old candy store — a boutique is there now — without thinking of "Old Dan" and Mr. Purvis, along with Mr. Matson, Mr. Hasbrook and the others.

"Old Dan" was a crackerjack carpenter, five-and-a-half days to the week, and he had three daughters to occupy most of his spare time and thoughts. But each Saturday when the whistles blew in high-noon, "Old Dan" gathered up his tools, peddled his bicycle home, washed, shaved, pressed his Sunday suit, and spent the remainder of the day at the "Ivanhoe."

Mr. Purvis's chief occupation, and love, was caring for Silas, his old horse. On Monday through Friday, Mr. Purvis "saw to" certain things. He and Silas went around the county selling oddments from a wagon.

Papa called him "our enterpreneur," and Papa wasn't mocking the elderly gentleman. Good God, no. I think

113

"enterpreneur" fitted Mr. Purvis. Besides, Mr. Ed Settle was exhilarated by the sound of "enterpreneur." It seemed to sprout flutes and rosebuds everytime Mr. Ed spoke it.

As I said, "Old Dan" was a splendid carpenter. Whenever anyone in Oxford did any task well, people would say: "Old Dan Tucker couldn't have done it any better." This was applied to everything from essays written at school, to Tom Day's "Deluxe Sundaes," to a winning home-run, to Papa's trying a mean case well, to a painting by Miss Daisy, to Dr. Henley's curing a patient of pneumonia, when hope and care were the only antibiotics.

Whenever aristocracy was mentioned, Papa always said "Old Dan" was a genuine aristocrat, a real blue-blood. This puzzled me at first because Mr. Tucker wasn't rich, book-educated, and his folks hadn't lived on any plantation. The local Tuckers weren't in any history books I had ever read.

"You're fooled by those fake aristocrats dreamed by such third-rate magicians as Thomas Nelson Page and the UDC," Papa said. "Old Dan is a thorough aristocrat, just like his father and his grandfather. They never used shoddy material or did a cover-up job. They never watched the clock. They were never satisfied just to get a job done and collect their pay. Whenever they built a house, a barn, or a stile, they meant it to last until Judgment Day.

"No one ever watched them because they were just as proud of their work as Rodin, Edison, Ty Cobb, Winslow Homer, and Woodrow Wilson."

"Old Dan's father, also called 'Old Dan,' got gangrene in his right arm from a hunting accident. Dr. Henley told him he would die if his arm wasn't amputated. Still he wouldn't let Doc take his right arm off. He said he never saw a good one-armed carpenter, especially a good one-armed, wrong-armed carpenter. He died, but the present Old Dan took his place, you understand?

"You understand, son. The old man preferred death to being a burden on his folks."

My Mr. Tucker was christened "Francis Asbury," just as his father and grandfather were, but everyone in Oxford called all three "Old Dan."

"Old Dan Tucker, III" is chisled on his tombstone in large letters. Just below, in parentheses, "Francis Asbury," appears in smaller letters.

He always rode a red bicycle to and from work. Many cold mornings I heard his bell dingling in the icy mists as I lay snug in bed. When I heard his bell I thought the world, despite the chilly winds, was in excellent hands.

He did a lot of work out in the country, and I heard his bell many times when he returned home, amid utter darkness. Sometimes we'd be eating. It was almost as if an engineer was ringing for a crossing. Papa would put down the carving knife and nod, almost imperceptibly, as if he had been given a clear talisman against gloom and fear. And the way "Old Dan's" daughters ran out to meet him always reminded me of the return of a hero from some interminable war.

His face was sun or wind-burned the year around. He always wore a felt cap, and when he took his cap off his hair was really as dark as a raven's. I had seen some photographs of Jack London, the virile writer, and I thought, and I still think, Mr. Tucker's face had a strong resemblance. He had tremendous shoulders, chest, and arms, and he walked on the balls of his feet, like an athlete in finest trim.

Yet, it seemed to give him enormous pain if he accidentally hurt any living creature, even if he stepped on a cockroach, even accidentally. Papa swore he never saw Mr. Tucker kill a fly. He just shooed them away, but Papa also said that "Old Dan" was too damned strong to be a man and not quite strong enough to be the stoutest bull-elephant that ever laughed at Teddy Roosevelt.

Each morning he was up early to fix things for his three daughters, each of whom went to school. He laid out the dresses, and he saw to it that each girl had a pair of white, clean stockings to wear, and that the three pairs of shoes were polished to a real glow.

Ever so often he stopped by the ladies' department at Bengough's to buy a few yards of red, yellow, and white hair ribbon. A yard was about right for a single hair ribbon. Frequently, he put a piece of ribbon with the dress, for the girl he thought it suited best.

Strangely enough, Mr. Purvis taught the girls what they knew about sewing. Mr. Purvis always carried a big sewing basket, a Necessaire, in his wagon, and when he was in the "Ivanhoe," on Saturdays, the Necessaire was always on the floor beside his chair.

His hands were old, gnarled, and filled with splotches, but his needle seemed to be a silver bird in flight. His Necessaire always had some bright oddments, swatches and bits of cloth in it, and I saw the fingers and thumb on his right hand as a sudden flight of gulls diving at a sea of silken blue. Again, they were swans perching in a field of wild orchids. When he rested his hand in his basket his fingers were supple, silver birds sailing out of sight in green foliage, to reappear in white orchards and rolling meadows made of scraps of odds and ends.

Mr. Purvis loved the old tune, "Narcissus," by "Miss" Ethlebert Nevins, and Mr. Matson would put the warped record on Mr. Hasbrook's "dog-victrola" as Mr. Purvis sewed. His hand kept time to the delicate music, and he always seemed to bite his thread at the end of a bar, as a sort of punctuation mark.

I'm sure Stonewall Jackson and Jack Dempsey, combined, didn't have the guts to call Mr. Purvis a sissy, certainly not in front of the "Ivanhoe's" coterie, but if some friendly person out in the country asked him why he sewed, he would smile sweetly and reply: "It doesn't seem fair for the ladies to have all of the fun."

At least once a month Mr. Purvis went to "Old Dan's" house to repair and to alter the family's clothing. Simultaneously, he taught the three daughters the intricate arts of sewing. "Old Dan" bought a pump sewing machine, and Mr. Purvis taught the daughters to cut out material for it.

"Old Dan" was too considerate of Mr. Purvis's feelings to offer to put him money for sewing for the family. However, "Old Dan" had a fine vegetable garden and orchard. He kept Silas supplied with corn and he kept Mr. Purvis supplied with fresh fruit, with canned fruit and preserves.

In cold weather "Old Dan" got up and fixed the fires while his daughters slept. The girls all slept in the same room, and the grate was blazing nicely when they got up and dressed for school. He checked the school lunches which he and his eldest daughter, Estelle, then about 16, fixed each night for the day following.

Most kids took their lunch to school in brown paper sacks, in small lard buckets, or in wicker baskets. Each of "Old Dan's" daughters had a regular lunch-box, the kind that was bought from a mail-order house. And they were among the first kids who had a thermos bottle at school. I don't remember any other kids having hot cocoa for lunch, not until the President's wife, Mrs. Ashton-Brown and some other rich mothers got thermos bottles for their kids.

After checking the school lunches "Old Dan" milked the cow and chopped and stacked enough wood to last until he returned from the job. He always made sure the pump on the back porch and the one at the kitchen sink were working. Normally his daughters, and the rest of us, bathed at night so we wouldn't catch pneumonia when we went outdoors. But if a daughter had to bathe before school, because she was in a play or something like that,

Mr. Tucker had plenty of hot water on the enormous kitchen range.

Sometimes he caught a couple of sleepy chickens. He killed them, picked them, and dressed them for supper. If he had made up dough, the night before, he rolled it and cut the lovely white stuff into big, round biscuits.

He put the round biscuits in a pan and left the pan on top of the warming-closet of the huge kitchen range. Then he set out the breakfast dishes, the milk glasses, the knives and forks, on the round eating table in the kitchen. The table was covered with oil-cloth that had been washed so many times it seemed to have a glistening sort of anemia.

If the children were to have waffles or battercakes for breakfast, he whipped up the batter in the large blue bowl his wife had received for a bridal present, from Mr. Bengough. "Old Dan" and his daughters always referred to it as "Mister Bengough's mixing bowl." On the mornings that the children were to have toast for breakfast, he cut fat slices from loaves that he and Estelle baked in their oven.

When he had sliced the bread, using "Mister Hasbrook's bread-knife," which was almost as hefty as a saber, and had a fine bone-handle, he took a rag and cleaned off the special eye on the range, the one that his daughters never spat upon to see the wondrous spittle sizzle and pop and play Humpty-Dumpty. It was the middle eye, just above the fire-box, that was reserved for browning toast.

If, during the season, the children were supposed to take flowers to school, Mr. Tucker cut the roses or the scotchbroom or picked the violets.

He kept some pigs, never many, in a pen at the extreme end of his lot. Many times, after the first hard, killing frost of winter, he killed a shoat and dressed it and hung it up in his meat-house before he left for work.

His wife, Rosalee Gooch Tucker, had died from typhoid, or from "the typhoid fever" as everyone called it, when the youngest child, Sarah, was a baby. Sarah was about ten at the time of which I am writing. For a year, perhaps, Mr. Tucker's sister lived with the family and kept house. But she fell in love with a man from Chattanooga, a salesman who came to Oxford four times a year selling "Stark's Dixie Plows." She moved to Chattanooga. For nine years Mr. Tucker and his girls had kept batch.

Each morning he left a note, what used to be called an "Etiquette," meaning a ticket with instructions or pertinent remarks written on it, on the kitchen table, under Estelle's milk glass. The daily note, written heavily in pencil, detailed the duties of each child after school recessed for the afternoon. The note concluded with the phrase, "Bee smart and hapy." Sometimes he said: "Bee nice and swete."

I almost forgot this: The state Congress of Parents and Teachers was organized in 1919. Oxford got a unit in Oxford in 1922. Mrs. Ashton-Brown was the first president of the local unit, naturally. But "Old Dan" Tucker was the second person to be the local president. Just about everyone said the president should be a woman everytime, but men, husbands, belonged. Both parents had to stand up when their children's home rooms were called out at the monthly meetings.

"Brer" Thompson made a fine, brief speech. He said "Old Dan" was not only father and mother but mother's brother's angel child, too. I can't say that Mr. Tucker's tenure as president of the local PTA made Oxford an instant Athens. But he built two bath-houses along the belly part of Sweetgum Creek, where he had dammed up a swimming hole. He rolled and lined-off two tennis courts, and he organized, with P. A. Duncan's help, the first Girls'

Scout troop in town.

I always suspected that Mr. Matson had someone to watch out for Mr. Tucker when "Old Dan" came down town about one o'clock each Saturday. Anyway, by the time the stout carpenter turned the corner of Main Street and started down College Street to the "Ivanhoe" Mr. Matson was singing,

Get out the way, Old Dan Tucker,
Get out the way, old Dan Tucker,
Get out the way, old Dan Tucker,
You're too late to come to supper.

The "per" part of "supper," seemed to be a wagon wheel, with a chirping axle, rolling on and on down College Street.

Mr. Hasbrook and Mr. Matson both came out the front door to escort Mr. Tucker into the "Ivanhoe." As they brought him in, each holding to an elbow, both broke into song, as did just about anyone else who might be in the store, except Mr. Purvis. Mr. Purvis kept his seat. He might flash a facsimile of a hum, as he bit a piece of thread in two. However, he was too feeble to jump and holler and shout the way the others did on Saturday afternoons.

Before Mr. Tucker sat down, in his wicker chair over by the Rental Library, six or eight were singing lustily:

I came to town the other night,
I heard the noise and I saw the fight,
The watchman he came running round,
Shouting 'Old Dan Tucker's come to town'.

The singing was audible up and down the street. Whenever Papa heard the singing, he smiled, raised and shook his right fist as if it were an exclamation mark and said: "Everything's all right now. Let the afternoon rip. Let 'er rip, my boy."

If "Struttin' Bud" Davenport was down town, he'd run to the "Ivanhoe," wind-up and throw his hard, high smoke ball and a couple of fadeaways, without any ball or glove, of course.

Mr. Tucker, in his wicker chair, was a catcher, for a minute. Sometimes "Struttin' Bud" called him "Ray," after Ray Schalk, and again Mr. Tucker was "the Duke of Tralee," after Roger Bresnahan, and sometimes the carpenter was "Muddy," after Muddy Ruel.

Mr. Tucker held out both hands, good-naturedly, as "Struttin' Bud" pitched to three or four imaginary batters. Once or twice, during each charade, he got mad as hell at the umpire.

"It got the corner, you blind bastard," he yelled to the imaginary umpire. At least once "Struttin' Bud" turned his head and looked down to indicate that the batter hit the ball on the ground. Then he'd sling his imaginary glove on the floor, the ground, and stomp it. "Damn bush league shortstop! Couldn't catch the clap in an Armenian whorehouse."

Nonetheless, "Struttin' Bud" struck out the side. He shook Mr. Tucker's hand. "Hank Gowdy can't tote your mitt, Dan'l." Then he would buy candy or ice cream, whatever anyone wanted, for everyone in the store. His usual custom was to give Mr. Hasbrook a five dollar bill and to holler, as he left the store: "Set 'em up, Amos, long as the fiver lasts."

"Struttin' Bud" was the richest man in town, and he was the ugliest man, in the face, I ever saw. Papa said if Moses had ever seen "Struttin' Bud" we would have eleven commandments instead of ten. And he had the wildest house I ever saw. But all that is a story unto itself. I'll tell you about "Struttin' Bud" and his crazy house later on.

As I have said, Mr. Hasbrook never cracked the ice cream freezer until Mr. Tucker arrived. If some boy insisted on a dish, prematurely, Mr. Matson would walk up: "Go suck your thumb, boy, and call it tutti-frutti."

Mr. Tucker always bought a nickel's worth of something, licorice, usually, just to help out Mr. Hasbrook, to assume the role of a customer.

He passed this around. Most of the time he forgot to ask for his sack of licorice back.

He was known throughout the county for his skill at cards and checkers. He never played poker, because he said if he couldn't afford to lose, he couldn't risk winning, either. He didn't play auction bridge. This new game, with its strange nomenclature, was just getting established in town. For several years it remained the card game of the "privileged classes," the same as golf. But no one could beat him at whist, hearts, set-back, or pinochle.

Hardly anyone could beat Mr. Tucker two in a row at checkers. He won the county checker championship several times. Everyone thought he could win the state championship, but he never could find the time off from work to attend the statewide tournament.

He didn't drink whiskey although he took a glass of short beer on festive occasions, to go along with the crowd.

I still see him now, with his long black hair, his Jack London face, his booming shoulder, his chest almost busting his shirt open, and his small, hard waist. Papa said "Old Dan" had the grace of running deer. He did, too. The way he walked so erectly, and always on the balls of feet, made me think he would galvanize into a clog-dance any second.

He was the only man in town who could jump into the air and click his heels together twice while his feet were still up in the air, even if he never put on any public exhibitions. If somebody just had to see him do this stunt, he slipped quietly down into Ransome's Alley.

His incredible dexterity caused Mr. Matson to call him "Steve Brodie." Mr. Matson explained: "Steve Brodie was the feller 'at jumped over the Brooklyn Bridge."

The first time the President heard him say Steve Brodie had jumped over the Brooklyn Bridge, the ground almost caught fire where he spat. "He jumped off the bridge, not over it, you old fool."

"Off it? Off it?" muttered Mr. Matson, tugging at his pigtail, his face distraught with stark incredulity. "I thought he jumped over it. Any damn fool can jump off a bridge, even you, you damn note-shaver."

During lulls in the Saturday card games Mr. Tucker drew lines on pieces of paper. These were plans for a house he was going to build for his own family. The other gentlemen looked over his massive shoulders, while he explained what each room was for and how it would be built.

It would have a wide, long front porch and a side porch, in place of the present covered stoop. But between the front and side porch there would be an open space, poured with concrete, about 16 feet square. It would have holes for evergreens and places for window-boxes and for potted plants.

Steps, leading from the side porch, would lead to a flower garden with a summer-house in it. And a white picket fence would run around the entire lot. (Mr. Matson never really butted in. Occasionally, though, he said: "Less make at fence green, Old Dan." So, the fence was green.)

The new house would have two stories. Downstairs

there would be a big parlor and next to that, almost a part of it, would be the dining-room, reached through double French doors.

The kitchen and Mr. Tucker's bedroom would be downstairs, along with a bathroom, with running water, hot as well as cold water. There would be four bedrooms upstairs, one for each of the girls, and a spare for company. There would be bathrooms connecting the two bedrooms on each side of the upstairs. In the front upstairs hall there would be a small sewing room for the girls.

They all agreed a piano and lots of shelves for books would be essential. The books were no problem. Mr. Hasbrook could order books, but the piano was something else.

Pianos were terribly expensive. That bothered Mr. Tucker. Mr. Hasbrook and Mr. Matson hated to see Piano Hutchins get any fatter, especially on "Old Dan."

It was Mr. Matson who solved the financial problem: "Go easy on them druggets, Old Dan. The biggest fool thing a man ever did was to putt in a fine floor and cover it with druggets so you can't see the damned floor. I gar-un-tree you can save enought on druggets to get a fine piany all the way from Baldy-Mo, Maryland."

The piano was placed by the east windows, in the parlor. Mr. Matson was right, Mr. Tucker, conceded, about the druggets, but, after all, it would be a low-down trick not to buy the piano from Piano Hutchins, from a fellow-townsman.

A few years later when I read Poe's "Philosophy of Furniture," I thought of this dream-house that sprang up in the fertile acres of love and wistfulness in the old "Ivanhoe." From what I know about Poe, he probably never owned two sticks of furniture, simultaneously, in his forty years on this earth.

"Old Dan" must have volunteered a hundred times to fix the roof on the "Ivanhoe," on his Saturdays off, and for friendship. Mr. Hasbrook shook off the kind suggestion: "Naw, thank you, kindly, Old Dan. 'Twould be my luck to give up the ghost jess you drove the lass nail. I couldn't ress in my grave knowin' them stinking in-laws in Foreginger would get her. Tin cans is best on-surance, I reckon."

Once, "Brer" Thompson said, sweetly enough: "Well, we all have to cross the river, you know." Mr. Matson harrumphed: "Well, me and Amos aint got no damn business to tend ter in Foreginger." But "Brer" Thompson didn't explalin that he was talking about the Jordan and not the Roanoke.

Aside from the weekly sketches, the closest Mr. Tucker got to building his own house was some wall-paper samples Mr. Hasbrook ordered from Baltimore, or Richmond. "Old Dan" and the others were overwhelmed with so many brilliant choices. They hit upon the happy expedient of papering different rooms differently.

Mr. Tucker was drawing up plans until the chilly day he dropped dead as he laid out the breakfast dishes for his children. He lived longer than Poe had lived, but he didn't make it to forty-five.

The wall paper samples stayed on in the "Ivanhoe." The President came across them one day in the middle of a stack of magazine. They were dirty and he threw them in the wood-box by the stove.

Papa was in the store at the time. I was with him but he really didn't see me. I saw fire coming from his eyes and nose. "Listen to me Tom Quigg (the President really had a name, Thomas Quigg), you put those samples back where you found them or I'll beat a whole skillet full of piss out your hide."

The President did precisely as Papa suggested, and right speedily, too. "Brer" Thompson said to Papa: "Your interest rate just went up to twenty per cent, but God loves you and I love you, Alexander."

Old Dan was as free of camouflage as a brass door knob. (Papa said once that there are three things that can't be camouflaged long: A little pregnancy, a manure pile, and a son of a bitch.) But Old Dan was in on one glorious, surreptitious act that was Oxford's best kept secret for a generation.

There was this Negro man named Moses Plummer, who lived on a farm about five miles from Oxford. He made a barrel of money farming, growing whopping, golden wrappers, the best quality tobacco. Mr. Ed Settle said Moses Plummer knew more about planting, raising, and curing tobacco than any man for nine counties around.

He had eleven children, and nine graduated from college at a time when few whites and practically no Negroes around home went off to school. The two who didn't go to college "weren't up to it." They stayed at home and farmed with their father.

Moses Plummer's big problem was what to do about his sizeable fortune. If it were known, generally, that he had big money, his own race would worry him to death trying to borrow and the white peckerwoods would hate his guts. So, he bought land, quietly, and he lent out money, on land, quietly, through Papa.

He wanted a nice house, a real home, but he knew if he built one that attracted attention he'd be a marked man. So he and "Old Dan" worked it this way:

Mr. Tucker built a find house inside an old unpainted, square clapboard house. Mr. Tucker left the old porch. He patched the floor and the roof, but it was never painted. Mr. Tucker left the front room, off the porch, as it was, for visitors. But behind and all around were fine walls and ceilings, and the prettiest floors original growth hardwood could make.

There was a well in the front yard, and Moses Plummer and his family drew water from it regularly. However, there was real plumbing inside the house. The fake front room was lighted by a kerosene lamp. The remainder of the house had real lights, Delco lights.

Unlike Mr. Tucker, Mr. Plummer had to order his pianola from Baltimore. All of his fine furniture was shipped in on the train, too. It was all hauled away and unloaded after dark.

One of my greatest joys was peddling out "Twelfth Street Rag" on the Plummer's pianola. And I am sure the greatest confidence ever reposed in me was knowledge of the wonderful house the Plummer's had inside that bunch of weather-beaten old boards.

But none of the few who knew about the house ever said anything about it, not even to each other, insofar as I know. Papa and the Plummers were mighty close friends. I imagine I was taken in because of Papa.

Today Henry Plummer, who is my age, lives in the house "Old Dan" built for his father. The clapboard camouglage was torn away some years ago, during Papa's lifetime. It's too bad some learned sociologist couldn't have written about this marvelous unmasking. The false-front, the facade, that was ripped off exposed a little progress for mankind, but, of course, it exposed much more of dark evil.

Henry still has the pianola his father ordered all the way from Baltimore. It still works, and only last week when I dropped in to have a drink with Henry, we took turns "playing" the old pianola. Henry and I took turns pumping out "Nola," "Kitten on the Keys," and of course, "Twelfth Street Rag."

After "Twelfth Street Rag," Henry lured me away from the pianola for a minute or two. While we were in the kitchen, the whole house seemed to get up and start doing a clog-dance. The pianola was playing "Old Dan Tucker," just as if the magic of music had just been invented.

Henry had lured me away so that his daughter, Matilda, could put on the "Old Dan Tucker" roll of music. I learned that Henry had ransacked second-hand stores for several years seeking the roll.

We cut-the-buck on the kitchen floor. I pretended I was Matt Venable, the nimblest, grandest dancer of them all. Henry got a hat and held it for me to kick. I hit the crown with my right big toe, the first kick, and, mercifully, I got my leg back without damage.

The tune played in my head, in my heart, and on my lips all the way to Oxford. It's a wonder I kept the car on the road. I could see Mr. Matson and Mr. Hasbrook ushering "Old Dan" into the "Ivanhoe," and I could hear the cult belting out the song. And Papa's big, raised fist was flailing the air, and he was booming out, in his mellifluous basso, "Let the afternoon rip."

There are times when I am afraid I may forget the rapt expectancy of Christmas Eve, or the sounds hoof beats made on the wooden bridge that used to span Sweetgum Creek. If I live long enough, I may even forget the taste and the smell of ripe scuppernongs, but I'll never forget those white handkerchiefs Mr. Virginius Purvis used to wash out so painstakingly and then plaster on the window-panes of the "Ivanhoe" to dry.

He did all of his own washing, in a big wooden tub, in the "Old Reliable," the horse and mule sales' stable run by Mr. Sim Stickney. Mr. Purvis lived in the "Old Reliable," in an empty tack room, near to the stall lived in by his old horse, Silas. At one time he had two horses and a two-horse wagon. I never saw Paul, the horse that had pulled the wagon with Silas.

The other stuff — shirts and socks and long under-wear — were hung on a line that was stretched from one side of the hayloft to the other. Mr. Purvis was too feeble, or unstable, to climb the ladder to the hay-loft. His friends helped him put his washing on the line. I don't think he ever asked anyone. People saw him bent over his wooden tub. They volunteered. All the "Ivanhoes" helped, and so did Boot Ransome. Too, as a boy, as one of Mr. Matson's "larrikins," I made a habit of ambling by the "Old Reliable" whenever I remembered Mr. Purvis' washing-day, Saturday morning, world without end.

There weren't any windows on the tack room, and the panes in front of the "Old Reliable" were so dirty Papa said Francis Asbury gave up on them in 1786.

On Saturday, after he washed, Mr. Purvis, with the help of Mr. Hasbrook and Matson, plastered ten or twelve large linen handkerchiefs on the window-panes at the "Ivanhoe".

The sun dried them long before it tucked its red tail to make room for Saturday night. They looked so pure and so stiff I thought they might be used for miniature flying-carpets, such as the great Solomon made and commanded the wind to fly, with a canopy of birds over-head to keep out the rain or sun.

The handkerchiefs looked as I imagined "the milk of paradise" might look, when frozen stiff. I never saw any such milk, but Papa used to quote "Kubla Khan" a lot. Sometimes Mr. Matson made Papa give "er key-man formance." The recitation always went well until Papa got to the part about the Abyssinian maid, with the dulcimer. No one heard the remainder of the poem because Mr. Matson always started doing what he called the "hootch-a-mee-kootch-a-mee." He sang snatches of "Meet Me In St. Louie, Louie," and he told about visiting the great World's Fair in St. Louis, in "ought foah."

Some of the ladies complained about those handkerchiefs on the window-panes. But they were at a disadvantage. Mr. Purvis was known, everywhere, for always carrying three large, white, linen handkerchiefs: one in the breast pocket of his tattered coat, one in his hip pocket, if he just had to blow his nose, and one in his side coat pocket, to mop his brow.

Such a stickler for clean, white handkerchiefs could not be all bad because this was a time when a mother's last question to a child, going to a party, going anywhere, was: "Have you got a clean pocket handkerchief?" You might not have a cent, and your underwear might be made of old flour sacks, but to be bereft of a clean, white handkerchief was indecent exposure, certainly in local mores.

Mr. Purvis's cronies called him "Vi." His face, once massive, was as wrinkled as a frost-bitten apple or persimmon. His hair was white and long and neatly combed, although he never carried a comb in public, of course. His moustache was white and full and always clean as dewy cotton. He wore a white felt hat the year around. He had two white coats. I'm pretty sure the frayed summer one, patched and repatched by his own hands, was linen. His winter coat was some kind of white duster, but it was made of heavier material.

I remember how I saw him one time, leaning heavily

on his cane, barely putting one foot in front of the other, during a heavy snow storm. At first I thought he was a walking snow-man. You know, one of Hans Christian Anderson's real-life creations.

Every spring he went around taking photographs of children. The attraction was that a child could have his picture taken sitting on Silas. I still have a fairly clear one of me on Silas. I am firing a cap-pistol, from my right hand, with the pistol hand across my bent left arm, in true William S. Hart fashion.

There is one of Sister, in what Mother called her "ballerina costume." Sister is atop Silas, pirouetting, I suppose. I know, for a fact, I was hoping she would fall off and bust her tail. But Silas was so gentle I doubt a leaf would have fallen off his back. Anyway, I remember that Sister got choked on a fish-bone that same night, and I wondered if my evil thoughts at the picture-taking had carried over to the accident at supper.

I guess Mr. Purvis was like the athlete in Housman's poem: His body lived on when his deeds were cobwebs. One of his local contributions, forgotten even when I was a boy, was bringing the "steam towel" to town.

Mr. Purvis heard of a man in South Hill, Va., who ran a "steam towel barber shop." Mr. Purvis rode up on the train, and he came back with the new barber. Mr. Purvis had talked with all of the "Ivanhoe" crowd and each had agreed to give his shaving business to the new man with the "steam towel." Until the "steam towel" came, getting shaved in a barber shop was frequently referred to as getting "Custered," after the unfortunate general.

The new barber's name was Aaron Ricks. He had such a soft touch with his razor Dr. Henley called him

"Sir William Osler." Before long, just about everyone called Aaron Ricks "Sir William," although hardly anyone knew why. Then people started calling him "Bill" Ricks. In a few years, "Bill" supplanted "Sir William." "Aaron" was lost in the shuffle completely. His son is called "Bill" Ricks today.

The sign in front of the old barbershop, now a thing of chrome and tile, reads: "Elite Barbershop . . . Bill Ricks and Son, Props . . ." It's hard to find any one who remembers about Dr. Henley and "Sir William Osler."

As I say, Mr. Purvis's contribution was forgotten, even when I was a young marble-shooter, save for the "Ivanhoes." If Mr. Matson saw some blade coming from the barbershop, all freshly shaved and spruced up, the old man would mumble: "Look at at damn tack-si–derm-is, the ungrateful pig-lover."

When some outsider asked what a "tack-si-derm-is" was, Mr. Matson shook his old head and pigtail sadly, as he explained, laboriously, that a taxidermist was a fellow who mounted animals, hence a pig, goat, or sheep-lover.

Before I was born, and then some, Mr. Purvis and his brother, Hosea, operated a small, fairly lucrative tobacco manufacturing business in Oxford.

From about 1890 to 1910 "Purvis Brothers" manufactured "Sweet Lorena," a tailor-made cigarette that sold for ten cents for a package of twenty. I never saw any of the cigarettes, but I have seen some of the picture-cards with which "Purvis Brothers" bolstered their flimsy packages in the pre-cellophane days.

For a while, virtually all cigarette manufacturers put a bolstering card in each package. Mr. Purvis is alleged to have originated the picture-card. Some manufacturers had a whole series of pictures. Some depicted national heroes and national shrines. Others showed ball players, theatrical luminaries, and national personalities. "Purvis Brothers" had picture-cards of local flowers, cultivated and wild flowers, and pictures of writers, "arthurs," as they were known in Oxford.

Boys used to hang around drug stores and tobacco stores to mooch cards from men who bought packages of cigarettes. A viable group of art-collectors arose in every town. Many boys specialized in a certain series of cards, and it was common to hear a boy say to his pal, "I'll swap you two Sitting Bulls for one Yosemite."

Many exhibitions were displayed at public schools, especially those that depicted national shrines, geography, and wild life. These were the first examples of "visual" education, in the current sense, and the enthusiastic young school-boy collector supplied the "audio" portion of his lecture.

"Sweet Lorena," known as a "mild smoke," was named for Mrs. Purvis, nee Lorena Barksdale, who died long before my time. I understand it was made from flue-cured tobacco, chiefly, and that it was cased with nitroglycerin and sugar. This made it a smooth, sweet smoke. Indeed, this casing process became almost standard with modern cigarettes.

The old cigarette factory, a three story building, was built on the bank of Sweetgum Creek, about a mile from the present corporate limits of Oxford. I understand "Purvis Brothers" employed as many as two hundred hands.

"Sweet Lorena," although never a big seller, did sell well in Virginia and in the Carolinas. Mr. Purvis made a good living from the sales of "Sweet Lorena," but he never became really rich. Then about 1910 "Purvis

Brothers" was forced out of business by the larger companies, by those with large advertizing budgets.

Our Mr. Purvis received a nice chunk of money, from the sale of the business, but he invested it in a soft drink called "Big Rooster." I understand his brother, Hosea, got the formula for the soft drink from a lady who was selling pitchers of a homemade concoction at a church bazaar.

According to local tradition the bottle drink was named "Big Rooster" in deference to Hosea Purvis's sexual prowess, but I have no real way of knowing if he was really "handy with the ladies" or whether he was just bragging.

The cigarette factory was converted into the bottling works, and when the bottling works failed, Mr. Purvis lost the building and the property as well as his cash investment.

The "Ivanhoe" crowd always said Mr. Pruvis's real doom came when he made his big trip to Boston and to Concord, Mass. And there was sense of corporate guilt because his going north, on the big trip, was a town project.

Mr. Purvis's idea of heaven was to visit Boston and Concord and to stand at Walden Pond, immortalized by Henry David Thoreau, whose writings Mr. Purvis read everyday of his life.

He had been too busy to make the trip, in the plush days of "Purvis Brothers," and ever since he had been too poor to make the pilgrimage. He decided he would buy a ticket for his white hat. His hat would go to Boston and Concord and back.

I suppose Mr. Purvis thought that everytime he put his hat on, after the trip, he would have the sacred essence of New England close to him, at least vicariously, anyway.

Then Mr. Matson read about a contest some soap company sponsored. One of the deluxe prizes was a free trip to any destination in the United States, with all expenses paid and a week at the town or site. As I understood it, the contestants had to finish a sentence, in twenty-five words or less, on "Why I Like" whatever soap it was.

Mr. Purvis, at the insistence of his friends, entered. He didn't win anything, but Mr. Shelton, the grumpy Western-Union operator, agreed to go along with a fake telegram that said Mr. Purvis won a trip to any place he wished to visit. The telegram said the prize money would come by wire the next day.

Mr. Ed Settle collected the necessary funds, quietly. I am sure he would have given the entire amount — I think it was $500.00 — but many other people in town insisted on the privilege of contributing.

To put the trimming on the tree, Captain Wade had a piece on the front page of the *Torchlight* announcing that Mr. Purvis had won the trip. However, Captain Wade wrote around the details. The soap company wasn't involved in the news story.

First off, at the suggestion of our one and only world-traveler, Oliphant Mason, Mr. Purvis sewed a $20.00 bill in each leg of his long underwear. He might get lost or knocked in the head. Even so, he'd go down with some hard cash to get him back to Oxford.

I think everyone in town went to the depot when Mr. Purvis left. I am sure Miss Bertha Hornbuckle salted the time ahead. At any event, we got from school in plenty of time to see Mr. Purvis get on the "three somep'n" train going north.

The Silver Cornet Band led the way to the station,

playing "At A Georgia Camp-Meeting," the old cake-
-walk rousement. At the station the band, in their natty
uniforms and directed by the Per-fessor, Max Schmidt,
played "Narcissus," a tune they had to practice up on
for three nights, since it wasn't in their habitual repertoire.

Everyone smiled, including Just Plain Snake
Imboden, because people knew it was a dear favorite of
Mr. Matson, Mr. Hasbrook, and Mr. Purvis. The three
men were always trying to find a picture of "Miss"
Ethelbert Nevin, who wrote "Narcissus." The other two
reminded Mr. Purvis to watch out for Miss Ethelbert, or
her picture, as he passed through the big cities.

When he got on the train his return ticket was tied
around his neck; and people had brought him enough
hampers of fried chicken and apple pies to last out a
trip to the moon or to Oregon.

I'll never forget that day, with the band playing
"Narcissus" and "Lorena." When the train hove to the
depot, some crewmen opened the baggage car. They
thought they were to take a casket aboard, what with
so many people standing around.

"Struttin' Bud" Davenport came by long enough to
strike out five straight batters. "Old Dan" Tucker
caught him. It would have been unthinkable for "Old
Dan" not to have taken off from work to see Mr.
Purvis off to that far country up yonder. However, the
sixth batter hit a towering fly, at least 500 feet, all the
way to the town water tank. I think it was a greater
catch than the one that rookie, Gionfriodo, made when
he reached in the bleachers and robbed Joe DiMaggio of
a home run. "Struttin' Bud" leaped across one baggage-
truck, and he scooted under another one. He scattered
the Ladies' Cultural and Improvement Society, never

taking his eye off that imaginary ball. Then he climbed up the first eight or ten iron rungs on the town tank and caught that ball, back-handed over his right shoulder.

I'm sure "Struttin' Bud" could hear us hollering when he got home, half a mile away.

After a week, Mr. Hasbrook got a telegram saying Mr. Purvis would arrive the day following on the "five somep'n train from Richmond." The crowd that went to the depot to meet Mr. Purvis was larger, if anything, than the one that saw him off. But the man who left wasn't the one who got off. The man who shuffled off the train was much older, and he looked as if he didn't have as much blood in him as a fishing worm.

While the train was groaning to a stop, throwing a small fit and shaking cinders the way a tramp hound shakes fleas, Sheriff Venable made a place in front of the Silver Cornet band for Mr. Matson, Mr. Hasbrook, and Mr. Tucker. The three were at the car before the porter put down the stool.

"Tell us how it was, Vi," Mr. Matson shouted. "Tell us about Boston, Concord, and Mister Henry David Thoreau's pond."

"Bless God," Mr. Purvis moaned, "There aren't any such places and there isn't any such man. It's Bas-tun, Conquered, and Henry Thorough."

But I know now, he was walking to deep shadows, not made of shade, when he walked away from the depot the day he returned from Boston. Finally, his chief source of income was selling razor-blades, can-openers, shoe strings, stove polish, chiclets, glass pistols filled with candy, celluloid collars, watch-fobs, tin pie plates, and numerous other oddments, from his wagon.

For a while he sold Skiddoo. This produced a volatile issue among the Ladies' Society. Most of the missionary societies sold Skiddoo. Therefore, Mr. Purvis was impeding the Lord's work. He was getting money that should go to save lost souls in darkest Africa and in China, whatever color that country might have been then.

Mr. Purvis acquiesed, immediately and graciously. He gave his remaining jars of Skiddoo to Mrs. Ashton-Brown to be divided among the white missionary societies.

Papa said if Skiddoo was the way to salvation, there had been enough sold in Oxford, alone, to make the world as clean as a dried fish bone. I almost forgot this: Mother and her sister, my Aunt Emma, used to talk along the 'phone about sickness and funerals, principally. One day Papa struck the end of the hall-tree at home and bellowed: "I'll swear, Mary. If you and Emma were missionaries and if you could spread the gospel as fast as you spread bad news, there wouldn't be a damned heathen on earth by breakfast time."

It was rumored around school, in a red-faced, giggling, but strangely titillating way that Mr. Purvis sold rubber condoms from his wagon. This merchandise was referred to, undeviatingly, as "conjum rubbers." I never learned if "conjum" was a corruption of condom or if the spooky word "conjure" had entered a bit.

One day I tried to ask Papa if this was true. But my mind couldn't get together on the precise phrase.

"Are you asking if Mr. Purvis sells some kind of illicit merchandise?"

I nodded yes.

"Don't talk like such a blamed fool, Sandy." Then looking me up and down, as if he were counting my stupid effrontery by the half-inch, Papa came back: "Do you equate a gentleman such as Virginius Purvis with a blatherskite such as Just Plain Snake Imboden?"

I knew Papa wouldn't lie to me about Mr. Purvis, or about anything else. I thought his statement settled the big issue of the "conjum rubbers." When I say "big issue," I mean it had all of the sassy, surreptitious evocations to kids that the painting "September Morn" and Eugene Field's clandestine poem, "When Willie Wet the Bed" had for grown men.

Still, I am not sure about those "conjum rubbers." At Mr. Purvis's funeral Pansy Alice, or P. A. Duncan, our liberated woman, was the only lady present. The way she bit her lip to try to keep from crying made me think there might have been something in Mr. Purvis's wagon that Papa didn't see, or didn't admit.

As we say today, P. A. was really hung-up on Margaret Sanger. I have wondered if there wasn't some vicarious attunement with Mr. Purvis's purveying birth control materials.

In addition to traveling around the county and selling oddments (no one ever called him a peddler or a huckster) Mr. Purvis was the official representative of "Goose Grease," *the goose grease*, which was considered excellent for check colds, croup, nasal infections, cuts, burns, bruises, and galded shanks or crotches. Most people thought "Goose Grease" was the best thing on the top-side of the earth for the "middle-aged man's prostrate condition." Mr. Matson used to chortle and add "brides" to the list of things "Goose Grease" was so good for, but, frankly, his allusion escaped me at that particular time.

Once a year, for many years, two giant geese, George Greene and Jacob Fuller, came to town to advertize the salve, with a brief parade that was almost over before it

started. After Mr. Purvis became the official local representative, no one but him knew when the geese would
come to town. As a matter of record, George Greene and
Jacob Fuller, or their progeny, made these furtive parades
through small Southern towns from the first administration
of Cleveland down to Hoover's time.

They were handled by an elderly Negro man, who
looked as if he had been cut from the best grade of
mahagony. The old Negro and the geese just turned up,
apropos to nothing, without fanfare. One minute they were
sashshaying down Main Street. The next minute they were
gone, as if they had used the same cloud Elisha had taken.

I imagined the old Negro was Jehu, from what I had
heard about Jehu, as he walked along holding the reins and
wearing "Goose Greese" sandwich boards. (I knew about
the "sandwich man" from the *Sketches of Boz* which Papa
read to me.)

George Greene and Jacob Fuller strutted like show
horses as they pulled a tiny wagon that held a cardboard
thing made into the shape of a tub of "Goose Grease."

But no one ever spoke of these geese as geese. No, they
were always George Greene and Jacob Fuller. A stranger
would be bound to think we were talking about two
outstanding local citizens.

Their spontaneous visit usually came on a sultry afternoon during "Dog Day's," roughly, July 15, to September
1, when the square was virtually deserted. But these visita-
tions were time-markers and foot-notes. Someone might say
that some event occurred at such and such a time. Some
history expert would shoot back: "It ain't no such a damn
thing. It happened two days after George Greene and Jacob
Fuller came to Oxford that summer when "Struttin' Bud"
pitched a perfect game on the dee-po platform, the same as
Addie Joss done against the White Sox."

Perhaps, the furtive glimpse, seen by only a few, was a gambit of the "Goose Grease" moguls. I really don't know, but there was intensive and far-ranging vibrance.

I never heard anyone say the originals were bound to be dead. Thus George Greene and Jacob Fuller were as ageless as larkspur, as imminent as Thanksgiving. They never grew old or feeble. Finally, they just faded away, when better roads and faster cars brought infinite changes into mercantile mores. More mortals died, but for forty years George Greene and Jacob Fuller walked rapidly, majestically, down Main Street.

We could count on them as we counted on the unblemished saints of our innocent childhoods. (This was not the same thing that occurred when local women, and women everywhere, continued to write Lydia E. Pinkham, and receive her personal answers to highly personal problems, for 22 years after the death of the priestess of the nostrums.)

On the big day, Mr. Purvis, with help from his friends, curried Silas and brushed him until he shone as brightly as Mrs. Ashton-Brown's lustrous silverware that was too fancy to be used for food. But Mr. Purvis never decorated the buggy, nor did he put any flowers on Silas. He merely shook his head at any such suggestions. He never added that he thought such decorations were in poor taste or that they would mock poor Silas.

Mr. Purvis met the venerable Negro, and George Greene and Jacob Fuller, in Ransome's Alley. Once he was on Main Street the Negro blew a cornet. Then the inertia, the stillness, and the sticky torpor of "Dog Days" were broken by mighty blasts. The tune was always the same: "The Campbell's Are Coming, Tra, Tra, Tra, Tra," which represented, "Goose Grease is coming, Tra, Tra, Tra."

Mr. Purvis and Silas led off but by the time they

141

reached the Confederate monument, George Green and Jacob Fuller had passed them. Before Silas and Mr. Purvis got to the Opera House George Green and Jacob Fuller were gone, in the flesh, until the next year.

Few people in town mentioned anything about Mr. Purvis' part in this short, fast parade. I guess few folks were aware of his identification with the parade, even if the "Ivanhoes" all said nice things to him. I remember, distinctly, towards the last how Papa said: "Well, Vi, that was the best parade you've had yet."

But people out in the county wanted to know every detail. When they saw Mr. Purvis and Silas, they flocked to the buggy to hear all the intimate details of the recent visit to Oxford of George Green and Jacob Fuller.

Towards the end of his life, Mr. Purvis would fall asleep in the buggy, almost every afternoon. Silas always walked slowly to the "Old Reliable." Papa, or "Brer" Thompson, or Dr. Henley or some other friend would see Silas trudging along, and someone who understood always followed on to the livery stable, to help Mr. Purvis down.

Silas was the first to die. Dr. Henley said the horse didn't die so much as he just didn't wake up that morning.

Mr. Matson and Mr. Hasbrook tried their best to cheer up Mr. Purvis. He was grateful but he just didn't seem to be able to respond. "Brer" Thompson, without Mr. Purvis' knowledge, started collecting money to buy a new horse. When Mr. Ed Settle heard about this, he offered to make up any amount that was needed.

It would be a horse, not a mare. Some thought Barnabas would be the right name. There wasn't a fuss, but Timothy seemed to suit better. The new horse would be young Timothy, all agreed. And if they had to have an excuse, Miss Bertha Hornbuckle and Papa would swear to a white liza-jane. They would say the "Goose Grease" headquarters, in Atlanta, I think, it was, had called long distance to say the company was giving Mr. Purvis the new horse. That would spare his feelings, they all agreed.

But three days after Silas died, Mr. Matson went to the "Old Reliable" to check on Mr. Purvis and found this note:

"Old Silas is dead and I want to die too. Goodbye, my dear friends."

There wasn't any name signed to the note. None was needed.

Dr. Henley announced that Mr. Purvis died of heart failure. He really died from a big overdose of laudanum. The word "suicide" wasn't mentioned, not to my knowledge.

I was walking home with Papa that afternoon. Dr. Henley came along in his brand-new Buick and gave us a lift. Papa looked at Dr. Henley lovingly and almost whispered: "Heart attack, Joe?"

Dr. Henley said, almost gruffly: "Hell, yes, Alexander, heart failure. That's what all of us die of anyway."

Most of Mr. Purvis's friends thought it over proper that he be buried in Silas' grave, or that Silas be moved to his grave. But "Brer" Thompson said the loves and fortunes of the two were forevermore joined, even in their separate graves. There wasn't any church funeral for Mr. Purvis, only a graveside service. "Brer" Thompson quoted Mark Twain: "When you go to heaven leave your dog or horse outside. Heaven goes by favor. If it went by merit the faithful animal would get in and you would be thrown out."

Oxford, June 10, 1961:

The population of Oxford is just above 7000. I am told that 40% of the population is composed of adults. I am reasonably sure this ratio is high relative to the national ratio of adults and youngsters, but we have an unusually large number of old people in Oxford.

Anyway if there are 2800 adults, there must be close to 2500 memberships in a wide assortment of social, civic, fraternal, patriotic, religious, and cultural organizations. Indeed, most of the 2500 belong to several such organizations.

There is a chapter of every civic club of which I have ever heard, but most of our local ones are relatively new, certainly in relationship to the long history of the town.

To my own knowledge, there are at least 27 women's literary clubs that meet regularly. But if there is a single literary organization for males, I am unaware of its existence. There used to be one, "Sans-Souci," or "the History Club," as it was commonly designated.

"Sans-Souci" faded many years ago, when I was a boy. Its dissolution was simply a tragic matter of the attrition of death. The membership died off, and no suitable replacements seemed to be available.

However, I think the demise of "Sans-Souci" related more to swiftly changing mores, especially to the incessant flood of new entertainments. Again, "Sans-Souci" was not an eating club, primarily. It held no "Ladies' Nights," and it bucked for no industries. It was not even remotely geared to civic improvement, not in the current sense, certainly.

For many years new members were not taken in save when an old member died. It was said that the President waited his turn for two decades. He was never tapped, although he spent a long, abortive apprenticeship boning up on Sidney Lanier so he would be ready when the great hour came.

I don't know the real extent of the President's special study of Sidney Lanier, but I know it to be a fact that he owned — had acquired in some fashion — one of the collected editions of Lanier's poems, *Poems of Sidney Lanier*, which the poet's widow got out in 1884. The President also had copies of such posthumous works of Lanier's as *The English Novel, Music and Poetry, Letters of Sidney Lanier,* and *Shakspere and His Forerunners.* (And Shakespeare is spelled "Shakspere.")

The President owned the biography of Lanier written by Professor Edwin Mims, in 1905. (Mims, who taught Papa at Trinity College, went on to Vanderbilt and lived through and saw through the unrealistic hogwash of the celebrated "Fugitive Movement.") The President's *piece de resistance* was his copy of *Tiger Lilies*, published in 1867, during Lanier's lifetime.

For many years the President has an annual display of his Lanier collection on February 3, the poet's birthday. (The UDC always had a big program at school on February 3, honoring Lanier. Indeed, I think I thought this was a national holiday until I left Oxford for college.)

The President displayed his fabulous collection under glass. We kids could look at, but never touch, sacred immortality.

The President loved to quote the passage from "Song of the Chattahoochie" that tells how:

The white quartz shone and the smooth brook-stone
Did bar me passage with friendly brawl,
And many a luminous jewel lone
-Crystals clear or a-cloud with mist,
Ruby, garnett, and amethyst-

The President's eyes glittered as brightly as the show-window at Mr. I. Ferguson's jewelry store, and his mouth watered the way I imagined Silas Marner's mouth

145

watered with ecstasy when he counted his gold.

Papa always came back by quoting the opening of Lanier's long poem, "The Symphony:"

O Trade! O Trade! would thou wert dead!
The Time needs heart — 'tis tired of head:
'We're all for love, the violins said.
'Of what avail the rigorous tale
Of bill for coin and box for bale'?

This was pretty shifty of Papa. It upset the President as much as Mr. Matson's malicious innuendoes about bank examiners.

I am sure vanity had much to do with the unchanging composition of "Sans-Souci." Papa used to smile, indulgently, and quote Mencken: "The essence of a self-reliant and autonomous culture is an unshakable egoism." Papa was alluding to the difficulty of gaining membership.

Getting in "Sans-Souci" reminded me of something "Brer" Thompson told Mrs. Piano Hutchins, who weighed a ton. Mrs. Hutchins asked how she could inherit eternal life.

"Eat less," "Brer" Thompson replied, "For the gate to heaven is exceedingly narrow."

Whatever "Sans-Souci" was, it was the fruitful antithesis of Carlyle's, "Such is SOCIETY, the vital articulation of many individuals into a new collective individual."

I was allowed to sit in a corner, in total silence, each time Papa was the host for "Sans-Souci," when it met at our house. Many years later I remembered a paper "Governor Poly" read on Johnson Jones Hooper's marvelously outrageous book, *The Adventures of Captain Simon Suggs*. The "Guv" said the Duke, in *Huckleberry Finn*, was the literary reincarnation of Captain Simon Suggs, that ingratiating devil. I mentioned this in an English class at Duke, some years later, and I seemed to have impressed my professor.

The "Sans-Souci" was founded in 1872, in the back room of the Eagle Tavern And Bar, by George Worley, a Confederate colonel, scion of a long-line of local gentry, and a lawyer.

The membership was limited to eight. One story says Colonel Worley limited the "Sans-Souci" to eight because nine or more made an awkward poker game. Another account says that eight was hit upon because there are 16 ounces of whiskey in a pint. Thus, eight men could get two ounces each, or what was called "a small eye-opener," or "enough for a hollow tooth."

Colonel Worley, rendered completely destitute by the Civil War, made a precarious living, barely an existence, from 1865 to 1870, by tutoring a few children in Greek and Latin and by investing his small stipend at the poker table in the back room of the Eagle.

One day in 1872 he found a Sunday school lesson on the floor of the bar-room, one dropped, evidently, by some thirsty farmer. Worley read the lesson and pronounced it, "The poorest damned attempt I ever read."

The bar-keeper dared him to do better. "By, God, I will," Colonel Worley said, picking up the gauntlet. So, acquiring Bible, tracts, paper and ink he proceeded to write some sample lessons.

Shortly, he was commissioned to write the International Sunday School Lesson. Papa said his father told him it was generally understood that Colonel Worley was paid the munificent sum of $50.00 a month for his contributions.

For four years the Biblical scribe led a life of affluence and luxury, all the while using the back room of the Eagle for his study.

Then in 1876 the editor of the magazine that published

147

the International Sunday School Lesson came to Philadelphia to attend some British-American brotherhood assembly. Since he was only a few hundred miles from Oxford, the British divine decided he must come to Oxford to pay his personal respects to "the Reverend Dr. Worley," his lucid and consecrated scribe.

In his zeal to pay deference to Oxford's Gamaliel, the British divine seems to have neglected to announce his intention. At any event he alighted from the stage coach, at the old stand in front of the courthouse. (The railroad did not come to Oxford until 1881.)

He asked someone where he could find "the Reverend Dr. Worley" and his informant merely pointed to the Eagle. Perhaps, the English gentleman was so aflame with rapt expectancy he was not aware of his surroundings. Nay more, he may have been totally unfamiliar with the interior of American saloons.

Attaining the Eagle he asked the bar-keeper the location of the good Reverend's study, and the publican pointed, wordlessly, to the back room. Still abysmally ignorant of imminent disaster, the pilgrim strode on to the back room. He knocked and when he was admitted, there sat "the Reverend Doctor Worley" holding a heart flush. His Bible, tracts, and writing materials were stacked by his chair. A bottle was at his right hand, and a "soiled dove," a painted saloon-woman, was leaning over his left shoulder.

Colonel Worley was fired by an unintelligible shriek of incredulity and righteous indignation, and by the steady retreat of two horrified feet.

To this very hour, a heart flush is sometimes called "an Indian massacre" in Oxford. It amuses me whenever I hear the phrase because the speaker has never heard of the hand in relationship to Colonel Worley's literary demise. Indeed, the modern poker player has never heard of the Colonel, much less of his writing the International Sunday School Lesson.

Beyond peradventure, "an Indian massacre" predates "Dead Man's Hand" in conjunction to the two pairs, aces and eights, Wild Bill Hickok held when he was shot and killed.

Colonel Worley's first associate in the "Sans-Souci" was Benjamin Thorpe, another impoverished scion, who was twenty-five in 1872. "Squire Ben," as he came to be called, lived until 1915. Although he died before I was born, I have always felt that I knew "Squire Ben" in the flesh, and intimately.

At Gettysburg, as a sixteen-year-old sharpshooter in the 26th North Carolina Infantry, Ben Thorpe was stationed, on the first day of the battle, in the region of the McPherson farm, on the east. Young Thorpe was placed atop of one of McPherson's cherry trees, and he was armed with one of the few telescopic rifles in the Confederate army. Ben's lieutenant, who had positioned him atop the cherry tree, stood near by to observe the enemy through binoculars.

From his perch Ben saw a group of Union officers halt on a knoll several hundred yards away. The lieutenant surveyed the group through his field glasses. (For the following dialogue I am indebted to my friend, Glenn Tucker and his "Lee and Longstreet At Gettysburg," published by Bobbs Merrill).

"Ben," he shouted up, "do you see that tall, straight man in the center of the group? He is evidently an officer of some high rank and is directing operations. Sight your gun at 700 yards and see if you can reach him."

These were the precise words, as Tucker records and as "Squire Ben" remembered them, in a conversation with Papa.

149

The first shot fell short.

"That was a little short, Ben," said the lieutenant. "Sight her at 900 yards this time and hold steady, for we must have him."

Ben sighted carefully, resting his long-barreled rifle on a limb of the cherry tree. He held his aim and squeezed the trigger. "I knew before the report died away that the shot had been a good one."

Later Ben learned that he had killed General John Reynolds, ("the great and good Reynolds," as "Squire Ben" told it to Papa,) who was in command of the Union Army the first day at Gettysburg, in the temporary absence of General George Meade.

"I've been sorry ever since," he said whenever he recalled the incident.

General Reynolds was reburied in his home town, Lancaster, Pa., and it is an irrefutable fact that "Squire Ben" arranged for flowers to be placed on the grave, on several occasions. He had some correspondence with Reynold's widow.

I understand Mrs. Reynolds was bitter when "Squire Ben" began his correspondence, but, in time, she accepted his sincere regret, his active sense of personal sorrow and guilt.

Papa, who acceded to the "Sans-Souci" upon "Squire Ben's" death in 1915, always referred to the old gentleman as one of the Civil War's most tragic casualties. Apparently, there was never a day for fifty-two years, from 1863 to his death in 1915, in which Reynolds did not occupy a portion of "Squire Ben's" thoughts.

While he was not a religious man in the orthodox sense, he went to Old St. Mark's church almost every day for an interlude of meditation or lamentation. He rode a horse, to the end of his days, and he was always followed by several hounds, even when he came to town to buy something or to attend the meetings of "Sans-Souci."

Apparently, he never used the word "bitch". No, female hounds were "little ladies."

His hounds went to Old St. Mark's whenever he went. The church was built on the Thorpe ancestral plantation, about 1820. It had six short pews on either side of a narrow aisle, and there was a small slave balcony. The wood for the building, for the pews, for all of the church furniture, and for the communion cups came from trees grown on "Old Goshen," the Thorpe plantation.

Towards the last of "Squire Ben's" life he was the only communicant left at Old St. Mark's. There was no rector, of course, but the rector in Oxford would drive out three or four times a year to give communion to "Squire Ben."

I remember a conversation when Papa and "Brer" Thompson were talking about old "Squire Ben," about how it was that he lived with guilt as intimately as other men live with love, as intimately as flowers live with sunshine and rain.

"Brer" Thompson said there should be a literal heaven just so old "Squire Ben" could speak his piece with General Reynolds, make his peace and find his peace. Each tried to project the scene. Each tried to conjure the words old "Squire Ben" would say to the man he had killed.

Finally, Papa and "Brer" Thompson agreed that the meeting would be along the lines of one of Lord Byron's stanzas:

If I should meet thee
After long years,
How should I greet thee? —
With silence and tears.

I spoke of the difficulty of getting into "Sans-Souci," of

the President's lengthy, empty vigil. One of the most ingenious devices at ingratiation was done by Mr. Gus Tulgin, father of Jo-Jo. Mr. Tulgin, who made, installed, and repaired house gutters, had a handsome collection of arrowheads and sundry Indian relics.

He invited the membership of "Sans-Souci," solely as individuals, mind you, to a barbecue and to an exhibition of his Indian artifacts.

At noon, on the big day, Mr. Tulgin filled two huge wooden buckets two-thirds full with well water. He placed the buckets on a shelf on his back porch. He gave Jo-Jo a quarter. Jo-Jo was to ride his bicycle to the ice plant at five o'clock and bring back two bits worth of ice. That would be about as large a piece as one could put into the basket of a bicycle. Jo-Jo was to chop the ice into chunks and to fill the two buckets with the pieces of ice.

Thus, the water would be good and cold for the juleps when Mr. Tulgin came home from his gutter shop. But Jo-Jo spent the two bits. As I recall, Jo-Jo went to the movie matinee. When he came home, about five o'clock, he filled both buckets with lumps of coal, from Mr. Tulgin's back yard coal pile.

Mr. Tulgin shook both buckets when he got home. It was about dark by then. The "ice" sloshed around nicely in the buckets. When he tasted the water to test it, it was lukewarm. He figured the ice hadn't been in long enough to cool the water.

When he made a second test, about thirty minutes later, the water tasted even hotter. He wondered what was wrong with the ice. He explained his vexation to his wife. She told him ice didn't make water hotter, that he was so filled with whiskey everything tasted hot to him.

The next time he drank he got coal dust and dirt all over his face. Mrs. Tulgin screamed. She said Mr. Tulgin had "the black foot in the mouth," or some kind of new and pernicious "hoof and mouth disease."

He looked at himself in the mirror, and he really went off his rocker. Mrs. Tulgin called Dr. Henley, and the doctor gave Mr. Tulgin something to calm his nerves.

In the meantime Jo-Jo, seeing the havoc he had caused, "borrowed" 35 cents of his mother's egg money, went to the ice-plant, and half-filled both buckets with real ice.

By then Dr. Henley's medicine, or shot, had quieted Mr. Tulgin. He wanted to show Dr. Henley he really wasn't crazy. He led the doctor to the back porch. "Now, see for yourself, Doc. That ice water is hot enough to shave with."

Both men sipped, and when the icy cold water hit Mr. Tulgin's mouth he really "broke bad." This time Dr. Henley had to give him a big shot of morphine to get him under control.

It was several years before Jo-Jo found the courage, or gall, to explain to his father what had really happened. The event quickly became a vibrant foot-maker, a book-marker, a time-marker, in local history. Until fairly recently, many events were equated, in time, "To the night when Gus Tulgin tried to make time with the history club and went crazy doing it."

Oxford, August 26, 1970

Today is the day of the national strike by women. As I understand it, the Women's Lib wants the American woman to strike all the way from the kitchen, to the washing machine, to the vacuum cleaner, to the bed.

As I have noted, Mrs. Ashton-Brown advocated such a strike many years ago; albeit, Abagail Adams implied a similar strike in a letter she wrote to her husband, John Adams, while he was President.

153

Pansy Alice Duncan, P.A. as she preferred to be called, practiced many of the tenets and proposals of the Women's Lib years ago. To my knowledge, she was the only person in town who resented having doors opened for her. That and hat-tipping and similar amenities were scathingly rejected by P.A. as masculine attempts to traduce and to enslave women.

I believe she was the first woman in town to smoke on the streets, in public. She resisted all efforts by men to hold a light for her cigarette. She used a long cigarette-holder. She held the holder in her teeth with a rakish, defiant, uphill slant, much the same way that FDR did.

She abhorred all terms of endearment and all adjectives such as cute, sweet, precious, and vivacious. She blew all of her fuses if she heard a woman designated as pert, dimpled, blonde, or stacked. Such words were snide male ruses, overt attempts at debasement.

At the same time she referred to some of the men of the town as bald-headed, skinny, grizzled, bitch-faced, pussel-gutted, bulbous-nosed, and so on. One day Papa told her she was blatantly inconsistent.

Immediately, she used Papa as a surrogate. She apologized to the men of town, through Papa, and, insofar as I can determine, she never made any such references to males again.

P.A. was the best-looking woman in Oxford, with the possible exception of Dovey Simpson, Jimmy's wife. She hardly ever wore make-up, and she kept her hair short. She hardly ever wore a dress. Her usual attire was a man's shirt and jeans, or jodhpurs. I never saw her in a hat, winter or summer, not even at a funeral. She never wore jewelry or furs. In cold weather she wore short coats. Some were made of corduroy. Some were leather and others were suede.

154

If she tried to conceal her marvelous feminity, she was never successful. Even in her rough, masculine garb she glowed. Her beauty had the magnetic sparkle of a newly-minted penny. Physically, she was the same irresistible challenge to the blades of the town that Mt. Everest was to the mountain-climbers. Yet she seemed as unobtainable as Eldorado. When she walked along our sidewalks, it was as if the composite male loin had usurped the composite male eyes.

All eyes flashed as if the sum of masculine knowledge and ambition was reduced to criminal assault. I don't mean that the men of town had active notions of rape, but each one seemed aflame with insatiable lust, with the intransigent desire for physical conquest.

I suppose P.A. opened all the cages, released all the savage beasts that resided within us. Conversely, when Dovey Simpson walked by, she set violins and flutes to playing rhapsodic paeans. Dovey transformed us into love-lyricists. P.A. induced an incurable epidemic of sheer, undiluted physical confrontation.

P.A.'s hair and face always reminded me of Poe's description of "Helen:" "Thy hyacinth hair, thy classic face." Her short hair was naturally curly. Mother said P.A. never used any curlers. Nor did she go to the beauty parlor.

I have ransacked my mind, but the cliche, peaches and cream, really describes her face. Her face was always tanned from the sun, but it always sparkled as if she had just given it a hard washing. Her mouth was full and sensuous, and it was sensual as hell, too.

Whenever I saw her, I thought it must be a terrible, tragic thing when she cut out the light and went to bed each night, when all that unadorned radiance was wasted in the darkness.

She had large breasts, the kind men whistle at even

when they don't pucker their lips. It was said that she never wore a brassiere, but, of course, I really don't know. She equated the corset with the Chinese custom of binding the feet of small females. One of P.A.'s favorite women was Caresse Crosby (nee Mary P. Jacob), the Parisian expatriate who, from her own funds, published the works of many unknown American writers who became famous.

In her anti-corset talk, P.A. told how Caresse Crosby, or Mary P. Jacob, a young New York debutante, had helped liberate women by inventing the brassiere. According to P.A., Miss Jacob found the corset meanly immobilizing. One night, before a dance, Miss Jacob had improvised a bra from two pocket handkerchiefs, a bit of ribbon, and some thread. P.A. referred to Miss Jacob-Caresse Crosby as a "beautiful person," and she explained that "beautiful" had nothing to do with good looks.

I'm sure P.A. didn't invent the phrase, "the beautiful people," but she was the first I ever heard use it in the modern context.

Her rough clothes, her pants, couldn't conceal her exciting figure any more than thick leaves can conceal the magic of the singing of an unseen bird.

Papa said P.A.'s camouflaging her remarkable figure in britches and in men's shirts reminded him of something Oliver Wendell Homes, Sr. wrote about his Harvard class-mate, Samuel F. Smith, author of "America:"

And there's a nice youngster of excellent pith,
Fate tried to conceal him by calling him Smith.

In summer, when P.A. went swimming, in her bathing suit, the local males gathered at the water as if the Old Testament prophecy were about to be fulfilled, as if creation were about to be destroyed by fire. She seemed taller in her bathing suit, "A daughter of the gods, divinely tall,/ And most divinely fair," as Tennyson said so well, as he so well said so many things.

She was the walking essence of summer skies and yellow roses. Surely, it seemed that all of the world's knowledge reposed somewhere upon P.A.'s long, golden legs.

As I may have mentioned, she was an excellent rider. She had two fine saddle-horses, Big Bill, a large bay, whom she had named for Big Bill Heywood, the oldtime labor organizer, and Meg, a sorrel whom she had named for Margaret Sanger, the birth-control advocate and slums-worker.

Two or three times a week she rode one or the other of her horses to the local cotton mill village to harrangue the workers while they were eating their lunch.

She spoke from the saddle. Big Bill reared and tossed his mane repeatedly. I don't know, but, perhaps, P.A. touched him with her heels to make him stand on his hind legs. Anyway, Big Bill's dramatics added zest to P.A.'s verbal fireworks.

As she enjoined the mill workers to unite, she berated the mill owners. Management was the old Russian Czar. The cotton mill was a cruel feudal system. The company store was the secret police, and the workers' homes, owned by the mill, were the salt mines of Siberia.

The President, Mr. Entwhistle, Mrs. Ashton-Brown and some of the other large stockholders asked Mr. Saxon, the superintendent, to put a stop to P.A.'s incendiary oratory. She was the first person in Oxford to be called "Red" and "Bolshevik." In fact, many of the mill workers called her "Miss Red Bolshevik" the same way William Sydney Porter had been called O. Henry.

Mr. Saxon told the irate stockholders he wouldn't stop P.A.'s noonday speeches for something pretty. No, he explained, the visits made the mornings pass faster, easier. P.A. gave the workers something to look forward to, to cherish.

And after her speech was over, all the hands returned to the afternoon's work in pleasant, friendly moods.

Many of the mill workers were small farmers who moved to Oxford for steady work after wrestling unsuccessfully with the wilt and low tobacco prices. Many of them were bound to be related to P.A. Obviously, some knew they were kin to Old Man Rufe or to Miss Texanna, but there is no evidence that any worker ever addressed her as "Cudin."

However, as I think back, P.A.'s influence on Oxford was much more oblique than direct. We talked about her much as the characters in Beckett's play, "Waiting For Godot," talk about the man who isn't present.

She was a gadfly, but she was more the smell of the rose than the rose, itself, more the peach switch in the corner of the kitchen than the actual lash of the thong.

I don't know, but it's possible she would have gone virtually unnoticed if she had been a homely girl. Perhaps, she could not have carried off her volatilities if she had been fat, or knock-kneed, or bespectacled and scrawny.

The modern psychiatrist might say that P.A. reacted from her father, from Old Man Rufe. Actually, she was strong and hardy, as her mother, Miss Texanna, was strong and hardy. And P.A. added lots of pepper to the earthy, salty heritage she inherited from her mother.

Once, she spelled Miss Bertha for a couple of hours at the central's office. Apparently, she plugged in some wrong numbers. Some lines were badly crossed during P.A.'s brief operation of the switchboard. The President thought he was talking excessively intimate business to Mr. Caleb Entwhistle. Before he caught himself, the President discovered he was divulging top secrets to Tom Day, at Hill's Drug Store.

Wrathfully, the President demanded an explanation. P.A. told him: "Go soak your head. I stuck the plug in my bottom, by mistake, and you got Mexico City."

Today, that phrase is used, infrequently, in Oxford, to explain some inadvertent blunder or some contretemps, but the new breed has no real notion of what is meant by the word "plug."

P.A. was "not with the movement," as people used to put it. She never attended church services. She was an "aetheist," an "agnostic," or a "free thinker," depending upon the person describing her.

This attitude made her stick out in Oxford the way the giant figures of Lee, Jackson, and Jefferson Davis stick out on Stone Mountain, Georgia. But denunciation of organized religion was never a portion of her verbal pyrotechnics. She didn't believe in the "Word" but others were free to believe.

Occasionally, she stopped to hear Just Plain Snake Imboden jabber from a street corner, when a particular batch of his white mule induced a call to preach. When Just Plain Snake, or some other itinerant revivalist, gave the call for sinners to confess, P.A. would march to the mobile altar on a street corner or by the water's edge and confess to innumerable sins. Most of her alleged sins were heinous crimes that ran a violent gamut from the Haymarket bombings, which occurred long before she was born, to the assassination of William McKinley, which also occurred before she was born, to the unsolved murders of William Desmond Taylor, the Hollywood director, and Star Faithfull, the New York girl.

It didn't take the rambling preachers long to catch on to P.A. Her catalogue of confessions usurped the meeting. No other sinner had a chance to confess, and, of course, this was very bad for the free-will offering.

One day she was riding Big Bill when Gimp Younger, a wart remover and jack-leg preacher, was holding a revival on a bank of Tar River. When Gimp issued the call, P.A.

started to the front. Gimp took one look at the empty hat he would pass.

"Naw, you ain't, damit it. Git chore ast back on at hoss, Missy. You done confessed yisstiddy in Oxford toe uvathing but putting alum in the Sunday School picnic lemonade."

P.A. was party to one prank that still brings the balm of laughter to her contemporaries. One August a bellows-lunged evangelist named Cyclone McPherson held a meeting in the Banner Warehouse. The Warehouse had (still has) a tin roof, and although the meetings were held at night, the warehouse was as hot as a blow-torch, almost literally.

P.A. convinced Matt Venable, our fire chief, that it was a good idea to cool down the building by playing a hose on the tin roof. As I recall, P.A. was assisted in this humanitarian endeavor by Ramsay Davis, Tom Day, and "Struttin' Bud" Davenport. Apparently, no one inside the warehouse was aware of this civic gesture. Tom Day said P.A. had told the men it should be "a nice surprise."

The warehouse had (has) several doors on one side, and it was through these doors that the collect left when the last sinner had been ransomed. One old gentleman went to a side door, saw the cloudburst, removed his good shoes and socks, rolled up his britches, turned up his coat collar, tucked his straw hat under his coat, and sped out into the "hard rain."

When he had pranced ten yards, his barefeet were kicking up dust. Nay more, the moon was shining brightly, despite the fact "rain" was pelting the earth just behind him. He ran back into the warehouse, wiped the "rain" from his face and head, gave Cyclone Mac his last two dollars and swore off liquor forever.

There were many other similar examples of confusion and consternation. P.A. and her friends wobbled the nozzle all about, perhaps, to prove out the Biblical dictum that rain falls on the unjust as well as on the just. Worshippers who went out one door found themselves in a torrent while those who walked out the next door encountered starlight and moonbeams. One lady would reach a door and raise her parasol as her friend stepped out into feathery dust three inches deep.

Some folks thought they had lost their minds, and some others related the phenomenon to Cyclone Mac's "influence upstairs."

Mr. Entwhistle, although a "High" Episcopalian, had attended the meeting, and he was sufficiently astute to figure out that there was trickery involved, even though he had been "caught," too. A tycoon couldn't take off his shoes and socks in public, but many people saw Mr. Entwhistle when he put his expensive Panama hat under his coat.

The next day Mr. Entwhistle went to the Banner — he owned it, by the way — just as Tom Day was rolling up the hose. Arming himself with a stout hickory felloe, Mr. Entwhistle made for Tom. Mr. Entwhistle, his eyes rasping as fiercely as two cotton-mouths, started chasing Tom around the building. The first time the two came around the building Tom hollered, "Stop him. Somebody stop him or I'll kill him."

Someone in the small crowd of watchers, seeing the irony in the situation, yelled back: "How you gonna kill him, Tom?"

Tom didn't have time to answer on that trip, but the next time around he hollered: "Damit, I'll run him to death."

If Mr. Entwhistle wasn't as rich as "Struttin' Bud", he was a millionaire, and then some. He began, about 1890, as a very young man, as a Methodist exhorter. That is, he went around to regular church revivals to lead the singing and to whip up the congregation.

He got a certain percent of the collection, and he always showed up a few days prior to the meeting to put out the rousements. He visited the stores and the farming communities, holding informal prayer meetings and hymn-singings. And the same procedure was followed each day of the meeting.

At this time he lived out in the Shakerag community, fourteen miles from Oxford, in a three room log house. Apparently, his exhorting was fairly lucrative, and he saved enough money to buy farm land.

When he wasn't exhorting, he worked as a second-string tobacco auctioneer. His prospects were not bright because he had no style. He had a fine voice but he lacked style. Then one time when he was visiting in Richmond a friend took him to a Roman Catholic service.

He evolved a smooth sing-song from hearing the Georgian Chant. He became the first sure-enough "singing auctioneer." Indeed, his style of patter has been adhered to ever since.

He auctioneered and speculated on tobacco on the side. Then in 1903 he built the first of his warehouses, the Banner. He invited thousands of his farmer friends up and down the Virginia-Carolina line, many of whom he first encountered in his days as a Methodist exhorter, to give him a brick for the Banner. This seemed to be a modest request, and it is believed that Mr. Entwhistle got all the bricks free. (The Banner was among the first, if not the very first, brick warehouse in the state.)

Even more important than the free bricks was the patronage cemented by the contributions. The men who donated the bricks felt that they had a stake in the Banner.

By this time Mr. Entwhistle had built the large Victorian

house on Spottswood Street. As I said before, the family had gone from outdoor plumbing to fingerbowls and servants, and Mrs. Entwhistle had gone from Mattie to Matilda.

In 1920 he had endowed a Chair of Philosophy at Piedmont College by creating a trust fund that paid $1000.00 a year for philosophical research.

Mr. Entwhistle was a large, rather florid man. He always wore a bat-wing collar, even in his auctioneering days, and a jim-swinger coat, split in the tail. In physical appearance and in dress he always reminded me of the pictures of William E. Gladstone, the old British prime minister.

Papa told me that Mr. Entwhistle was twenty years old before he learned to read and write. His teacher, in many surreptitious night sessions, was "Governor Poly." He spoke well enough, and what he said was impressive because he had a deep, melodious voice.

He didn't make many mistakes in grammar, although "Governor Poly" carried him through the rudiments of reading and writing, only. Papa said Mr. Entwhistle owed his clarity and his absence of grammatical errors to the fact that he had the judgment to avoid complex construction.

However, to the end of his days he said "hope" for "help", and he pronounced "put" as "putt," and "to" as "toe." Occasionally he said "cheer" for "chair," and ever so often "might" came out as "maught."

For all that, I may have picked up a few oddments from Mr. Entwhistle, facts I understand he gleaned from conversations with "Governor Poly."

He liked to tell how Fort Duquesne was changed to Pittsburg in honor of William Pitt, the Elder, the First Earl of Chatham. Mr. Entwhistle brought this in sometimes when there was a discussion of the Pirates, but he always mentioned the fact as if it had just occurred to him, after

163

lying dormant for many years. It was done almost *sotto voce*, and I had a crazy mental image of William Pitt's standing in line to clean up the bases after Paul and Lloyd Waner and Pie Traynor filled the bases.

He knew that Rhodesia was named for Cecil Rhodes, the empire builder, the first white man to explore the region. And he knew how the fund for American scholars honored Rhodes. I am sure Mr. Entwhistle would be delighted to know that a tobacco auction market operates in Rhodesia today.

Obviously, the Boer War wasn't mentioned often in Oxford, but on those episodic occasions when it was mentioned, Mr. Entwhistle explained, with disarming ingratiation, that Boer was the equivalent to the German word "bauer," meaning a farmer. Indeed, this fact seemed enlightening to Otto Bauer, a local truck farmer, a second generation German, whose main interest was growing delicious cauliflower, which Papa called "cabbage with a top hat."

Inevitably, some of the oldest families in town called the Entwhistles poseurs. Some of the hardest-up, and, thereby, the most resentful, called the Entwhistles "tacky," money, butler, chauffeur, and "Cheer of Philosophy," not withstanding.

But their three children, a boy and two girls, turned out well. Caleb, Jr. succeeded his father in the tobacco business, after going to college here and in Europe. Annabelle, nee Annie, relinquished a life of affluence to become a registered nurse. The younger girl, Sophia, nee Sofie, married a medical missionary.

The Entwhistles lived diagonally across the street from P. A., Miss Texanna, and Old Man Rufe. There was no enmity between the two families, despite Old Man Rufe's running vendetta with the Entwhistle's aristocratic bull dog.

164

Obviously, P. A.'s antics were anathema to Mr. and Mrs. Entwhistle, but they regarded her more as something in the funny page than as a creature of flesh and blood.

P. A. was a few years older than I, if her advanced ideas and general maturity made her seem much older. We were in a play together once, when I was in the third grade and she was several grades ahead of me.

I don't remember too much about the play, but I was a bee. Some of us third-graders, dressed in bee costumes, sang "Be My Little Baby Bumble Bee" ("Buzz around, buzz around.") I did the main "buzzing around" in the skit. I think I "buzzed" the older students.

As I recall, our skit related to the coming of spring. The whole cast practiced together a few times, and I heard P. A. singing and whistling a "low-down" song several times, during intermissions.

I remember one terse couplet:

Old Uncle Jake, the jelly-role king,
Got a hump on his back from shaking that thing.

I was reasonably sure P. A. was the literal incarnation of Jezebel. The fact that she knew such words was prima facie evidence. The fact that she had the consummate gall to sing the words in public was indisputable proof.

Anyway, during the play someone off-stage twittered like a bird. P. A. went to a stage-window, looked out and exclaimed:

The lilacs are in blossom,
The cherry boughs are white;
I hear a sound above me,
A twitter of delight;
It is my friend, the robin,

As sure as I'm alive.
I'm very glad to see you:
Pray, when did you arrive?

When P. A. finished her lines, she curtseyed and began a little ballet step, back to her place in the center of the stage. This boy, Ira Tulgin, Jo-Jo's older brother, was sitting on the front row in the auditorium. He yelled out: "What happened to Old Unca Jake, the jelly-roll king."

I was "buzzing around," and P. A. knocked me down when she bolted from the stage, leaped off the front, a la John Wilkes Booth, and made for Ira Tulgin. With one hand she yanked his hair as the flat of her other hand gave the back of his neck what is now known as a karate-chop.

It's entirely possible that P. A.'s liberation, counter-revolution, disaffiliation, whatever it was, had its real incubation in the incident with Ira Tulgin, and in the brief aftermath.

For a while boys of the town taunted P. A. with all sorts of allusions to "my friend the robin." Some twittered when they passed her on the street and others stretched out their arms and pretended their arms were a bird's wings. Others greeted her by saying, "It is my friend the robin, as sure as I'm alive." This was substituted for "Good morning" and for "Hello, Pansy Alice."

The first few times these things happened she struck back tempestuously. She bopped one boy in the head with her heavy book-bag, and she chased another boy through all three departments of Bengough's, striking at him with a heavy ruler.

Then she pretended not to notice. It was as if the teasing words turned to ice. When she stopped her hostile reactions, the boys let her alone.

If her big change didn't really stem from the play

incident, I am sure it was at this time that she rejected "Pansy Alice" to become P. A.

Apparently, Miss Texanna accepted P. A.'s eccentricities the same way a mother would accept a child's green eyes, or the fact that a child was an albino. I always got the impression that there was much love between Miss Texanna and P. A. Miss Texanna was not one who exhibited her emotions, nor did she wear her good qualities as if they were campaign ribbons. But she was as resolute as P. A., even if her resolves took a different turn.

There used to be a saying: Each of us is a wagon in which our ancestors ride. This was probably truer of P. A. than it seemed to be.

Her mother was more the firm, gentle shepherdess keeping silent watch than the mother hen hovering protectively over a lone chick. Actually, a rather obvious dualism devolved upon Miss Texanna.

She was mother, housewife, high priestess of pots, pans, and druggets, as well as the mistress of home and premises. She was also the boss-lady of three productive farms, a grist mill, and several sorghum mills.

In tobacco planting time and during the priming, curing and selling seasons she was up and out in her buggy while the sun was still cat-napping in his bed. Often she didn't return until dusky-dark. She had to be the boss-lady because Old Man Rufe hadn't hit a lick since hatchet was a hammer.

But vigilant stewardship was deep in her blood and marrow. She had the Anglo-Saxon reverence for land, for property. Waste was original sin. It was said of her: "You can't cut a switch on one of her farms unless you plant a tree in its place. You can't draw a bucket of water unless you find a new spring."

Nevertheless, she certainly wasn't grasping. She treated

all of her numerous tenants handsomely. People liked to tend her land. She gave her folks a fair shake, and then some. She made money, but she seemed to measure wealth more in apples, eggs, ears of corn, and trees rather than in cash, bank deposits, stock, and bonds.

Tobacco was the money crop, but no one could tend her land unless he planted an enormous vegetable garden, kept good milk cows, plenty of laying hens, and lots of hogs.

She made all of her folks plant large corn crops. Her cribs were always full. There was always more than enough for everyone to eat.

Provisions were always available. Hence, Miss Texanna's tenants hardly ever borrowed money from the President or charged supplies at the "Time" store. And her folks always had something to sell almost everytime they came to town — sweet and Irish potatoes, apples, grapes, hams, sides of beef, homemade wine, eggs, butter, and chickens.

If they required financing to make a crop of tobacco, she lent the money herself. Papa said Miss Texanna rarely ever charged interest, but she got a much larger return than six per cent because her people worked harder, had more pride. Since her folks didn't have to pay the tremendous mark-ups and carrying-charges at the "Time" store, most of them had a little "ready-money" the year around.

I always heard she was the first person in the county to use charcoal to cure tobacco. She guarded her pines as zealously as Mr. Ed Settle guarded his. She rotated crops, and long before the day of expert agricultural advisers she replenished her land with manure, lime, and ground oyster shells.

She put up fences and she kept them painted. All of her folks planted cane, not on the scale in vogue in the deep South, but sufficiently to make enough molasses to last the year around, with many barrels left over for commercial sale.

An acre of good cane produced about 100 gallons of molasses. It had to be cut before frost. First, the thin folder was knocked from the stalk with a stick. Farmers such as Miss Texanna's folks left the thin, green fodder on the ground to enrich the soil, but "plugs," or second-rate farmers, fed the fodder to horses. Most mules turned up their mighty nostrils at cane fodder.

The heads of the stalks were cut off and these were fed to chickens and hogs. It was good food for both. Then the slender stalks were cut and taken by wagon to the sorghum mill. Miss Texanna had three, one on each farm. The cane was fed into a "mill," between two rollers. A horse, hitched to a long pole, walked around and around, like a drunk man with his peg-leg caught in a hole in a wooden bridge. This ground the cane into green juice.

The green juice ran from the "mill" in a pipe to an evaporator. The pipe had a cut-off so that the flow of the green juice could be stopped, when it was necessary to do so. A fire under the evaporator cooked the green juice until it became luscious, gold molasses, a flood of liquid double-eagles, as sweet as a million pots of honey, and as redolent with earth perfume as the toilet water used by hearty, he-man angels.

No one ever related the heady odor of cooking molasses to a lovely girl, or to a flower, or to grass wet and fresh and sparkling after a sudden freshet. It was a manly, robust smell. It was as if perfumery had sprouted powerful biceps, big shoulders, and a barreled chest. The permeations got you by the nose, of course, but they grabbed you by the spine. They worked down to your marrow and your gastric juices seemed to have been struck by a benign sort of lightning.

There was a stopper, at the bottom of the evaporator. This was pulled by a lever at the top. The cooked molasses ran out into large pans, even as more was being cooked. The pans were dumped into the empty barrels until they were filled with molasses. Miss Texanna, unlike the "plugs," always had two or three tenants who were "middlin'-fair," or better, coopers. All her barrels were "rived" from oaks, made of stout oak staves, smoothed down by a hand-lath to a fine finish.

Miss Texanna allowed each group of her tenants "to steal" one barrel of molasses "for mischief." Sugar was added to the molasses. It fermented the way Lefty Grove pitched shut-outs. The fermented stuff was called "molasses wine."

Molasses "wine," more nearly rum, was as deceptive as a pretty girl with a blackjack in her purse. It kissed sweetly, but it knocked the nails off your toes. I have had a few dippers of it, and I can testify that a small toddy would make a hummingbird try to assault an eagle.

Of course, Miss Texanna knew her folks made molasses "wine" each fall, but she pretended not to notice. This was an unwritten law with considerate landlords. It was the same as the "miller's toll."

Old Man Rufe and Miss Texanna were second cousins on one side of the family and they were third cousins on the other side. Sometimes, P. A. called her mother "Cousin Tex," but she always called Old Man Rufe "Pa." They were married nine years before Pansy Alice was born. Sometimes Old Man Rufe told his cronies in the "mossy-lee" that the girl should have been named "Artesian." They asked why and he replied: "Well, I show had to dig a long time afore we got her."

Old Man Rufe had inherited one of the three farms. It had 1,882 acres and ten "settlements" on it. Miss Texanna

170

repaired the tenant houses and out-buildings, all of which had deteriorated when she and Old Man Rufe had married. She kept ten tenant families on the farm, one family for each 100 acres. All the tenant houses were painted. While these houses didn't have "town conveniences," they were all attractive, durable homes.

The grist mill was on a cliff at a bend of the Tar, where the river snake-hipped through "McCausland's Quarters." Miss Texanna was a McCausland, and she had inherited the farm, 1,467 acres, and eight "settlements," from her father, Willie (pronounced "Wiley") McCausland. After her marriage she had bought another farm, one that adjoined "McCausland's Quarters," which contained 800 odd acres.

The mill, a vast dishevelment of planks, was a split-level long before the term was ever applied to local architecture. It resembled an elephant. The "legs" along the rocky river embankment stuck into the water. The "body" was along a rocky plateau about fifty feet above the river, and the "head and snout" creased the earth about forty feet above the "body".

The mill was reached, from the "Oxford side," by a wooden bridge almost sixty yards long, the middle thirty yards of which was a covered bridge, the last surviving covered bridge in the county. When Pansy Alice was young, she loved to zoom across the bridge and through the covered portion in the buggy with Miss Texanna.

The covered portion was a sort of magnetic looking-glass made of bare boards. In fact, I made the trip with Miss Texanna a couple of times. Just before the horse reached the bridge his hooves sent fire-flies sailing when the iron shoes struck the rocky road. But once on the bridge the sounds of the hooves were mighty barrels being rolled, the wild sound of summer thunder, the trumpets of Judgment Day. Inside the covered bridge the welling sounds were a roaring water-fall, a surging cataract. The world stood on its toes and jumped in my lap. I was Atlas, in a buggy, holding the world between my spindly legs.

I saw the covered bridge, as I am sure Pansy Alice saw it, as the New York subway. The whole bridge was O. Henry's Bagdad-on-the-Hudson. The crazy, elephantine mill was a castle. One came from the dull, prosaic world of Oxford into an exciting, mysterious tunnel. One came from the mysterious tunnel into a world of fantasy. For, surely, the grist mill was Camelot, and Merlin was the water-powered mill-stone.

The mill-stones were selected by Miss Texanna's grandfather, Luke McCausland. The stones were chiseled down until they were perfectly flat. Both stones were identical, thirty-six inches across. The bottom stone had several small trenches drilled into it, by hand. It remained still as the stone above it went around and around. Ears of corn were put into a sheller and the sheller was turned by hand. The cobs flew out and the grains of corn stayed inside in the pan, in the sheller, until scattered on the bottom stone for grinding.

If a customer wanted corn meal, as most people preferred, the miller lowered the top stone with a peg that served as a lever. The more the top stone was lowered, the finer the corn was ground. But if a customer wanted hominy, the top stone was raised a bit. The meal, or hominy, flew from the trenches in the bottom stone into a big, wooden box. From the box it was sacked.

The top stone was turned by the mill-wheel, an enormous, iron wheel. Water from the Tar came from the mill-trace to the mill-wheel. The water always hit the mill-wheel on the top. Then it went down, along the deep indentations, as if it were descending a flight of stairs. When the water reached the bottom of the wheel it poured back

172

into the trace.

For the duration of my knowledge of the mill, Miss Texanna's cousin, Erk (nee Urquart) McCausland was the miller. But it didn't matter about his Christian name, or about any miller's real names. A miller was always called "Dusty Miller." The sobriquet fitted. Everytime old Erk shook his head, small snow flakes seemed to fly. His eyes seemed to repose, eternally, in a mass of powdered sugar. When he slapped his pants or shirt, the air seemed to fill with fine chicken feathers. He always walked in a blizzard and on snow shoes.

The grist mill was a lucrative enterprize for several generations, but the demand for meal and hominy had slacked off by my time. But most people in Oxford still bought "McCausland's White Rose Meal" and "McCausland's Top-Grade Hominy." Most people bought their meal and hominy retail from one of the local merchants — Jimmy Simpson or Bengough's — but a lot of folks, Papa was one, drove out to the mill for purchases. The trip was lovely, in spring and in autumn. And it was as fascinating to adults to watch the milling operation as it was to children.

So, several Oxford people used the direct purchase of meal or hominy as an excuse to visit the covered bridge, the "old elephant," "Dusty Miller," and the lithesome, sleek, muscular Tar, in its pre-progress, or unpolluted, condition.

Actually, Miss Texanna's milling products, especially "McCausland's White Rose Meal," were sold in stores across several counties until the late 1930's.

Some folks accused Erk, "Dusty," of being slow. "Brer" Thompson said he fished for six hours while he waited for "Dusty" to grind two pecks of meal. "You know, 'Dusty,' Mr. Entwhistle's bull dog can eat meal faster than you can grind it."

173

"How long could he do that, 'Brer' Thompson?"

"Until he starved to death."

Hayriders, picnickers, and sparkers came to the mill and the covered bridge regularly in warm weather. The covered bridge offered protection in a storm and a hurricane always seemed imminent when courting couples went in that direction.

Unromantically enough, the fundamental purpose in covering any bridge was to protect the timbers of the bridge, but the place had long vibrance as a trysting rendezvous, or a "honey hole," to use the local phrase.

The Maine poet and Pulitzer Prize winner, Robert P. Tristram Coffin, wrote a fine poem about covered bridges. Coffin said a covered bridge gave the warm illusion of "a home away from home." One had the sense of taking some portion of his home with him every time he rested in a covered bridge or took refuge in one.

As I said, Miss Texanna usually drove a buggy on her rounds to her farms and to the grist mill, although P. A. drove her in the Buick when the weather was rough and wet. Miss Texanna carried a pearl handled Smith and Wesson revolver, .32 caliber, in the "budget," the small carpetbag, or over-sized pocketbook, that held her note and account books. She knew how to use the Smith and Wesson, too. One night she shot a carnival worker in the hindquarters when he tried to climb into a window of the Duncan home.

People used to laugh about the regular procedure that occurred whenever any unusual noise was heard in the night in or around the Duncan home: Old Man Rufe, the "hero" of the Spanish-American War, the intrepid ex-soldier, toted the lantern while Miss Texanna carried the gun.

I should think Miss Texanna was a pretty young girl.

Even as a middle-aged lady she bore a strong resemblance to P. A. She was smaller than P. A. but she had strong hands, and she walked the same floating sort of way. People would say: "Miss Texanna, I believe your daughter got her good looks from you."

Old Man Rufe would slap his thighs and chortle: "Damn, she musta tuck all Texanna had."

The Duncan home, Miss Texanna's house, was two and a half stories. It was painted white, and it had a mansard roof and dormer windows. The parlor, on one side, and Miss Texanna's sewing room, on the other side, had large bay-windows, with long, cushioned window-seats. While these two big bay-windows were not unattractive, they always reminded me of a boy with both jaws swollen from mumps. There were six rooms downstairs, three on either side of a long hall that ran the length of the house and opened on a large, screened-in back porch.

The third floor was the sweetest smelling place this side of the orchards and melon patches of Beulah Land. In it Miss Texanna kept barrels of molasses, molasses "wine," home-made brandy, locust-and-persimmon beer, and bins of ripening apples and pears. There were baskets of nutmegs and baskets of those half-scrubby green-leaved spices called sage. Stalks of dill stood in the four corners of the big "plunder room," and long strings of red and boll peppers were hung on the wall on strings.

Miss Texanna kept the only key to the "plunder room". It was on a key-belt that kept the keys to the house, the smoke-house, and keys to numerous other properties. The "plunder room" had a double-lock. I always assumed the double-lock was extra protection against invasion by Old Man Rufe.

Sometimes when Old Man Rufe felt what George Ade lamented: "No time for mirth, no time for laughter-/The cold gray dawn of the morning after." he'd implore: "Don't shake them keys, Miss Texanna. Don't mock my infirmity." And he would tell his cronies: "When I rilly need some jump-steady and when I hear Miss Texanna a-rattling of them keys, I feel like I'm on shore, in a bear-trap, and the lass ferry-boat to heaven's-a-blowing in midstream, going tuther way."

One night when she was in bed, Miss Texanna heard a gurgling sound. A big barrel of molasses had sprung a leak. I think the bung, or the spigot, was faulty. She got molasses all over her bare feet, hands, and flannel night gown. She ran downstairs to get something to catch the escaping molasses and to stop the leak. She called to Old Man Rufe for help.

She grabbed a couple of dish pans and a hammer, and when she started up the stairs again, spreading molasses everywhere, she yelled to Old Man Rufe again.

He floundered out, in his woolen night gown and cap: "Patience, Miss Texanna. Patience. Old Job had patience."

"I'll betcha Job never lost a barrel of molasses in his whole life," she yelled back.

During cold weather a goose, or a turkey, was always at one end of the sideboard in Miss Texanna's dining-room, and an old ham was always at the other end. In between were cut-glass bowls filled with chow-chow, dill and watermelon rind pickles, pickled peaches, pickled okra, and small onions.

Two large wicker baskets, covered with huge damask napkins, were filled with beaten, drop, cream, and scratch biscuits. When herrings ran on the river, late in summer, Miss Texanna always put up a couple of barrels of smoked-herring. A plate of these was on the sideboard, and there was always a decanter of blackberry or scuppernong wine, and a stout pitcher of locust-and-persimmon beer.

The stuff on the sideboard was for "grazing," not for meals. The food and drink were for anyone who dropped in. Miss Texanna called the sideboard the "snack table."

Old Man Rufe might invite five or six people to dinner or supper and then forget, completely, he had invited guests. But the sumptuous, ever-ready buffet provided most handsomely for anyone who came, expected or unexpected.

Each September Miss Texanna had special days inexorably set aside to make sauerkraut and catsup in her big backyard. This was a real event, and I am sure Miss Texanna would have made "kraut" and catsup, on the appointed day, if she had known the world would be destroyed the next day.

I always made a point of coming by to "help" her, and I still recall the heady excitement. If the transformation of cabbage into "kraut" and of tomatoes into catsup was not up to water into wine, or to the loaves and fishes, the annual ritual had elements of the miraculous for me. Withal, it was a bucolic, back-yard Mardi Gras.

P. A. brought a two-horse wagon load of cabbages from the vegetable garden, and under Miss Texanna's expert tutelage, we shucked off the larger outer leaves of the cabbages. When they were stripped down to lustrous white noggings we cut them into fine ribbons. We crushed the delicate, white ribbons with big wooden stompers. Then we put fine, feathery whiteness into heavy earthen crocks. P. A. and I carted the crocks to the cellar, where they sat in stony silence to await the transformation into rough, wry, ultra masculine sauerkraut.

The same wagon that brought the cabbages brought a load of tomatoes. The catsup kettle, made of brass and large enough to hold five gallons, rested on bricks. Miss Texanna made a charcoal fire on the ground, between the bricks, and P. A. and I plopped the tomatoes into the

177

enormous kettle. As the tomatoes bounced and bobbed around the kettle, P. A. said they were red friars off on a pilgrimage. Miss Texanna smiled warmly, despite her lack of understanding, and she scooped up a huge wooden spoonful of the ruby-rich texture, blew upon it, and gave P. A. a taste.

But no one tended the fire or the stirring except Miss Texanna. She guarded the fire as if it were the last dab of heat on earth. I thought of the American Indian legend about the turkey:

At the beginning of a particular fearsome winter, all the fire on earth went out save a few coals in the trunk of a hollow tree. A noble turkey stood and fanned the flame with his wings. When the coals were fanned to fire, the flames burned the top of the turkey's head and his neck. And that's why the turkey is bald-headed and pock-marked today.

I can see Miss Texanna now, tending the fire and stirring the catsup kettle, absorbed, half-smiling, and sure, stirring, tasting, and measuring, with the precision of a religious ritual.

Too, near the end of September grapes oozed royal blood over the fire. How, oh, how, I marveled, could such tender vessels hold such favulous cargoes. Some of the blue and some of the purple blood was bottled for wine and some went into jams and jellies. And near by, long string beans or snaps, as we called them, were thin, green fish swimming around in pans of clear water.

If memory is likely to be as blurred as a faded photograph, my memory of these September rituals slices away the years with the precision of a surgeon's scalpel. The picture is clearer than the one on the television tube.

How charged with energy and excitement those September days were! The brisk, busy days come back, all fired up with September sunshine, with a foretaste of autumn in the late afternoon air, and the smell of dying and burning leaves, filling our neighborhood with an exotic, highly personalized, incense.

I remember it as it was at twilight when the whole community's eyes smarted from the smoke of those burning leaves, from those funeral pyres. There always seemed to be a mist that fell as a seasonal benediction. When the fields were picked down to fish bones and birds started flying south, I never knew if a bird, or a season, or a way of life was flying over the dark, wet heads of Mr. Ed Settle's beautiful trees.

Oxford, April 15, 1970:

Obviously, I know more about men than I know about women, more about boys than I know about girls. From a boy's perspective the first really serious romance is a combination of celestial lightning and electric-shock. The boy is Columbus but he discovers a world far beyond the ken of great captains and navigators.

The boy's days and nights are set to flutes and violins but these days and nights are harassed by cold sweats, by chills and fevers that are impervious to any known medications, any antibiotics.

Young Lochinvar is truly a disembodied spirit. He really uses white and blue clouds for flagstones. Even so he steps into quagmires and he is lacerated by briars. The world is his very own merry-go-round. The spotted horses race to the music of his heartbeats, but the gallant chargers throw many shoes. They shy and they toss him into the meanest gullies.

The world is his own love song, but he can't keep the tune because the melody is dominated by the idea of the

179

song, itself. An hour apart from his true-love is a life sentence in solitary confinement, but a whole evening spent together seems to pass as quickly as the clock strikes one.

First love is glorious and heroic and it is likely to be inglorious and tragic. But it is immortal, somehow, even when it passes rapidly and hides its face in a crowd of stars. He may forget her face but the touch of her fingertip survives countless inner and outer hurricanes. First love is beautiful and terrible. It is ecstasy and anquish. But if the "perfect" rose fades and dies and is blown to sea by cold, impersonal winds, the divinity of its fragrance is eternal.

Hopefully, it works both ways. She may not remember his name but the adoration of his voice endures. He becomes faceless, perhaps, but something about the grandeur, or the pathetic desperation, of his kisses goes on. Perhaps, the words his heart framed, the words his mind lacked the power to express, become a wisp of a benediction. When all else is gone, it may be that the kisses that their eyes once mirrored continue as a talisman.

My first profound romance was with Rose Blatz. We were juniors in high school. We had "home room" together and we sat near each other. I knew her, was aware of her, somewhat hazily, before we were put in the same home room. Then I looked across the row one morning, almost apropos to nothing, and there sat Rose.

In ten seconds I knew exactly how Benjamin Franklin had felt when he discovered electricity. My insides felt as if someone were using them to shoot off all of the firecrackers and Roman candles that our whole town shot off on Christmas Eve.

Rose was a strawberry blonde. Her long hair spilled over her shoulders, a river of cherries. I knew if I ever touched her long hair it would speak, through my fingertips, in all the tongues known and unknown. Sometimes she wore a white ribbon and I thought it was the Milky Way, and again it was a slender moonbeam, pretending to be a bit of yellow ribbon.

We read Milton's "Lycidas," as an assignment, and two of the poet's lines, just lines to me ordinarily, took intensely personal dramatic shape:

To sport with Amaryllis in the shade
Or with the tangles of Nearera's hair.

We read another couplet from Pope's "The Rape of the Lock:"

Fair tresses man's imperial race ensnare,
And beauty draws us with a single hair.

Papa said Pope got the second line from a proverb written by James Howell, along about 1620: "One hair of a woman can draw more than a hundred pair of oxen."

I was ecstatically ensnared. Surely, one of Rose's hairs could reach from Oxford to heaven and draw me along to the Pearly Gates.

I thought her eyes were two stars, when only two stars were burning at night, and when she walked she seemed to float, to glide. Some years later, when she was gone, I saw Degas's famous painting of the ballet dancers, and I conjured Rose, walking along the street but barely touching the sidewalk.

I exclaimed: "It's Rose, Rose Blatz, from the old days in Oxford."

Her face beat anything I had ever seen. It was strong enough to surmount centuries of infamy and social injustice, yet it was as thin, as marvelously delicate, as Mrs. Ashton-Brown's finest, hand-painted china cup. There were a few freckles on her lovely face. I thought these freckles were pure gold nuggets, of infinitestimal size. One day I told her the freckles were "faery-dust." I didn't know what "faery-dust" was, but I ran across the expression in Rupert Brooke's poem, the "Great Lover."

Rose laughed softly: "Meshugge," she whispered. From my association with her I knew that meant "silly boy" more than it meant "crazy." Her smile was a sliver of starlight, at high-noon. But when we went walking on fall nights, her forehead, her nose, and her lips seemed to be magnets on which tiny tatters of moonbeams did arabesques, and I always imagined that the yellow slivers were angels seeing how many could dance on a pin-point, that they used the tip of Rose's nose for the pin-point.

She never laughed loudly, even when she was thoroughly amused, but when she smiled her own special smile, I thought it had the magic of a gentle spring rain putting a necklace around the throat of a red flower. If her laughter was slight it was as warm as the south wind is warm when it rolls and tumbles in the light-leaved fingers of late April.

If I was Rose's beau, I was still a shaygets, a Gentile boy. I picked up a phrase from a boy named Hymie Schwartz, whose people came to Oxford after Mr. S. Blatz, Rose's father, had sort of founded the local Jewish community. The phrase was "Shayn vi zibben velten," or "Beautiful as the seven world."

One day when Rose and I, and two or three other couples were sitting around one of the marble-topped tables in Hill's Drug Store I said the words to her.

I smiled and I said, "Shayn vi zibben velten," as casually as I would say, "It's a nice afternoon." At any event, that is the effect I wanted, the one I tried to create. Even so I felt what I said because I loved her, because I thought she was as beautiful as seven worlds.

182

But, of course, I was showing-off, too, feeling my ginger and my mustard. I imagined that I was debonair George Brent, in a movie, speaking Yiddish to Norma Shearer, or to some virgin Queen of Sheba. And I'll admit, now, it was surpassingly exhilarating to talk excessively intimately and to use a language beyond the comprehension of our Gentile friends.

Rose let it pass the first time, and we continued to sip a single cherry-smash through two straws. Economy really wasn't the vital factor for our sharing a nickel drink. It was romantic, intimate, and glamorous for a boy and girl to sip from the same cup. Or so I thought. Indeed, I thought it was swashbuckling.

And it was titillating, even passionate, the way I maneuvered my straw so that it touched Rose's straw at the bottom of the cup.

I had the distinct impression that I was acting out the intransigent intimacy of a current movie, *Jungle Torment*, as I recall the title, in which George Brent lay on the ground in a forest, in a feverish coma. He couldn't swallow and he was dying of thirst. His girl friend — Heather Angel, I think — sucked some juice from a coconut and then she kissed the life-saving fluid into George Brent's mouth.

Of course, it was Rose who kissed the coconut juice into my blistered lips. I turned to her to thank her for saving my life: "Shayn vi zibben velten," I said, amid the urgency of unutterable gratitude.

She whispered testily: "Shemen zich in dein veiten haldz," or "You ought to be ashamed of yourself down to the bottom of your throat."

Rose's rebuke stung more sharply in Yiddish, and, thus, she didn't wash our personal laundry in public at Hill's Drug Store.

I touched her knee, tenderly, impulsively, to let her

know I was sorry, but, evidently, she thought I was using the anonymity below the marble-topped table as an excuse to get fresh.

"Shmuck. Shmuck. Shmuck." She repeated the word three times, with increasing asperity.

On the way to her home, I explained and I apologized. When I turned to leave, she said, "Shalom," and I knew she really wanted to be at peace with me.

After dark, when we took our leave of each other I always said "Gutte noch," but I always said "Shalom," by day. In our county there is an Old Salem and a New Salem church, and there is a large farming community in Salem Township. When I was going with Rose, I used to tell my Gentile friends that we appropriated Salem from the Jews, from shalom, but, as I recall, I didn't make much headway.

Sometimes when Rose had to recite at school (we stood to recite) or when she had to write something on the blackboard, I might whisper "lots of nochos, Rose," wishing her good luck. If I whispered, I still said "lots of nochos" clearly enough for the words to be distinctly audible. If she did well on her recitation, and she was an "A" student, I whispered, "Mazel-tov, Rose," to congratulate her.

Rose visited our home many times, especially in the afternoon, after school. Usually she walked home with Sister and me, but Mother introduced Rose as "Sandy's friend," rather than as "Sister's friend."

We listened to the victrola and I taught her to dance by putting pieces of newspaper on the parlor floor and doing what was known as "the Box." We ate ladyfingers, gingerbread, and Lady Baltimore cake, which Mother and Sister made, and we washed the food down with homemade drinks such as "vanilla floats," royal raspberry acid (an early do-it-yourself version of Kool-Aid) and with locust-and-persimmon beer.

(I was never sure why "acid" was appended to "royal raspberry" and other "fruit drinks." "Acid" was the juice that accumulated when raspberries and other fruits were boiled for preserves. "Acid" was poured into pop bottles. The bottles were capped and stored in the basement during winter. The next summer "acid" was mixed with water to make a drink. I think the proportion was one part "acid" to three parts water.)

(We made a big batch of locust-and-persimmon beer each fall. The process was simple: We placed alternate rows of locusts, broomstraw, and persimmons in a large, wooden barrel. Then the barrel was filled with water, and the wooden barrel-top was banded on. Each barrel had a tap, a wooden spigot.

(The taste was delicious, just sharp enough to make you want to smack your mouth. Of course, this "beer" would get as hard as the President's heart if it "worked" long enough, but Mother always tapped ours "before it actually lost its virginity," as Papa put it.)

Rose ate supper with us, ever so often. But when Mother invited Rose "to take pot-luck with us," it was on nights when were not having pork chops, sausage, or ham. The first time Rose ever ate with us Papa mumbled the blessing. The only audible word was "amen."

Mother spoke up: "I couldn't hear a word you said, Alexander." Papa replied, "I wasn't talking to you, my dear." Then their eyes met the way a key fits a riddle. Mother understood that Papa thought the Christian blessing might be awkward. From then on, Papa mumbled some incoherency whenever Rose "took pot-luck" with us.

I visited the Blatz home more often than Rose visited ours, and although I hardly ever stayed for supper, I

185

developed a taste for chopped chicken livers and Gefilte fish; albeit, I almost turned in the fire alarm the last time I ate the fish, cooked in the skin and almost aflame with red horse-radish.

Rose and I studied together, two or three times a week. She thought of herself as a "greeny kuzziny," as I got the phrase, or "the green cousin," in relationship to Oxford's mores. When we were alone, I called her "Cudin Rose" because just about everyone in Oxford was related, in some nebulous fashion, back then. Even if the old designation, "kissing-cousin," or "cudin," as we called it, was likely to be a polite euphemism, the wide use of the term illustrates the extensive and the intensive sweep of our tribal nuances.

People in Oxford rejoiced to sing an old song, "It Ain't No Sin To Hug And Kiss Your Cousin," and endless smooching, and more, was done in the guise of family fealty. Just as it was impossible for two people to sit in a hammock and to remain physical strangers, one could always establish some "cudinship" with an attractive girl.

Even before the other Jewish families settled in Oxford, the second floor of the Blatz home, a white clapboard house on McClanahan Street, was set aside as the Shul, the sanctuary for minyan and discussion.

When Mr. S. Blatz first brought his family to McClanahan Street, he closed his store, "The Emporium," each Saturday, on the Sabbath. Traveling men who were Jews came to the improvised synagogue. Then after some Jewish families settled in Oxford, Mr. Blatz was the "undeclared Rov."

Mr. Blatz wore a frock coat, whenever he mounted his jerry-built pulpit. Perhaps, he was too absorbed in his "davening," swaying slowly from the east to the west, amid profound meditation, to realize how ruinous it was for him to close "The Emporium" on Saturdays, in Oxford. Saturday was the big day for shopping.

All the farm families came to town to shop, to see the sights, and to socialize with their Oxford friends and relatives. All the stores stayed open until ten o'clock Saturday night. Late Saturday afternoon, virtually all the town folks took their mandatory "Saturday baths," dressed-up, and went "down town" to shop and to chat with the people from the country.

Ere long Mr. Blatz understood his "mish-mosh," his fouled-up mercantile state of things. I am positive the phrase wasn't "mish-mash" because it always rhymed with "pish-posh" whenever it was spoken by any Hebrew in Oxford.

I suppose Mr. Blatz was about fifty, at this time, but he seemed as ageless to me as a rugged oak tree. He was short and his dark eyes blazed from his bearded face the way a cat's eyes blaze in the darkness. Mr. Blatz's beard was so heavy and black he reminded me of one of the prophets in our illustrated Sunday school lessons. When he smoked one of his Fatima cigarettes I thought he was half-Moses and half-burning bush.

I was invited to Passover two or three times, although Mr. Blatz did not put one of the little black skull caps on my head. But I learned the difference between Rosh-Hashanah and Yom Kippur, and about the ram's horn and the Book of Judgment.

In turn I told Rose about local history, about our institutions and families. It was hard to untangle the maze that devolved upon what Papa called the "Gentile Sanhedrin."

Rose had more trouble with local names than she had with irregular verbs. It was hard to explain that "Taliaferro" was (is) called "Tolliver;" that "Morton" was "Motun;" that "Currin" was "Kern;" that "Herbert" was

187

"Hub-but;" that "Alexander" was "Eleck-zandah;" that "daughter" was "dorta;" that "Tuesday" was "Chewsday;" that "business" was "bidness;" that "Mary" was "merry;" that "supple" was "soup-pul;" that "syrup" was "sir-rup."

Whenever we talked about local names and mores, I thought of Rose as a lovely Ruth, plunked down in a strange land. If she came to accept most of the quiddities of our bizarre nomenclature, a sign on Main Street remained hilariously enigmatic. The sign said: "Andrew Beauchamp-China and Silverware."

Of course, "Beauchamp" is called "Beech-um," here and in many other places. Rose would look at the sign and if someone happened to say, "Why, hell-low, Mistah Beechum," Rose acted as if she had heard Eleanor Roosevelt was subbing for Sally Rand.

Just the unadorned sound of the word "Beech-um" became a marvelously pulsating private joke for Rose and me. When we were delighted by some spontaneous joy, or when we worked out a difficult problem in solid geometry, we said "Beech-um" in unison.

As we said "Beech-um" in spontaneous unison, I got the impression we were throwing champagne glasses against a fire-place, the way characters did in some of the British novels and in some of the British-type movies. As I have said, Rose never laughed uproariously, but "Beech-um" sent her delectable little freckles turning somersaults.

She was enchanted with an old saw that children chanted as they played hop-scotch, frog-in-the-middle, farmer-in-the-dell, and hiding:

Hacker backer soda cracker,
Hacker backer boo;
Hacker backer soda cracker
Out goes you.

Rose loved to chat the meaningless words, although she was quick to point out that "goes" in the last line should be "go." Papa had told me the same thing, several years before, but I always said "goes" so no one would accuse me of being too big for my britches.

Rose agreed that it was better to say "goes," in public. To say "go" might make her a "shlimazl," an unlucky person, a loser, in today's parlance. According to Rose, as she got it from her father, "When a shlimazl kills a chicken, it walks; when he sells umbrellas, the sun comes out; when he sells shrouds, people stop dying." As I heard the word it was pronounced "shli-moz-zl," to rhyme with "thin nozzle."

My friendship with Rose, and my part-time job with Mr. S. Blatz, which I will get to directly, led to several charges of "Jew-tile," and I had a few minor altercations and one real fight, with Jo-Jo Tulgin. Jo-Jo broke my nose, but it was Mother who fainted, not I. The fight occurred near the "Ivanhoe," and I sat on the steps to the candy store while Dr. Henley set my nose with his fingers.

Mr. Matson brought me a glass of short-beer to "bolsterate" me. He said I had fought for "the scattered nation," but I didn't know what he meant. Too, the short-beer made me sort of tight.

Mother didn't see the fight. She fainted when she saw my bloody face and shirt. Papa said: "Our boy is like the late Union General, Ambrose Burnside, He will fight, even if he never learns how."

Rose must have heard about the fight, but she never mentioned it. When I had to explain the cause of the fight, I said Jo-Jo had called me an ugly name. That required no explanation since it could mean only one thing. I certainly didn't want Rose to know that she had been involved, even obliquely, in a street brawl, but I am sure she guessed the real reason.

I learned about Chanukah, the "feast of lights," the eight day Jewish celebration that usually came in December but which came before our Christmas. I gave her a present at the commencement of Chanukah, and she gave me mine on Christmas Eve. But once or twice, we gave presents to each other at Chanukah and at Christmas.

Because of Rose I was the only Christian in town to see Christmas things early in September. About the first of each September Mr. Blatz and Rose studied the fat catalogues put out by two big wholesale houses in Baltimore. These were the catalogues from the celebrated "Baltimore Bargain House" and the famous "Butler Brothers."

Mr. Blatz ordered the Christmas "necessities," which were luxuries, too: Shirts, dresses, ties, britches, coats, hats, and two-pants' suits. But Rose picked out all of the dolls, books, and toys which she thought would appeal to youngsters. Mr. Blatz deferred to her tastes completely. After all, Rose knew gentile children. She went to school with them. She knew many things, such as the fact there was no word pronounced as "Beauchamp."

When the Christmas stuff came, the scuppernongs might be getting ripe but the persimmons were not pink around the gills and the trees were still girls in green skirts too tight at the hips. I helped Rose unpack and check the Christmas stuff. Then we stored all of the gleaming oddments and the pungent, earthy-smelling books in the Shul, on the second floor of the Blatz home.

Long before fall came to town to put up her yellow circus tents, I was blowing "Christmas" mouth-organs and Jews-harps in the synagogue. Long before frost put the first faint moustache on the corn shocks, I was shooting Christmas marbles, being careful to keep them uncracked and glistening, and although I was too big for such kid shenani-

190

gans, I played with a long toy hook-and-ladder truck. It was the first hook-and-ladder I ever saw, toy or otherwise. I ran the hook-and-ladder all over the floor of the Shul, putting out raging fires and rescuing helpless, pretty girls and children, if they didn't pop chewing gum in my ears as I was hauling them down the ladder.

I remember that I forgot to clean and dust my knees. Papa looked at my baggy, dirty knees, I mean the cloth in my britches. "There are only three ways a boy can mess up his trousers around the knees — the way yours are messed up."

I didn't say anything and he continued: "We can eliminate praying, in your case, I think. That brings us to shooting craps? My boy, are you a devotee of that form of gambling?"

I told him, truthfully, that the only times I had ever handled dice was when I played parchesi with him and Sister.

Then he said, sadly, or, perhaps, with poignant resignation: "If you find yourself the defendant in a bastardy charge, I want you to appear as your own counsel. We lawyers have a saying that goes this way, dear boy: 'If a lawyer defends himself, he has a damned fool for a client.' And I think you will qualify, Sandy."

I started to tell him I had been playing with the toy hook-and-ladder, but I guess I feared being called sissy more than I feared being called a carnal sinner. Playing with the hook-and-ladder not only seemed less defensible. It was privileged communication. No one but me knew that Mr. S. Blatz's stock of Christmas items came to Oxford before autumn started whetting its grind-stone.

Rose loved our local weather. She told me many times she was lucky to live where the four seasons had distinctive personalities all of their own, even though they merged into one enduringly exciting whole.

She loved the early spring mornings when every tree was a glee-club of birds, when the singing of one small, hidden bird in a boxwood seemed bigger than the bush, itself. She loved to wander among the forests, flowers, and creeks, but there was never any insatiable impulse to own these wonders, to summarize them in precise definitions.

Rose was content to let nature spread itself without any overt help from her. Thus, she was eternally the bug-eyed pilgrim, the ebullient young seeker. I stumbled across something in a copy of Walt Whitman's "Specimen Days," lent me by "Brer" Thompson, that revealed Rose in all of her innocent intensity:

You must not know too much, or be too precise or scientific about birds and trees and flowers and watercraft; a certain free margin, or even vagueness-perhaps ignorance, credulity-helps your enjoyment of these things.

She loved the great, white wolf called winter, too. She spoke of this lean, raw-boned time as "the good shivering." She avoided the skaters on the ice-ponds and all the hosannas and hullabuloos, but she made snow men that were first-rate genre art. She was wild for the taste of snow cream, when I taught her how to make it.

She hated rabbit-boxes. Once she said she wondered how it would be if rabbits made "boy-boxes" to trap live children? Of course, hog-killings were brutally profane, for Rose, and everytime she smelled the odor of sausage in our kitchen, I was permeated with such a sense of impropriety I almost felt I was an unredeemed sinner. I am sure my sense of outrage was specious. As soon as Rose went home, I laid into the sausage as vigorously as Macduff and Macbeth laid into each other.

Rose attuned to summer's lazy, hazy indolence, to the endless torpor of the parched days and to the endless rapture of the deep, purple nights. I don't think she really ever let go on a hay-ride or a gypsy-tea, as combination picnics and swimming outings were called, but she could never get enough of local flower gardens. Just about everyone in town planted flowers, and in the immaculate stillness of the night, when silence seemed to be pristine wisdom, the town smelled as if all of the perfume and spice ships in the history of the East had smashed up in Oxford.

She liked, particularly, the long twilights, when late afternoon was a gorgeous diva giving one "farewell" performance after another. Finally, when twilight was a dapple fawn being chased, but never really menaced, by the dark hounds of nightime, Rose liked to walk our streets and hear the tots singing and shouting, "Ain't No Buggar-Bears Out Tonight."

Warm weather and days as long as Tar River galvanized small kids with ringing bravado. Everywhere they ran and shrieked, "Ain't No Buggar-Bears Out Tonight."

I knew full well, and Rose understood thoroughly, that this was the same kind of courage many grown men got from pulling hard on Just Plain Snake Imboden's rot-gut.

Each shadow was a snake-pit and shrubs were lions and tigers, but these children-eaters were kept at bay with the blacker magic of taunting songs.

Rose told me about the Evil-Eye and how the Jews placated it. I told her of my terrible fear of lightning storms, how when I was little, my grandma forbade any sounds, any playing, even any reading during a storm.

I knew, beyond peradventure, that any extraneous sound, even an inadvertent swish of a sleeve against a wall, would send the lightning upon our miserable heads. I explained to Rose that everytime a lightning storm ended I always felt that miraculously, and without deserving it, I had somehow managed to escape a ghastly death. I told her I had always felt as if I were a gentile Lazarus.

She asked if I had conquered my pagan fear. I lied boldly. But she knew I was lying, and I'd be lying now if I said I don't pray for temporary lockjaw to smite the big-mouthed heathen who gabble during intense lightning storms.

A few two-for-a-nickel hills are visible from Oxford; and when these were heavy with the first misty garments of the evening, Rose said the hills were going somewhere. She said these hills had been walking steadily, if barely perceptibly, since the beginning of time. They would never get where they were headed, but they would keep on shuffling along.

If a cloud gave our hills a hump, Rose said they were camels. If they were really black and arched, I said they were cats, like Edgar Allan Poe's, but Rose didn't like cats, or Poe, whom she referred to as "Meester Tintinnabulation." So, we compromised and let the moving hills act out a dog and pony show.

We sauntered around at night when every lawn was a sachet bag. I'd tell Rose about our beginnings, as I had heard about them. Sometimes I was so caught up in the drama of the early days I was almost hypnotized by my own poignance and eloquence. My voice, and my heart, throbbed like Mr. Hutchin's best organ.

If you can imagine David's getting thoroughly choked-up on his own harp playing, you can fix me in my role as personal historical dramatist to lovely young Rose Blatz.

As I told her how civilization came to Oxford and environs, by dint of long rifle, Bible, and fiddle, I was pretty sure Rose was prepared to hear the Tuscarora braves dancing in Mr. Ed Settle's gorgeous woodland. Surely, she expected to see a deer leap Mrs. Ashton-Brown's heavy iron

194

fence and then go flying down Spottswood Street.

What I didn't know, I improvised, but the first time she asked me about slavery days I felt that she was holding me personally responsible for all of the terrible sins of my fathers.

The Confederate Monument puzzled her. It amused and angered her, too. I think I defended the monument along the lines of Henry Timrod's:

Stoop, angels, hither from the skies!
There is no holier spot of ground
Than where defeated valor lies,
By mourning beauty crowned.

To Rose, the monument was a memorial to inhumanity and stupidity. "When you grow up and ged good sense, the monumund will remind you of your sins."

Rose made excellent marks in English, especially in the vocabulary tests. She read the dictionary every day for sheer delight, as if it were the most enthralling continued mystery story extant. And her melodious voice had a definite Southern accent, although it wasn't burdened with magnolia and mushmellons. But she never quite got some words down precisely, ones such as "get" and "monument," but these vagaries merely intensified her charm, made me love her even more.

It amused her that birds nested on the "Monumund," and she asked why the "U.D. and C's" didn't explain to the sparrows that they were committing a sacrilege. These "damn dumb buds" always left bits of straw and thread, as foot-notes of their tenancy, when they flew off to Florida.

Occasionally some demented woodpecker would go rat-ta-ta-tat on the bronzed man, but many birds used the man and his pedestal for a public "garden house."

In summer, the old soldier's forage cap was always besmirched with bird-droppings. I still remember the towering embarrassment that seared my tongue when Rose asked me why little boys and girls made sandals of big magnolia leaves and wore them on their bare feet in summer. The magnolia sandals, of course, were to keep bird and chicken-do's off the feet when you played in the yard.

Some children tied the leaves around with strings, but a real expert put the twig between his big toe and the next toe. When I was small, or pre-hobbledehoy, I wore out several pairs of sandals in a summer day. I carried extras in the hip pocket of my Bell Buckle overall britches, the same way many adults carried half-soles, which they affixed with glue.

Sometimes when I put on new sandals, I pretended I was a horse being shod. Mr. Matson caught on, and many times he backed me up to a power pole or to his chair in the "Ivanhoe" to shoe me. He was a smith and I was an infinite variety of horses, Traveller, Little Sorrell, Dan Patch, and that white beauty Buffalo Bill rode in the wild west show.

I, and every other boy, had to crimp up his toes to hold the twig tightly in place. Papa said I would get a club-foot, the same as Lord Byron's, but he said all other resemblances ceased, especially poetic similarities.

One night Rose and I stole by Boot Ransome's flower beds. We came as close to walking on air as mortals can come. We held hands, automatically, as if we were making ourselves into a single cloud, or one disembodied sprite.

We were intruding. We hadn't asked permission to gaze, to smell, to be anointed and enchanted. We stayed just long enough to learn that Boot's violets were the real eyes of the summer night.

It wasn't at all the same as looking at the sparkling gems

and the radiant silverware in the jewelry store window. Those splendors were on display for sale.

Rose and I felt we were trespassing on Eden, on Eden's first unsullied night.

I really think the old man heard us. Papa said old Boot couldn't hear a silver dollar hit the sidewalk five feet away, but he could hear a seed turning in the soil at the other end of the county. As we were leaving the wind came through the beds, a colt kicking up his heels jauntily, but wearing velvet in lieu of iron shoes. We were almost drowned by waves and waves of frankincense and myrrh, Rose and I. And as we were drowning so gloriously I thought of something "Brer" Thompson said:

He quoted Henry Ward Beecher: "Flowers are the sweetest things that God ever made and forgot to put a soul into."

"Brer" Thompson told Papa: "Beecher got it wrong. Flowers are all soul."

I usually pretended to pull a star for Rose to wear in her strawberry blonde hair. Once, I plucked the Big Dipper. She said it was too heavy for her head, that it was as gaudy as Mrs. Ashton-Brown's tiara.

However, a lone star, particularly some obscure star, was just fine for her hair, she told me, smiling warmly.

A few times I actually put a flower in her hair. Once it was a white rose. Again it was a bit of hyacinth. Once it was one of Mrs. Ashton-Brown's gardenias. I broke the commandment. I stole it for Rose. I was ten feet tall. I was Jimmy Valentine, O. Henry's marvelous thief. I was Francois Villon. I was the Highwayman, in Alfred Noyes poem, and Rose was Bess, the landlord's daughter. But, of course, the British soldiers didn't put a finger on me.

One night I broke a twig of blooming pear. She put the white astonishment in her hair. We went to the drug store for ice cream. I was sure everyone in front of the drug store and everyone reading magazines and lounging around inside was looking at the pear blossom.

Everyone knew Mr. S. Blatz didn't have a pear tree, and everyone knew we had several. Actually, I don't recall that there were any overt raspberries, but, inwardly, I was Jess Willard, "the great white hope" of the Jews. I snarled so rancorously in my guts my ice cream melted ten times as fast as it did normally. Or so it seemed to me. In my shell I was lashing out mercilessly, savagely, at every idiotic face. "Take this. Take that," my granite fists were saying.

Nonetheless, when we had finished our ice cream and when we were back in the sweet anonymity of the night, I felt as if I had been in the fiery furnace with Shadrach, Meshach, and Abednego, but had stayed a few days extra, after the Hebrew lads left.

I was enveloped by a strange dualism which I do not fathom completely to this day. Even as a boy I watched myself do everything I did. I was looking over my own shoulder, eternally, making notes on everything I did. I am sure I have missed a lot of loot for this penchant for tiny dramatizations.

When I saw Rose to Mr. S. Blatz's front door, after our leisurely nocturnal strolls, I usually made some kind of good-night speech, but she hardly ever said anything. Thus, the leave-taking was more filibuster than dialogue. When eloquence ran down, the way a wind-up train ran down, I'd give her a furtive peck on the cheek.

I suppose she thought anyone who talked that long, that ardently, without pausing for breath, was entitled to some commemorative memento . . . Most likely she said, to herself: "A lung un leber adf der noz," or "stop talking yourself into an illness."

There were many times, though, when she slipped in the

door, smiled through the closing crack, and was gone while I was still silently polishing the prologue to my good-night oration.

But one night we really did some hugging and kissing. It was in our flower garden, in a swing under the big rose trelis. Between kisses I told her she was the true "cudin of my heart."

She called me "Cousin Silly," but I guess we did turn-on a little, even if there was never the most remote danger of Rose's losing anything she brought with her to Mother's flower garden.

It was strange and unreal. One minute the crickets were having a quilting party, rattling their knitting needles so loudly my ears rang. Then next minute I couldn't hear the merry hell-raising of the insects for the fury of my breathing and panting.

I asked myself if my panting was what adults called passion? I asked myself if Jimmy Simpson panted so painfully when he was expressing his physical enthusiasm with his beautiful wife, Dovey?

When we left the trellis and started to her home I whistled snatches of "Love Divine, All Love's Excelling," if not in the precise mood that Charles Wesley intended his song. I was as strong as "Old Dan Tucker," or Galahad, because my heart was pure.

But did Rose know this? Did she think that I had been fresh with her because she was the daughter of a Jewish immigrant? Suddenly the nosegays in my insides turned to large hailstones.

I squeezed her hand, too hard, trying to be protective. She freed her hand from mine, but I put my arm around her shoulder to show that she was, truly, "the cudin of my heart." She shrugged loose. "Drai mir nit kain kop," she said, or "Stop bothering me." I knew I was being heavy-handed because she censured me in Yiddish.

That night I couldn't sleep for sour apples. I could hardly wait to see her again, to make matters right, but the sun seemed to have gone on strike. The small birds that chirped in each sunrise must have been aged crones when dawn finally came to Oxford the next morning.

I waited until eight o'clock to spring into action. I looked around on our back porch. Cantaloupes and roses would make a nice subterfuge. I put five or six of Mother's best cantaloupes into a basket, and I stuck several long-stem roses around the melons.

I would tell Rose that Mother was sending this stuff to Mrs. S. Blatz. I walked too rapidly. I broke into a sweat. I stopped a couple of times to sniff myself. My socks were wet. My sneakers gave off squshing sounds as I churned along.

When her exquisite innocence filled the door-way, I knew exactly what Papa meant when he said a man like Just Plain Snake Imboden could give hell a bad name, if he went there enough.

I intended to say, "OY VAY IZ MIR," or "Woe is me," the only Yiddish I knew to approximate my chagrin. I expected her to tell me I ought to be ashamed of myself: "Shemen zolstu zich in dein veiten haldtz." To my amazement, she kissed me, lightly on the lips, smiled, and said, explaining her morning kiss, in relationship to the night before, "Ir gefelt mir zaier." That meant I pleased her.

We held hands a second through the crack in the open screen door. She whispered, "Neshomeleh. Tei-yerinkeh." I think both meant "sweetheart." I am sure I could not have stood the sublimity of her saying "sweetheart" in English.

I ran a block, much faster than Man o'War. I still had the cantaloupes and roses in the basket, in my hand. I ran back, and placed the basket inside the screen door. I didn't want to see Rose again at the moment. One can't improve on heaven, and I was afraid any extraneous sound would make the dome of heaven fall and bury Oxford in broken bits of glass.

Fall, fat, full-bellied autumn, the old minstrel, the eternal gypsyman, was Rose's favorite season, principally, because we had the streets and the world more to ourselves. People were inside. Children were at tables, playing parchesi, or "Authors," instead of chanting "Ain't No Buggar Bears Out Tonight," on lawns.

Fall was always opulently succulent back then, and Rose and I began the annual pageant with scuppernong grapes, marveling how such tender vessels could hold such lavish cargoes. I shook down ripe locusts and persimmons for us, and we hunted along the creek banks for the nests of scaly-barks, the local hickory nuts that had the essence of Eden inside their tough shells.

She never went to a corn-shucking, except vicariously, but I told her about the big-meal that rewarded the shuckers for a hard day's work, how the tables held some of everything that ever had feathers or fur or scales, that ever grew above or below the ground. I told her how the fellow who found a red ear got to walk home with a pretty girl, without any chaperone.

I found a red ear of corn everytime I told Rose about somebody's having a corn-shucking.

When the gleaned fields were like picked chickens and the wind came by playing enny-meeny-minny-mo with creation's bare ribs, smoke started pouring from local chimneys, as troups of acrobatic black cats or as a host of gray foxes fleeing the howling wind's pack of hounds.

Rose almost made an anthology of local poetry, in form of smoke. She exuded from her eyes, and even from the tip of her nose, her incessant enchantment with our chimney

201

smoke. I think of this today, sometimes, when most chimneys are mere flues, long fingers that point accusingly to the sky as if trying to get someone's attention.

Back then, before smoke was a known menace, almost every chimney in Oxford seemed to have an incense and a tableau all of its own. The smell of fresh pine wood was a galvanizing, hearty greeting to company coming. Oak belched smoke that was a warm, fragrant epilogue to an evening around the upright piano, or a rousing trip around the world aboard that exalted charger called *The National Geographic*.

When grate fires were lighted, or re-charged, early of a zingingly crisp fall morning, scented smoke came tumbling wildly as a covey of baby birds flying more from exuberance and liberation than from skill. When fires were prancing red ponies, the smoke was a black banner defying the demonic threats of the great white wolf of winter, who waited, almost ready to pounce upon Oxford, just over the horizon. A bit later on in the day the smoke smelled like good pipe tobacco.

Frequently our Oxford smoke was wrinkled, the way Papa's face was wrinkled from incessant smiling. And when the sun called it quits and punched his time-card for the day, the smoke was as old as the serpent, without the original serpent's avarice. It crawled around in the sky on its perfumed belly, as if to erase the memory of that earlier upright reptile.

Well, that was a deeply personal time, even if the scope of human involvement was limited. But we were really excited by picayunes. Rose and I had never seen an art museum but we used our imaginations to translate chimney smoke into a kaleidoscopic gallery of intimate pictures, framed with love and longing and with all the heady spices that grew in the forests.

202

When frost was a billion white rabbits "skinning-the-cat" on the trees, leaping walls and fences, and scampering everywhere, Rose and I walked out at night. When the moon was dropping yellow puddles all over Oxford and the starlight was dribbling fireflies along the darkened hedges and lanes, we were the devisees of November's nocturnal splendor.

She had a muff and matching hat, made of gray rabbit fur, which she wore with a blue coat. Another muff and matching hat were velvet, but the ones made of gray rabbit fur have outlasted all the ensuing changes in fashions, in my heart.

I'd usually forget one of my gloves, on purpose. If Rose didn't notice my bare hand, on nights when the wind was a giant turtle biting down, I'd blow on my knuckles. The muff was "Ganaiden," the Garden of Eden, Paradise. My cold, cruelly neglected hand was "Kabtzen in ziben poless," a pauper in seven edges, a very poor man.

For a block or two Rose pretended not to notice my bare hand, although my huffing and puffing on it was as obvious as that done by the wolf on the straw house in the story about the "Three Little Pigs."

But, ultimately, my labored histrionics were rewarded: Rose made room in the muff for my bare hand. And I can still feel that soft fur, and Rose's fingers, and those chilly nights when the moon was an old steam-boat chugging down the sky's big and majestic rivers.

I felt, and I still feel, the exultation Balboa knew when he discovered the Pacific Ocean. Of course, Keats confused Balboa with Cortez in his immortal poem, "On First Looking Into Chapman's Homer." Today, the computer would throw a fit. It would say Keats was crazy as hell, because of his error in identification. But the poem retains its matchless exaltation, although Keats has been dead one hundred and fifty years.

The computer gives an immediate analysis of sea-water, but it can't remotely suggest the abiding essence of Masefield, Conrad and the others who wrote so well about the ocean and the men and the ships that traveled the ocean.

I'm sure the computer can zap up dozens of definitions for love, but it couldn't define Rose and me, two innocents at home, in a hundred years.

I think Rose was something I somehow didn't have to deserve, as Robert Frost said about home in "The Death of the Hired Man." Reverence has nothing to do with deserving. In a glorious sense, she remains eternally in the public domain for me, the way that late April, white orchards, the sounds of violins, the poetry of Whitman, and first frost remain in the public domain, remain in the tenderest sort of protective custody.

If he is superlatively blessed, every boy, every young man, has a love-affair with some adorable Rose. In time she becomes as immaterial as the shadows that go pussy-footing in June, but, apropos to nothing, she returns, sporadically, to get divinely mixed up with the salt on the table, the mown grass blades, the heroics of the children, and even the most fervent kisses of the wife.

She wasn't a Christian and she never thought in terms of any Christian heaven. But she had more than enough soul, in the old and in the present sense, to go to any heaven, without dying.

I leave her standing there, in Oxford's innocent days before the image came to town in the manner of Mr. Matson's Dalton gang. She stands there in her dotted Swiss, her hair ribbon, her sachet teasing the breeze. Or she stands there in her muff and hat, made of matching gray rabbit fur, in her blue coat, and I know that much of my better portion stands back there, too, on a deliciously nippy fall night, my cold, blue knuckles asking to come inside the muff.

Mr. S. Blatz had peddled, from his back, and then from a wagon, seven years before he saved enough money to open "The Emporium."

Just prior to immigrating to America, Mr. S. Blatz spent three years in the Czar's army. He slipped away, walking much of the time at night and hiding and sleeping in the woods by day, until he reached Le Havre. Some Jewish society got him a boat ticket to Buenos Aires.

Mr. S. Blatz was never sure why his ticket was to Buenos Aires, and I certainly don't know. He worked in Brazil for two years to save enough money to come to New York.

He told me, once, how the first Jews to reach America had come from Brazil. In 1654 23 Jews landed in what is now New York, aboard a ship called the *St. Charles*. Rose and I called the St. Charles the "Jewish *Mayflower*." I wrote a piece about the *St. Charles* which Captain Wade ran in the *Torchlight*. For a few days, Papa called me Lord Beaconfield, who had been Benjamin Disraeli, and Dr. Henley called me Harry Heine.

From Ellis Island Mr. Blatz came almost immediately to Yanceyville. His companion on the trip down was another Jewish immigrant, who became Mr. I. Ferguson. Nervous, and possessing scant English, he told the Irish immigration official, when asked his name, "Fergesen," or "I don't remember." So he went down as I. Ferguson. Mr. Ferguson came to Oxford, a few years after Mr. S. Blatz came. Mr. I. Ferguson was a jeweler. He was always in a hurry, and he used the Yiddish, "Ich eil zich" so often that many Oxonions called him Mr. I. "Ickelzich."

Several years before Mr. Blatz came south, a warehouse had been built at Yanceyville, ostensibly to supply stocks of goods to immigrant Jewish peddlers. Apparently, this warehouse was established by Mr. Fels, who attained national celebrity as the Philadelphia philanthropist. There is little doubt the warehouse was established solely to give immigrant Jews a chance in the new world.

Terms were generous and credit was easy. Apparently, Mr. Fels was satisfied to break even in the operation of the warehouse. For almost a year Mr. S. Blatz peddled from a pack on his back. He was given an itinerary, a map of sorts. The map kept him from getting lost in the vastness of this strange, new land. It told him where to expect friendly or vicious dogs, where springs could be found, and which families allowed a peddler to stay overnight in the house, in the barn, and which families wanted no over-night guests.

Triple stars were placed beside the names of families who purchased stuff regularly, and friendly dogs got double stars. Unfriendly families were marked with triples "X's" and dogs with double "X's".

For the first year, Mr. S. Blatz subsisted almost solely on hard-boiled eggs, while rambling around toting his pack. Eggs were Kosher, and hard-boiled eggs wouldn't spoil. Conversely, chicken would spoil, and there was no rabbi along the way to kill fresh chickens. For many years, around Oxford, many people called hard-boiled eggs, "Peddler's fruit." In time, Mr. Blatz learned that the by-ways of Caswell, Person, and Granville Counties, the terrain he peddled, were loaded with all sorts of luscious berries.

For as long as I can remember, raspberries, huckleberries, blackberries, and dewberries have been lumped together in one word, locally, — "jewberries." Every spring dozens of small boys come by my home hawking "jewberries," or pails brimming indiscriminately with all types of the local fruit. Some etymologists of regional folk-words say "jewberry" is merely an accidental corruption of "dew-

206

berry," but other students of local idioms ascribe "jew-berry" to the old-time peddler.

Mr. Blatz would pick berries until he overflowed one of the galvanized or wooden buckets he carried for sale on his wagon, when he graduated from back-pack to wagon. Placing the bucket between his legs he'd munch berries and read his Talmud, as his horse, "Freddie," drove himself.

At first, Mr. Blatz referred to this placid mare as "Ferd," the Yiddish idiom for horse. But kids construed "Ferd" to be "Fred," and I suppose they made it "Freddie" the way "funny" is fun, with a tail to it. Anyway, Freddie, often "Freddie Blatz," was the only mare around with such a name.

Children, of all races, made Mr. S. Blatz's way much easier for him. When they spied him and "Freddie" and the covered wagon, the shout went up, "The peddler's a-coming."

Fathers and mothers might say there wasn't a cent on the place, and there was always the excuse of drought, or too much rain, too much hail, boll weevil, or tobacco wilt. But Mr. Blatz learned quickly the wisdom of saying that even though he didn't expect the parents to buy anything he couldn't deprive the children the thrills of looking at his wares.

He laid out the stuff, and he identified each item as some proud conductor might call the names of exotic whistle-stops: "Colognes, t'hamburgs, t'threads, nee-duls, pinz, bud-duns, t'side combs, rib-binz, theme-buls, stick-pinz, t'sweet soap, reach combs, chell-you-loidt collars, ent t'zizz-zers."

Mr. S. Blatz wore a black derby hat, a jim-swinger coat, a stand-up collar, and a silk four-in-hand, perhaps, on instructions from Yanceyville. But this attire certainly set him apart from the hucksters who came chewing on match stems, wearing begrimed wool hats, who were always coatless in warm weather, and who, in all seasons, let a single collar button do the work of a shirt collar and tie.

Mr. Blatz wore a big stick-pin in his tie, and on the little finger of his left hand a tremendous glass ring sparkled in the sunshine. He sold lots of the same stick-pins and glass rings. The rings cost 35 cents each, and Mr. S. Blatz never pretended these rings had any value, but many poor boys bought them for engagement rings. If someone said a certain girl had been "Blatzed," it meant she was spoken for, wasn't up for any passionate grabs.

His luxuriant black beard was always neatly trimmed. The beard barely exposed the dark, swarthy face beneath it. His face, flashing here and there through the beard, reminded me of a hootchie-koochie dancer. Many farmers saw Mr. S. Blatz as stepping straight from the Old Testament. Many asked him to supper, hoping to get the nuance of a perplexing bit of scripture explained.

He gave away a few favors, now and then, usually small mirrors, for women and girls, and sticks of licorice for children. But once he had all of his glittering oddments laid out, many an adamant and "impoverished" wife raided her egg money, her "pig" — in reality an earthen jar and spelled "pygg," before piggy-bank came along — for the change to buy a few yards of lustrous hamburg lace, or a yellow top for a boy who was out of his mind with expectation.

He always opened a bottle of cologne, the same bottle, until it gave out. He would dab the stopper to a little girl's hair. The scent seemed to linger, in the child's mind, to become for all time a vital part of the odoriferous seduction of honeysuckle.

He laid out bars of sweet soap almost as if he were laying-on hands. The strongest wind from the west couldn't blow away the aromas. As the multi-colored bars lay in their cases, children saw them as perfumed pink clouds, scented green waves, or white clouds redolent with myrrh. Surely, surely to God — to ours and to Mr. S. Blatz's God — if these delectable bars of soap were put on flowing water, they would turn into those Nicean barks which so delighted Edgar Allen Poe.

At this particular juncture most country people made most of their own soap — lye soap — from animal fats, hickory ashes, and water. A less stringent brand, called "sweet soap," was made by cutting down the "lye" content.

Dr. Henley said Mr. S. Blatz brought the pleasure and the hygiene of bathing to our country friends and relatives. He sold them pretty bars of soap. The soap cried in bright colors and pungent scents for use. So, those who had restricted their bathing to "bird baths" and to "big baths" in creeks and mill ponds during hot weather, started heating water for "standing up" baths on the back porch. And those who had restricted bathing to heating water for the tub on Saturday night, started bathing on Wednesday night, before prayer meeting.

Beyond question Mr. S. Blatz was the founding-father of hair shampoo, in our rural section. He introduced "Golden Girl," a package of flakes. The flakes were mixed with water for the shampooing.

He gave away, as "favors," some ornate hair combs, the big-toothed kind women used to wear.

Papa said women wouldn't call attention to dirty, um-kempt hair by advertizing it with a big comb. So, everytime Mr. S. Blatz gave away a comb he won a permanent convert to the new-fangled shampoo, "Golden Girl."

After laying out the soap, he usually put out the cotton goods. They smelled like a bed, freshly made with clean sheets. As crisp as water cress salad in a brook, the cotton goods seemed to speak of a quiet, cool, gracious sanity far beyond the ken of the searing fields, the back-breaking toil of the tobacco rows, the stench of sweaty over-alls, or "over-halls," and the constant urinations and defecations of uninhibited mules and horses.

Some girls bought cotton goods on one of Mr. Blatz's visits to make a dress to go with a parosal they had bought from him on a previous visit. With other girls, it was the opposite way. Brighter than the most radiant hues of Camelot's tents, these parosals always reminded me of exotic birds pirouetting in mid-air. They were like luscious cones of tuitti-fruitti on sticks, these bright parosals were.

Mr. S. Blatz even sold silk stockings, but only intermittenly. While silk stockings were plentiful in my time, Mother said the first pair she ever wore was to her own wedding. She hadn't had any when she was in the May Court at Greensboro College.

Even when I was a boy there was some suggestions of the lascivious to silk stockings. I remember the talk of the town was a pair Ramsay Davis gave to P. A. Duncan for a Christmas present, and Miss Texanna made P. A. return the gift to Ramsay, as being an unbecoming token to a young lady . . . I'm sure P. A. didn't give a damn about the amenities or any such jim-cracked morality. Jimmy Simpson said P. A. told Ramsay that Miss Texanna said for him to put the stockings where the monkey put the nuts, but, of course, Miss Texanna didn't say that.

Whether a family bought oddments or not, the scents and colors remained, in fancy. Hence, when a child looked into her mirror she usually managed to see a fleeting glimpse, at least, of Mr. S. Blatz. His fabulous caravan remained long after the wagon had gone. When a boy spun his glistening yellow top or drew raucous music from his harmonica or jews'-harp, he could still see Mr. Blatz, in the yellow gyrations and in the spirited screeching, long after the wagon had vanished into that impenetrable snow storm made from the dust of a sandy, summer road.

Pots, pans, and buckets were lined-up on each side of the canvas that covered the wagon. These things were tied to a rope, and the rope resembled a trot-line across a stream. The assortment of pots, pans, and buckets dangling and floundering reminded many folks of fish, hooked on a trot-line.

They were flying-fish, the same as Kipling's, and musical fish, to boot. The pots, pans, and buckets, the iron skillets, and the old-fashioned coffee pots, kicked up a sprightly racket. Everytime the wheels rolled, these utensils used each other for cymbals, drums, and glockenspeils. When Mr. S. Blatz headed his mobile mercantile operation into Oxford the cacophony heralded him ere the wagon hove into view.

When Per-fess-or Max Schmidt heard the approaching sounds, he always clapped his hands, as if he were a superlatively happy child playing "patty-cake, patty-cake, the baker's man." He called the clinking-clanking sounds "The New World Anvil Chorus," and he always started directing the pots and bands, with his hands.

The creaking symphony in brass, tin, wood, and iron reminded "Brer" Thompson of a nursery rhyme, which he quoted with great feeling, and mirth, when Mr. S. Blatz, was all sound and no sight:

Gay go up and gay go down
To ring the bells of Oxford town.

Orange and lemons
Say the bells at St. Clement's.

When will you pay me?
Say the bells at Old Bailey?

When I grow rich,
Say the bells at Shoreditch.

As Papa stood, eagerly awaiting the appearance of the wagon and Mr. S. Blatz, snapping his fingers and patting his feet to the delightful hullabaloo, he quoted something from Ambrose Bierce, who vanished into Mexico about 1914:

All the wagon bells make a solemn din-
A fire-alarm to those who live in sin.

Actually, Bierce had "church" where Papa inserted "wagon," but Papa would shout the couplet and, turning to "Brer" Thompson, say, evenly: "Anytime you are ready, I'll be happy to receive your confession."

I suppose the sounds from the pots and pans created the same effect in town that the cologne, mirrors, tops, and other oddments created out in the country. But I know it is no trick of time or nostalgia when I say that the rolling concert salvaged for joy many a listless afternoon already rued to a bad crop, or to those terrible local ailments, the "jimmy-jaws" and the "eppezudicks," which remained adamant to Dr. Henley's science.

Mr. Blatz drove his wagon around the courthouse square much as the circus wagons paraded around town before the big show. Then he parked the wagon in Ransom's Alley and set-up shop for a day or two, at a time.

In Oxford, the parked wagon became the "Jew Store" before Mr. Blatz opened "The Emporium." Inevitably, some of the regular merchants disliked him because "Blatz

212

gets the hard money." That is, he didn't sell anything on credit, and he didn't pay any taxes, save for his privilege tax, his peddler's license.

I forgot a fabulous item. As Mother would put it, I clean forgot the clocks. Mr. Blatz must have had at least two of every kind and design of clock manufactured, from metal alarm clocks, to cuckoo clocks, to big "mantlepiece clocks."

I never knew his system of winding these clocks, but some cuckoo or imitation "Grandfather" was always striking an hour. One clock struck twelve as another struck five, and the others clicked, clucked, and spewed simultaneously.

People loved to ask Mr. Blatz the time of day. At such times his bearded lips broke into a vague facsimile of a smile: "Vell, vot time do you vont?" So saying, he would point to the wagon. Then he'd take out his heavy gold pocketwatch – it had a heavy gold chain and a winding key – and he'd swing the watch the way Svengali is supposed to have swung his to hypnotize the Czar's children.

Perhaps, the local Sunday school teachers missed a trick by not taking their classes to Mr. Blatz's wagon when they taught the lesson about the Tower of Babel.

Old Man Rufe Duncan was Mr. Blatz's first real friend in Oxford, and it was through Old Man Rufe that Mr. Blatz rented the store on Spring (originally Gum Spring) Street. Miss Texanna owned the building.

Mr. Blatz passed the cemetery in his wagon many, many times, and Old Man Rufe waved to him from his chair in the door-way of the "mossy-lee." Then one day Old Man Rufe stumbled from the "mossy-lee" to hail Mr. Blatz. Later on, when he told of this meeting, Mr. Blatz said he didn't know if Old Man Rufe was the devil or a local version of Pharoah. He said he would have hollered for help but he couldn't think of the English words. It would be futile to use the Yiddish, "Machen a g'vald." Hence, he thought it was wise to say a few words, ("Zog a por verter.")

Old Man Rufe included Mr. Blatz in the "mossy-lee's" coterie, post haste, and the total number never exceeded five. Too, Old Man Rufe was about the only Gentile who always addressed Mr. Blatz by his first name, "Saul."

I learned from Papa that it was Old Man Rufe, amid some spell of unparalleled lucidity, who suggested "The Emporium," as a store-name, and the slogan. Baldy Moore painted a large sign that said:

The Emporium

Clothing And Shoes For Ladies And Gents
Terms Strictly Cash-No Mark-Up Or Carrying Charges
S. Blatz Prop

The sign was written in gold letters, in what Baldy Moore proudly referred to as "My best Spensorium Scrit."

Some of his first customers were people from his old peddling route, but many came in because he looked and talked differently from the remainder of us. But the real key to his limited mercantile success lay in the fact that he was the first merchant in town to allow Negroes to try on shoes and items of clothing for size.

Papa said Mr. S. Blatz was blessed by a lovely defect. Papa said Mr. Blatz was "color blind." Even so, some irate merchants called Mr. Blatz "a Christ-killing son of a bitch," more especially when Negro trade was gravitating, perceptibly, to "The Emporium."

He was the first merchant in Oxford to sell things for amounts such as $1.98. This sounded a lot cheaper than

214

$2.00. Although the sign in pseudo-Spenserian script said "Cash," Mr. Blatz learned quickly that during the long, listless summer months cash was as short as the President's sense of humor. So, he was forced to let some items go, "for something down and the balance in the fall."

Papa gave him a list of notoriously bad credit risks, and highest on the list was Just Plain Snake Imboden. One day Mr. Blatz sold Just Plain Snake a pair of incredibly high-class and incredibly expensive patent-leather shoes, low-quarter ones that cost $4.98. Just Plain Snake paid $1.98 "down," and walked out with the shoes in a box under his arm.

Papa told Mr. Blatz he would never see Just Plain Snake, or the elegant shoes, again. Mr. Blatz smiled, almost through his beard and moustache: "The Just Snake vill return, be backt zoon. I pud 'em two leff shoes in dat box."

Not long after the opening of "The Emporium" Mr. Blatz went to Baltimore and he returned with Mrs. Blatz, his bride. It was told that Mrs. Blatz was a "mail-order -bride," but Rose told me that her father had known her mother, as a young girl, in "the old country."

Rose was born a year later. I always heard that Mrs. Blatz, Miriam, was never seen in public during her pregnancy. No, Mr. Blatz bought a Model T Ford, and each night, after dark, he took his Miriam for a spin around town.

Soon, there were six Jewish families in town, and although some of the gentile ladies paid calls to Mrs. Blatz she was inconspicuous in Oxford. She never "stayed" in "The Emporium," although Mrs. Ferguson "stayed" in her husband's jewelry store, Mrs. Lehmann "stayed" in her husband's furniture store, and when Mr. Fox opened the biggest, most up-to-date department store in town, Mrs.

215

Fox always "stayed" there.

As I said, Saturday, the Jewish Sabbath, was the king-bee in local economy. In time Mr. Blatz learned the mandatory necessity of keeping the store open on Saturday. He had a succession of Shabbat goyim, and I became a Shabbat goy.

I worked in the store on Saturdays, along with an older man, Tobias Tate, whose regular job was selling lightning-rods around the countryside. It was said that Mr. Tate had been struck by lightning two or three times when he was installing rods on roofs, once with such severity that his gold cuff links melted.

I don't know if all of that was true, but he had a definitely scorched appearance, and when he walked he looked as if a gaunt, human Tower of Pisa were in motion. Some folks said he smelled "sulphuric," but when I worked with him in "The Emporium," he smelled strongly of bayrum and that pink dusting powder used in pool rooms, the powder usually referred to as "whore's dust." Just the same, people avoided him, most sedulously, when the weather looked stormy.

Obviously, after Rose was big enough to "stay in the store," my acting as the Shabbat goy was a ruse to be near her. I'd come by late Friday afternoon to help Rose cut all of the paper and twine for Saturday's sales.

The store was heated by a coal stove. The hump-backed stove-pipe ran a good forty-five feet, way up high, to a hole in the far right wall. It reminded me of the biggest, blackest caterpillar in the entire history of the insect world.

You had to put a pan of water, some vessel of water, on hot stoves back then to humidify the air. Otherwise you caught a "head and nose cold." ("Sinus" wasn't in vogue in Oxford at the time.)

Most merchants put water in old coffee cans, but Mr.

Blatz used a variety of kettles. Perhaps, these kettles were left-over from his peddling days, but I remember several different ones. One was aluminum, or, maybe, zinc. It got to be magnificently tarnished — silver hair streaked with gray, just like "Mother Macree." One was iron, and blacker than molasses. I thought of the black kettle as "the ram," after a ditty Dr. Henley used to say:

 Richard had a rakish ram,
As black as black molasses;
He butted Richard in the rear
And gun him psorasis.

Another was copper. It jumped up and down as nimbly as Sheriff Matt Venable doing the "clog" dance. I told Rose the copper kettle was the sun, getting hot, turning up his damper, and flexing his muscles.

But she was more entranced by the sounds of the kettles. Sometimes they hissed, as if a paused locomotive were gossiping. Sometimes they were peanut roasters chanting strident rhythms. Again, they were cotton gin whistles screaming twelve o'clock on Saturday, and often they were hunters calling up their hounds through silver-plated fingers. Sometimes, a kettle would get religion and shake and cavort and yelp in Holy-roller tongues. Sometimes the vapor was a silver stallion prancing to the window to see the sights.

Ever so often the steam was a water-moccasin, according to Rose, hissing and crawling on its belly and getting ready to bite me because I had such "lascivious" thoughts.

I got bitten, repeatedly, but I can swear that snake bites are not antidotes for certain thoughts.

In cold weather we built a big fire Friday night. The coals weren't touched until Mr. Tate or I arrived on Saturday morning, although Mr. Blatz'd give the fire a chunk, or put in extra coal, when he came by Friday night at nine, on the dot, to cut out the light that burned on the outside of the store. If the people in Koningsberg set their watches by Immanuel Kant's daily constitutional, everyone in Oxford knew it was two minutes to nine when Mr. Blatz walked past the "Ivanhoe" on his way to cut the front light at "The Emporium."

Fellows lounging around, playing mumble-de-peg on the courthouse lawn or singing beneath a lamp-post, would yawn, automatically: "Well, there goes Mr. Blatz. It's bedtime, already."

Mr. Blatz was a "Yeshiva Bucher" and I construed that to mean a man of learning or one who loved solitude. If this image seems incongruous with the image of a small town merchant, Mr. Blatz spent all of each Saturday reading and meditating.

He sat behind the counter, in a chair, reading, thinking, and lighting one Fatima off another one. I am sure he never needed more than three matches a day.

American newspapers fascinated him. He read everything from the *Torchlight*, to *Grit*, to the metropolitan papers. The first rotagravure section I ever saw was in "The Emporium." The bright pictures seemed to walk and talk.

Papa said Mr. S. Blatz had the quickest aptitude for the languages of anyone in town, and I am sure he absorbed a wide, diverse, and bizarre range of local idioms from his friendship with Old Man Rufe Duncan. Too, he dropped in the "Ivanhoe," once or twice a week, en route to cutting out the store light, and this was comparable to special studies and a Ph.D. from Harvard, in colloquialisms.

He was, I think, more interested in American schools and colleges than anyone whom I had ever met, up to that time. He was always asking Rose and me about the local

218

school, and what it was we learned and how the subjects were taught. He said the same questions to Papa, Dr. Henley, to "Brer" Thompson about colleges.

He knew, already, many of the things Rose studied. Rose would ask, mystified: "How do you know these things, Tata, my father?"

"My child, long before you came into my life I was watching history being made." Thus, he related Oxford in terms of Russia and Brazil, and the other way around.

He was the first Jew in town to become a Mason, and although I am not a Mason, I understand much memory work is entailed in the ritual of being admitted. But even before he became a Mason, he was contributing small sums to the Masonic Orphanage, according to Papa.

He required Rose to write letters in Hebrew, or perhaps a mixture of Yiddish and Hebrew, to her relatives in Europe. This must have been Oxford's first cultural exchange program.

But Rose was an American. I think Mr. Blatz reminded her of this almost everyday. English, not Hebrew, was his primary tongue, but Hebrew was the well-spring of her soul, the soul of her lavish heritage.

Today, when the word "soul" is thrown around the way citronella used to be used in mosquito time, it amuses me that Rose had a way of designating people as "soul," "tongue," and "hands." Poets and musicians were "soul"; lawyers were "tongue"; and merchants were "hands." But I'm sure her father was "soul." And, of course, it was beautifully clear that "Old Dan Tucker," who had the strongest of all hands, was sheer "soul."

The other Jewish business men and merchants prospered, but Mr. Blatz, the scholar, didn't prosper. The family moved to Baltimore the year I left Oxford for college. Rose and I wrote to each other for a while, but I think I spent

219

so many words trying to prove that a mixed marriage would work out I made out a case against mixed marriages, by dint of insatiable fervor. Perhaps, I protested for unadulterated love too loudly.

I never saw her again. All of that happened long ago, in another world. But if it is "long ago and far away," as Kipling said, in "Mandalay," it is not entirely "shoved behind me."

Last December I was out one day seeking holly and mistletoe in the woods. The canned reverberations of "God Rest Ye Merry, Gentlemen" were still upon my ear when I remembered Chanukah, the "Feast of Lights."

After all these years I remembered that Chanukah, unlike the festivals of Succoth, Pesach, and Rosh Hashana, has no Biblical origin. It commemorates the victory of the Jewish Maccabees over Syrian despots. It was this fight, one for religious freedom, that rescued Judaism from extinction. I remembered that the Jews light candles eight days. One is lighted each evening on the nine-branched menorah, "men-AW-ra," or "candelabrum."

A ninth candle, the shames, or guardian, is taller than the other candles and is used to light the others. This is done to show that one can give love and light to others without losing any portion of one's own radiance. That's what Rose, and her family, did for me. In a long life, blessed with many loves, and many loves infinitely more active than my first love, Rose endures as the ninth candle, and the spiritual radiance grows with the years.

Oxford, September 15, 1970:

"Doing your own thing" is verbally and emotionally irrepressible today, but so much time is consumed in proclaiming this rarefied intention I wonder if much opportunity is left for execution?

However, a timeless spiritual puts the question much more succinctly, much more pertinently: "Everybody talkin' 'bout hebben ain't goin' there."

Conversely, "Struttin' Bud" Davenport was "doing his own thing" years before the phrase, as such, was ever spoken. He epitomized the buoyant essence without being overtly aware that he was doing anything.

If boredom is the ultimate evil, as Schopenhauer contended, "Struttin' Bud" must have been an angel, with arms and legs, using an imaginary baseball in lieu of a harp.

For, life was an orchard heavy with rich, red apples, and "Struttin' Bud" was smitten with an incurable appetite. His days were entire months of incessant excitements. He transformed idleness into a pulsating art.

Additionally, this bona fide off-beat was kind, generous, and tolerant. He was as natural as an inquisitive puppy given the total run of a sun-speckled morning. Indeed, "Struttin' Bud" was a happy, open-handed contrast to Oxford's uptight wheeler-dealers of this hour who are sure, as "Mr. Dooley" suggested, that God would do precisely as they do if He had the true facts of the case.

Some people in Oxford equated "Struttin' Bud" Davenport, who pitched so many imaginary baseball games, with Peter Pan. They said "Struttin' Bud" was an adult who never grew up, one who lived eternally in what would now be dubbed as some sort of Disneyland.

Others said he was a crank, but I never heard anyone say he was an out-and-out nut. A few put him down as an innate eccentric. I am not certain. It has occurred to me that "Struttin' Bud," revolting from a drab world, made of life an incessant, effervescent charade.

Perhaps, he began by playing a role, the same as a character in fiction. Perhaps, with time, he succumbed to the role completely. It may have been that the role became primary as the physical world, thy little monarchy of Oxford, became hazily secondary. Once, Papa told me that Oxford was too little to be a monarchy and too big to be a lunatic asylum.

"Struttin' Bud" was wealthy, as rich as cream, as the saying used to be. Obviously, a poor man couldn't have got by with his shenanigans, with his aberrations, if one insists on a stronger term. It is monstrously unfair, but we tolerate willingly the "idiosyncrasies" of the wealthy even as we berate the "idiocies" or the "tomfooleries" of the poor.

At the time of which I am writing — Oxford of the pre-image era — "Struttin' Bud" was in his forties. When he was 18 he had entered a poster in a competition the Big Bull Company, the famous sack-tobacco firm, was running to advertize its famous product.

"Struttin' Bud's" poster won, and his painting is the one that used to decorate the barns, billboards, and blank walls of the nation, the one that showed a majestic bull rearing on his hind legs while a love-smitten cow, separated by a fence, gazed with unvarnished admiration.

In lieu of a cash settlement, "Struttin' Bud" took his fee in stock. The stock became incredibly valuable when the sack-tobacco firm was amalgamated in the huge tobacco trust.

He didn't quit "art" after his financial triumph. From then on he painted and sketched for fun. For instance, he decorated one wall of the fire house with a huge painting of Bertha and Matt hitched to the wagon. He painted a good likeness of the two horses, but Pete Wood, the driver, resembles a caricature of W. C. Field.

I hardly ever saw him, on his pitching rounds, when he wasn't carrying a sketch-pad. Sometimes he would stop and use a mail-box or the fender of a car for a drawing-board.

222

He sketched rapidly, and as his pencil or piece of charcoal raced, he mimicked the person whom he was drawing. He rolled his eyes, twitched his face, puckered his lips, wiggled his nose, grunted, sighed, whistled, or did whatever it was that his subject did subconsciously.

I have read that Dickens and Sinclair Lewis mimicked the salient features of the characters whom they wrote about, that both authors looked into a mirror continually as they put down the unusual features of a face or a voice.

I am sure this was a reflex-action with "Struttin' Bud." Sometimes he sketched from the "Ivanhoe," and he laughed aloud when he thought he had captured some distinctive nuance. I've heard him clap his hands, ecstatically, and dance a little jig when he was pleased by something he saw and drew.

I have some of "Struttin' Bud's" street and "Ivanhoe" work. He gave it to Papa, and Mother gave the drawings to me when Papa went to the Happy Isles, to see the Great Achilles, whom he once knew, via Tennyson.

My collection shows "Old Man Rufe" Duncan ensconced in the doorway of his mossy-lee; Mr. Matson and Mr. Hasbrook toasting Miss Lillie; Mr. Ed Settle in his huge buggy; wonderful Old Dan Tucker going to work on his bicycle; the President crossing College Street and walking as if he has an egg up his tail and is afraid the egg will break; Miss Bertha seated at her switch-board; Doctor Henley toting his satchel; several of Papa; and there is one of the porch of the whorehouse, with Miss Opal surrounded by her male coterie.

Several times "Struttin' Bud" went to the annual State Fair in Raleigh, where he set-up as a sidewalk artist. He made charcoal drawings of some of the people, from all over the state, who attended the fair. I understand that his usual charge was fifty cents a portrait, although Papa said

"Struttin' Bud" gave away far more than he ever sold.

This always amuses me. I wonder how many of these on-the-spot drawings have survived, and I wonder, even more, how many of the sitters, or walkers, to be precise, ever realized that they had been drawn by Oxford's eccentric millionaire.

His house, unlike any other I have ever seen, had copious examples of "Struttin' Bud's" artwork. Several of the walls of the enormous rooms were filled with murals. Much of this reminded me of the convoluted paintings of Dali, whose works I saw afterwards.

"Struttin' Bud" may have been the first artist to incorporate baseball bats, balls, bases, gloves, and other paraphernalia into larger works. An entire wall, of what "Struttin' Bud" called the "talking room," had baseball equipment floating around the way diverse objects cavort in seances.

I suppose one would say that "Struttin' Bud" had "surrealism" imposed upon "representational" art, although I am positive he never heard either spoken or ever saw either in print. The representational work in the "talking room" was a sort of distorted kaleidoscope of Oxford personalities. Some of his figures were pygmy-sized and others were taller than the tallest of today's basketball players. The pygmies were fat, with huge heads, and the enlongated ones had pins for heads.

However, Mr. Matson's features were fairly distinctive, but the scalped portion of his head was green and the crazy pigtail was red. He stood in a blizzard of white bases, looking down at several dead bodies. Several of the bodies wore bandanas around their faces, and I assumed these were the Dalton boys, but one, bearded and haloed, with the strings of a sack of Bull Durham flowing from his shirt pocket, had to be Lord Tennyson. For a petrified fact, the gentle Lord smoked Bull Durham.

The opposite wall was cluttered with big-league ball players. The figure of a pitcher winding-up, at least ten feet tall, must have been Walter Johnson. "The Big Train" towered over Ty Cobb, painted hook-sliding into home-plate, Babe Ruth swinging at home-plate, John McGraw, throwing a tantrum, to one side, Tris Speaker, making an over-the-shoulder catch in centerfield, and a fast double-play, executed by Tinker, to Evers, to Chance.

A man in a blue suit held a whisk broom in his left hand, a tin cup, with pencils, in his right hand. The wizen-ed face of the blind umpire always reminded me of my mental conception of Blind Pew, in *Treasure Island*.

The crazy house was built in 1911 when "Struttin' Bud" was twenty-one or twenty-two. He called the house "The Bull Pen," and he always smiled to indicate the double-meaning, but Mrs. Davenport, nee Ethelene Talcott, called it "Xanadu," albeit, I never heard anyone allude to "Strut-tin' Bud" as Kubla Khan. Anyway, "Xanadu" was the official name given to the place in the book, *Famous Homes and Gardens of North Carolina*.

Many local people called it the "Nut House." It had three stories, in addition to a tremendous basement, or cellar, as basements used to be called. There were sixty-odd rooms, not counting those in the cellar. These included a ball room on the ground floor that was approximately 180 feet long and 100 feet wide. There was a theatre, of the same proportions, on the third floor. Each of these had four tremendous fire places, although the whole house had central heating, one of the few in Oxford to have that feature, at that time.

Xanadu had the only elevator in town. Marcus Downey, "Struttin' Bud's" yard-man, a strikingly handsome young black, doubled as elevator operator. There was a closet beside the elevator in which Marcus kept his "elevator suit." Whenever Marcus operated the elevator he slipped into a bellboy's cap and jacket.

Papa said Marcus's "elevator suit" resembled the cap and blouse worn by British admirals, and the sobriquet, "Admiral Marcus," stuck to the young black. Once, a magazine writer, who spent a night in town en route to Pinehurst, heard allusions to "Admiral Marcus," and thinking he might pick up a lively, unexpected feature story, rode out to Xanadu to interview the "retired admiral" about his naval experiences.

The whole house, including the wings and appendages, covered 3.4 acres. The exterior of the house was made from graystone, quarried in our region, and the roof was made of light red tile. "Struttin' Bud's" barn, containing stalls for his milk cows and prize bulls, was connected to the great-house on the east. The barn sloped to one story, as did the stable, on the west wing, which contained stalls for the master's riding, walking, and trotting horses.

There was a riding-ring, approximately 150 yards south of the house, and just beyond the ring was "Struttin' Bud's" race-track. The race-track had a covered grandstand, on one side. About twice a year the Davenports held a horse show, with sizeable cash prizes for gaited horses, walking horses, buggy-horses and the like.

When I was a boy, when paved roads were still scarce and when portable vans were virtually unknown, special trains came to Oxford for the semi-annual "Horse Show." "Struttin' Bud" was the ring-master, and he always wore a top-hat, a natty jacket, tight, sleek britches, and heavily polished riding boots. He had a specially made ivory-handled buggy-whip, with a red, silk snapper. He loved to crack it, and he made it sound as if Chick Hafey were hitting those sizzling line drives for which Hafey was so justifiably famous.

Semi-annually, the Davenports held the "Xanadu Cup Races." These came a week after the horse-show, and hefty prizes were given for the top three horses in the mile and a tenth race, and in the trotting contests.

Locally, the race-meets were called "Epsom Salts," an obvious take off on the famous British racing course, Epsom Downs.

The cellar contained a large kitchen. "Struttin' Bud" kept two special cooks on the job, in the cellar kitchen, each morning to make breakfast for hoboes. The "speciality-of-the-house" was pancakes, and often there would be a dozen, or more, hoboes in for breakfast.

"Struttin' Bud" loved to flip pancakes on a spatula and catch them on the spatula when they came down. Sometimes he went to the basement kitchen to give the two cooks a hand. On these mornings he wore a billowing, white chef's cap, the very same as the man used to wear on the "Wheatina" package. Once, I heard him tell Papa that he had flipped and caught, three times in a row, without a bobble, pancakes that went at least ten feet into the air.

Papa agreed that this must be a national record, and speaking of records, he asked it "Struttin' Bud" had ever read Owen Johnson's story, "The Great Pancake Record," the one in which the Tennessee Shad endeared himself to his fellow students by getting a holiday by dint of eating so many pancakes. "Struttin' Bud" hadn't, and Papa lent him the story. Until then Clarence Buddington Kelland, creator of Scattergood Baines, another big pancake devourer, was his favorite writer.

But "Struttin' Bud" was so taken with the Johnson story he wrote Johnson, in care of his publisher, asking him to pay a visit to the "Bull Pen." However, if Johnson ever made the pilgrimage, I am unaware of the fact.

227

Nonetheless, "Struttin' Bud" established the annual "Owen Johnson Pancake Eating Contest." For several years he put on an annual breakfast for the kids of Oxford. By the second year the breakfast was integrated, and it was the first fully integrated social event in the long history of Oxford.

He gave $50.00 to the boy who ate the most pancakes, $25.00 to the runner-up, and $15.00 to the third boy. Papa said "Struttin' Bud's" annual pancake contest anticipated Huey Long's "Share the Wealth" political gimmick: The grocery store, Jimmy Simpson's, sold large amounts of flour, eggs, bacon, and so on; Mr. Hill, the druggist, sold barrels of purgatives; and Dr. Henley and the other physicians spent at least three days making house calls to the homes of the contestants.

I think every kid in town attended the third annual breakfast. P. A. Duncan had written a blistering diatribe in the *Torchlight* in which she rocked "Struttin' Bud" because little girls weren't admitted. To be precise, girls were never excluded. I suppose "Struttin' Bud" thought his contest was unladylike, but he was happy to send the word to the little girls.

By the fourth year every room in the basement was filled. "Struttin' Bud" cooked, flipped pancakes with amazing dexterity, and he and Mrs. Davenport helped wait on the tables.

Along about the sixth year Papa and "Brer" Thompson suggested to "Struttin' Bud" that he extend the contest into an annual scholarship for some deserving boy or girl. Although the eating contest continued until "Struttin' Bud's" death, the "Owen Johnson Scholarship" was established, as a separate entity.

Papa and "Brer" Thompson told "Struttin' Bud" that the scholarship should bear his name, or Mrs. Davenport's.

But he wouldn't hear to it, and the "Owen Johnson Scholarship," an annual grant of $1000.00, continued until fairly recently. Papa served as trustee for many years, and he, Dr. Henley, and "Brer" Thompson were on the committee to make the annual selection of a bright, needy student.

The hoboes called "Struttin' Bud's" fabulous cellar "Big Rock Candy Mountain," or the "Rock," for sake of brevity and expediency. Among its other unusual features, the cellar had ten shower baths, and these were the only ones in town at that time, save for one in the back of Bill Rick's barbershop and two at the high school. The two at the high school were not available during summer, and as I can testify, personally, they never seemed to emit any hot water during winter, during the last portion of football season and during basketball season.

All the hoboes were required to take soap-showers before breakfast. At first, some hoboes demurred, but ultimately, the showers became an added inducement.

Many of the hoboes, hot, dusty, and dirty from the road and the by-ways, or saturated with soot, cinders, and aches from riding the rods, exulted in "Struttin' Bud's" showers to such an extent he decided he should share this opulent luxury, to have some "shower bath parties" for his local friends.

After all, the ladies of the town had "showers" for brides and babies constantly. Nonetheless, the "shower bath parties" didn't catch on with the grown men, save for a few perfunctory, polite acceptances. Just Plain Snake Imboden went a few times, but his brother, the "King of the Green Snakes," said "Snake's" taking a shower at "Struttin' Bud's" was bound to prejudice the hoboes against the place.

But kids went fairly often. I guess those showers were status-symbols for us boys, but the icy water, after the hot water and the soap, was supreme exhilaration during Dog Days when the sun sent mad hounds prancing across the sky.

"Struttin' Bud" had a bowling alley in the basement. It had three lanes, and he let us try our hands at bowling when we went for the showers. I always showered first and bowled afterwards. That gave me a valid excuse for a second shower. Papa said that "Struttin' Bud" did more to exemplify "cleanliness next to Godliness" than all the revivals held in the state.

The showers were in a big bath room, and a cake of ice was always placed at the bottom of each urinal. The hoboes called this "pissing on ice," but the term denoted privilege, status, or high living, rather than the obvious. The phrase encompassed the whopping free breakfasts, the deluxe handouts, the entire amalgam of "Struttin' Bud's" largesse.

For years I assumed that the term was local, or certainly confined to hoboes. Many years later I purchased a copy of the "Dictionary of American Slang," by Wentworth and Flexner (Crowell Publishing Co.) and I found the old phrase as a synonym for "living high on the hog."

The "Winter Garden" was on the first floor of the great-house, next to the stable. It was solid glass on two sides. The floors were made of the finest tile I ever saw. There was a pool in the center that had lily-pads, all sorts of bull-rushes, mossy little islands, and fish, tropical fish, allegedly. There were several frogs, and I am sure these were local frogs.

Even when I was used to the sounds it gave me a start to hear, apropos to nothing, apparently, several giant bull-frogs, going "Knee-deep, Knee-deep, Knee-deep," amid surroundings so splendiferous as Xanadu's.

The "Winter Garden" ran the depth of the widest point

of the house. Hence it was better than 100 feet and it was as long as the ballroom and the theatre. It would have taken a botanist to have classified all the flora, fauna, trees, flowers, and shrubs in the place. I was in the "Winter Garden" many times and I always felt as if I had walked into a jungle such as W. H. Hudson described in his classic, *The Green Mansions.*

"Struttin' Bud" said he fished in the pool, especially when he wanted fish, freshly caught, for breakfast. But this privilege was not extended to the people in Oxford. But it was told, reliably, that he and his wife went skinny-dipping in the pool, especially in the winter.

Occasionally, there was a rumor down town of a skinny-dipping party. I imagined such parties were literal translations of the wildest Roman orgies, even if I had no real way of knowing.

Ramsay Davis made some loose-lipped allusions to sporadic skinny-dipping parties, but I think he did this for two reasons: Obviously, he had never been invited to one, and, in his role as a perennial candidate for office, he was making a palpable appeal to the "moral element."

One day, when Ramsay was muttering some snide, oblique references to "Struttin' Bud's" alleged naked swimming parties, "Brer" Thompson spoke up, as if Ramsay weren't there: "The scriptures don't say anything about this, but I rejoice in thinking that the Master, and the twelve, after a hot, dusty day spent trudging those rough paths, could hardly wait until evening so that they could pull off their robes and dive into the Sea of Galilea. And they went swimming the same way they came into the world, the same way Michelangelo painted the saints on the ceiling of the Sistine Chapel."

I never knew whether or not any skinny-dipping occurred at Xanadu, but, ever so often, one of the rural Baptist ministers got permission to hold a baptizing in the pool in the "Winter Garden."

I didn't intend to neglect Mrs. Davenport. Ethelene, or "Lene," as her friends called her, was good-looking, without being beautiful. Whenever I think of her features, I think of Merle Oberon, the former movie star. Lene had the same high, strong cheek-bones, the same delicate skin tones.

Her hair was long and dark. I heard Papa quote Martin Luther to her one day: "The hair is the finest ornament women have. I like women to let their hair fall down their backs; 'tis a most agreeable sight."

But one didn't see the long, black hair very often. Lene wore wigs, an infinite variety of them. She played many roles. Consciously, or subconsciously, she must have put on the wig that attended some specific facet of her personality, her creativity.

She sculptured a lot, heads mainly, and she always wore a blonde wig above her smock. She spent many hours in solitary meditation. When she lay on the grass in the trees, "to get the true harmony of nature," she usually wore a rust wig.

Occasionally she had a showing of her sculptures. Most of her heads were modeled on characters in Greek mythology. Hence, most local patrons were unable to judge the accuracy of her likenesses. The best example of her work I ever saw was called "Aphrodite." Something about "Aphrodite" reminded me, pretty strongly, of the lovely face of Dovey Turner Simpson, the wife of Jimmy Simpson, groceryman and short-stop on our Oxford nine, our clean-up hitter.

Lavish refreshments were always served at Lene's exhibitions. Hence, her art-work always drew a sizeable crowd. I went with Papa and Mother once, when the piece de resistance was a copy of Venus d'Milo.

The torso of Venus, mounted on a stand, was draped with a velvet covering. At the dramatic moment, "Admiral" Marcus Downey, dressed in a cut-away, striped trousers, spats, a bat-wing collar and an Ascot tie, pulled the cord. When Venus was revealed Mr. Caleb Entwhistle nudged his wife so hard he almost knocked her down: "Great G-hos-e-fat, Mattie," he yelped, "somebody's done broke off boff her arms."

This artistic faux pas was not so egregiously gauche as Mr. Entwhistle's calling his wife "Mattie." She was "Mattie" when they had married, when they had outdoor plumbing, but in the financial rise from outdoor plumbing to finger-bowls, she had become "Matilda."

Lene sculptured, communed with nature, and she had "quiet hours" long before Oxford ever heard of the "Oxford (England) Movement." But the theater was her first love, her real joy. Four times a year she produced and directed plays that were put on in the theater on the third floor.

Sometimes she starred in these productions. At other times she did what she called "Interludes." These were impersonations of people such as Isadore Duncan and Ellen Terry, but I think the best ones were the "Interludes" in which she simulated wind, rain, flowers, passion, grief, or anger by her actions.

Her triumph must have been "The Saga of the Oak Tree," in which she began as an acorn, came up as a sapling, developed a trunk and great leafy branches. At the end she crashed to the floor so hard I thought Jack Dempsey had put the wood to Jack Sharkey. The felled oak depicted man's inhumanity to his environment, and I must confess I never saw anyone take a hard spill more gracefully or more convincingly.

"Struttin' Bud" always made and painted the sets and he acted as stage manager.

Occasionally, Lene hired some road company that was playing in Raleigh or Durham. A few times road companies were brought in all the way from Richmond. I think the actors liked to come to Xanadu. They were paid well, and, of course, they were treated handsomely.

I didn't see them, but two of the first shows brought in were *Hitchy-Koo* and *Irene*. The latter introduced "Alice Blue Gown" to Oxford. The song captivated our town completely. It may be a bit sugary, but it's still a good tune. In fact, I heard Lawrence Welk play it the other night. Jimmy Roberts and Norma Zimmer sang the duet, and I remembered all the stories of Lene Davenport's fabulous "Alice Blue Gowns." It was said she had a bluish wig to go with the gown, but that may be apocryphal.

When I was a small boy, I went one night, with my parents, to see a road show production of "Sally," with Jerome Kern's exquisite song, "Look for the Silver Lining." When Sally sang "Look for the Silver Lining," as she bent over her wash-tub, I slobbered all over my Sunday shirt. I was so enveloped with empathy, so galvanized by the words and the music, I wanted to go out and to do and die for something, for someone, for some adorable, deprived Sally.

Of course, it wasn't manly to cry, except at funerals, but I lost some of my sense of shame when I saw Mr. Ed Settle whimpering into a silk handkerchief that seemed as big as a small tablecloth.

Lene's transcending coup was getting the immortal Irish tenor, John McCormack, to Xanadu. A special Pullman brought him down from Richmond, where he was making a guest-appearance. Papa told me that Lene paid John Mc-Cormack a thousand dollars for one evening.

McCormack was billed, justifiably, as the rightful successor to the divine Enrico Caruso, at the "Met." As I recall, we had just two days to prepare for McCormack's concert. The guests, whom Lene invited, had a special session at the Woman's Club, with Per-fessor Max Schmidt, the German gentleman who taught music lessons in town. He played all of his operatic records, and we did our best to bone up on Verdi, Puccini, et al.

McCormack's singing was as resonant, as sweet, as rich as Keats's poetry. His voice was as intimate, as pulsating as the most passionate kiss, but he sang only two arias. There we were, cocked and primed for the complex hurricanes of opera, but what we got was "At Dawning," "Danny Boy" and some other Irish ballads, and "Memories," the song written by Gus Kahn.

I was astounded that John McCormack had ever heard of Charles Wakefield Cadman, who wrote "At Dawning;" Percy Granger, who arranged "Danny Boy;" or Gus Kahn. But the singing, if the antithesis of top-hat, was delightful, exquisite, simply enchanting.

Mrs. Ashton-Brown was appalled. She said McCormack had insulted our sensibilities with those popular songs. But I agreed with Papa. He quoted Anatole France: "It is better to understand a little than to misunderstand a lot."

During all the years that "Struttin' Bud" served free breakfast to all those hoboes, he served supper every night for one man. Each evening, at precisely five o'clock, never a minute before or after five, "Governor Poly," old Mr. Polycarp Marshburn, walked from his room located over "Tull's Billiard Parlor," and started the trek to Xanadu to supper. Come to think about it, Mr. Marshburn was the only person in town, aside from Mrs. Ashton-Brown and the Entwhistles, who had "dinner."

He always wore a frayed suit of tails, an opera hat, and he always carried a gold-headed cane. In cold weather he wore an opera-cape. If he had an over-coat, I never saw him wearing one.

In winter, when the gloaming came earlier in the day, I imagined that "Governor Poly" was a bat as he skimmed long the sidewalk. He had a habit of flinging out both arms, about every twenty yards, and this intensified the bat-image as he walked along in his ancient evening clothes.

He ate in a small room on the ground floor which "Struttin' Bud" fixed up as a dining-room, just for "Governor Poly." A waiter brought his dinner from the kitchen, and "Admiral" Marcus, dressed in a butler's uniform, served the meal. Apparently, "Governor Poly" ate the same food every night: A double-porterhouse steak, a side dish of aspargus tips, a huge side dish of hash-brown potatoes, and for dessert he had a large piece of deep-dish apple pie.

According to "Admiral Marcus," "Governor Poly" ate everything served him, and he sucked down the steak bones when he had eaten the meat. He could have had more, and he could have varied the meal. Apparently, he got exactly what he wanted, and in the precise amounts.

Before the meal, Marcus served him two large Scotch and sodas and an El Producto cigar. Even then, El Productos cost two for a quarter. He smoked his cigar as he had his two high-balls.

He was served wine, during the meal, and brandy with his dessert. When he had finished his dessert, his deep-dish apple pie, Marcus brought him two more El Productos. He took another hefty Scotch high-ball with his second cigar. The third cigar was for the trip back to his room over the billiard parlor.

Apparently "Governor Poly" had little contact with the Davenports, but this was in deference to the "Guv," to his important work. For as long as I knew him, and before I knew him in the flesh, he was writing a, or rather "the," comprehensive history of the state.

The magnitude of his work was so absorbing, so demanding, he never left his room save for his walk down to Xanadu for supper. I understand he had a little coffee-lace for breakfast, but he confined his eating to the one meal each evening at Xanadu.

Even when I was a boy, the appellations, "Governor Poly" and "the Guv," were pretty foggy. Newcomers and visitors assumed that "Governor" was appended in the British sense, a mere salutation, that "the Guv" was some sort of local joke, that Mr. Marshburn was a "guv" somewhat in the manner of Crighton, the butler, in Sir James Barrie's play, *The Admirable Crighton.*

Actually, he had been elected lieutenant-governor of the state about forty years before this time, when he was 28. I believe he was the youngest man ever to be elected lieutenant-governor. Strangely enough, he was never really keen on politics. He was elected at a time when there were no Democratic primaries, when candidates were nominated in convention.

He had inherited a large farm, and he was one of the early leaders in the Grange and in the Farmers' Alliance, even though he was strictly a "gentleman farmer." He had never attended a convention before he went to the one that nominated him for lieutenant-governor, and he went solely to nominate some man for Commissioner of Agriculture.

His speech, totally devoid of political rhetoric and bombast, captivated the delegates by dint of its effervescent contrast. Then, when an impasse developed in the nominations for lieutenant-governor, some of the weary leaders turned to the disarming young man who made such an attractive impression in his brief, maiden speech.

This occurred late at night, after countless, futile ballots. In other words, young Marshburn found himself in the same position as a crap shooter who picks up a pair of dice with nothing but sevens on them.

Republican opposition in the general election was nominal only, and Polycarp Marshburn, Esq. became "Governor Poly." Albeit, it seems he never went to Raleigh except when it was necessary for him to preside over the biennial sessions of the State Senate.

He had lost his farming interests, his capital, and his inheritance when his land was ravaged by the wilt, by downy mildew. "Struttin' Bud" paid his room-rent. He could have taken a room at Xanadu, but I suppose less stigma was attached to separate quarters, and, besides, no one ever interfered with his writing, ensconced as he was over the pool hall. I was in his room once, with Papa, and there was no place for anyone else to sit down.

Tremendous piles of papers, ledgers, old journals, maps, and assorted bric-a-brac completely usurped the room. There was one chair, at a drop-leaf desk. In a corner there was a rickety wash-stand, with a bowl and a pitcher. I understand "Governor Poly" got his drinking and shaving water downstairs, in the pool room. Apparently, he showered at Xanadu, ever so often.

I always understood that "Struttin' Bud" cared for "Governor Poly" because his father and the old gentleman had been close friends. He was with us, in my time, almost as a ghost and an echo. He nodded amiably enough, on the street, when he came out for his brief appearance each afternoon, but, otherwise, he was as immaterial as a shadow, as the permeations of lark-spur.

He had no interest at all in politics. Papa said he was the only ex-officer holder extant who didn't even trouble to vote, much less to stage a political come-back. To my knowledge, no one ever sought "Governor Poly's" political opinions or advice and he never dispensed any. But there was absolutely no derision in his nick-name.

His life's work was never published. I am not aware that he offered it for publication. The manuscript, in his own hand-writing, very small letters always written in an uphill slant, runs to more than 5000 pages. It covers, in detail, every facet of life. The portion relative to the Indians and the Colonial period runs more than 1500 hand-written pages.

The manuscript, in a packing crate, stayed in the vault in the county clerk's office for a long time. Now, it is under the aegis of the Oxford Historical Society. Despite staggering problems in editing, I should think "Governor Poly's" immense manuscript would make an interesting study for some aspirant to a master's degree in history.

I'll never forget two of "Struttin' Bud's" most memorable stunts, although he didn't consider them "stunts," certainly not in the normal context of the word.

A "tramp" pitcher, "Stuff" Malone, came to town. Our regular baseball players were amateurs who worked at something else for a living, but the fans did pass the hat to get up money for pitchers.

"Stuff" pitched for Oxford one summer, averaging eight or ten dollars a game. Our catcher, George Hargrove, said "Stuff" had the widest assortment of curves he ever saw. In fact, the other teams couldn't touch "Stuff." He was striking out fourteen to eighteen men each game. Then one day some of the Henderson players accused "Stuff" of working on the seam with a victrola needle.

The umpire's investigation disclosed a flat surface on the seam. As any player knows, Mia Farrow could be a whizz pitching a ball that has a flat surface on the seam.

From then on, the umpires searched "Stuff" before he took the mound, and from then on, he was just another pitcher.

Simultaneously, South Boston, Va., also in our semi-pro league, had a pitcher who was caught doctoring the ball with paraffin. He, too, was rendered virtually impotent, via official searchings.

"Struttin' Bud" decided it would be terrific fun, and a most interesting experiment, to have a game between Oxford and South Boston in which "Stuff" was turned loose to use his victrola needles and the other fellow was given free use of his paraffin cake.

The game was played in Oxford the day after the season closed officially, and I'll guarantee there never was one like it, not from Abner Doubleday's time down to the Mets. The game went five innings, before the other 16 men quit in disgust. No hitter, on either side, got to first base. No ball was knocked out of the infield.

Jimmy Simpson hit the longest ball of the day, a pop foul that went half-way down to third base. Hitters went to bat 30 times, and 23 struck out. The longest grounder hit almost got to the pitcher's box. And there were some fine hitters on both teams.

I saw this bizarre game, and there is no doubt in my mind it would have been a double-no-hitter if it had gone nine innings, or eighteen innings, for that matter.

The next year Tom Day showed me in the "Sporting News" that "Stuff" had won ten straight games, without a loss, in the Pacific Coast League, a league that was just under the majors back then. According to the news story, several big league teams were trying to sign "Stuff."

Along about the middle of July "Stuff" showed up in Oxford. Somebody asked him what happened. He answered: "Well, it seems them ball players and umps out yonder is fa-miller with the gramaphone, too."

The superlative stunt was the time "Struttin' Bud" bet Tom Day five bucks that he would serve fresh snow-cream on July 4. Tom ransacked all of the available almanacs before he put up his five dollars. There was no indication of snow in Oxford in July, nor had there ever been any snow in July.

Towards the end of June, when the town was panting from the ravages of a real heat-wave, "Struttin' Bud" passed the word around town that he would have a "Ben Hur chariot race" at his race track on July 4.

Tom Day made circular signs around his head, around his white cap: "Maybe so, but when's it go snow, Bud?"

"Struttin' Bud" smiled innocuously and told Tom not to miss the chariot race.

I guess a third of Oxford went to the race track at Xanadu on July 4. Just Plain Snake Imboden was peddling white booze from a wagon that was filled with turnip sallet, and the "King of the Green Snakes" Imboden was giving away luscious green-snake watermelons.

After a while, three chariots, each pulled by three of "Struttin' Bud's" horses, charged from the run-way. He drove one; Lene, in a sort of Julius Caesar wig, drove one; and "Admiral" Marcus drove the other one. She was dressed like Cleopatra, in the movie, and "Struttin' Bud" and Marcus wore the same garments Mark Anthony wore.

As I recall, Lene won the chariot race.

Right after the race, all of the Davenport's butlers, cooks, maids, and handy people came to the race track pushing wheelbarrows. Each wheelbarrow held several freezers of snow-cream. "Struttin' Bud" pocketed Tom Day's five bucks as if it were the Hope Diamond.

Papa, who was in on these stunts, told me that "Struttin' Bud" bought the three chariots from Ringling Brothers, or from one of the big circuses. He had put his entire force to gathering snow the February before. The snow was made into ice cream. The ice cream was packed into freezers, and

241

the freezers were stored in the ice plant in Oxford.

Captain Wade had both stories on the front page of the *Torchlight*, and some of the wire services picked it up. The snow story was garbled, a bit, in translation, and for a while some of the more facile of the sensational journalists were equating Oxford with the "Big Rock Candy Mountain," the place that had the lemonade springs and the gum-drop trees. But, then again, as I have already noted, the hoboes were calling Xanadu "Big Rock Candy Mountain" long before "Struttin' Bud" Davenport put on chariot races and served snow-cream, in Oxford, that wonderful July 4.

Oxford, November 18, 1960:

The old-timey, small-town whorehouse, such as we had in Oxford, must have gone to Kansas, or to hell, or somewhere, without a hack. I have not read any authoritative piece on the demise of the small-town sporting-house, and to my knowledge, there is no palpable point of embarkation such as Jerome Kern used in his old tune, "The Place Where the Good Songs Go."

But whether or not one admits the fact, anyone with the brains of a misbegotten amoeba knows that it was pitiless amateur competition that ran the madam and her girls out of town without so much as a testimonial fish fry from the alumni.

I don't know what happened to the high-steppers who clicked their heels on the sidewalk and who twirled their parasols so hypnotically back when corner lights were called iron lilies. Some of the preempted soiled doves may be in Florida watching shuffle-board, drawing Social Security, and contemplating their memoirs. Some may be in the cities, giving helpful hints to fallen sparrows who

242

want to fly again. Some may be giving "How To Succeed" lectures to incipient call-girls who get more in a night than Miss Opal's "young ladies" got in a month, combined.

Perhaps, Jim Bishop will write another gripping book, *The Day The Small-town Whorehouse Died.* Then we shall have answers as well as conjectures.

Today, here in Oxford, there is a drive-in bank where Miss Opal's place stretched in the sun and cowered in the icy wind. This drive-in bank is inside the corporate limits of the town. The corporate limits go way the hell out now.

At the time I'm writing about, when I was a bug-eyed boy smitten with a type of glandular fever restricted to growing boys, Miss Opal's place was about twenty yards behind the corporate limits of Oxford, on the west side of town.

Location was important. The place was beyond the "ordinary jurisdiction" of the Oxford police force. Actually, the town police had the right to make arrests, in certain extreme cases, one mile beyond the town limits. Naturally, the policemen would pursue and shoot at a bank-robber, but Luther Baggs, our chief, had great respect for the niceties and nuances of the minutiae of the law. As he explained it: "Unless it is a great emergency, I don't intercourse with the sheriff's business and he doesn't intercourse with mine." To my knowledge, Chief Baggs was the only person in town who used "intercourse" in this fashion; albeit, on occasion Mr. Matson might say, just for a change of pace, that the President was "intercoursing" with some poor widow's money.

Anyway, Chief Baggs worked in the daytime when things were relatively quiet at the whorehouse. You may think I'm lying, but Mr. Arnie Tatum, our night policeman, had the job ten years before his wife found out. He was always in bed by ten, at the latest.

Mr. Tatum sold chill tonic during the daytime. He probably made less selling chill tonic than the seventy-five dollars a month he got as night policeman. But his wife was supposed to be some aristocrat from Virginia. Apparently, Mr. Tatum thought she would think being a policeman wasn't couth, not in the old Virginia way.

Miss Opal's place was too near town for Matt Venable to go to all the trouble of cranking his Ford, for an official trip. And, besides, he walked down that way almost every summer night.

Miss Opal's place was painted gray, or what was known as "Wabash blue," like the celebrated train, the "Wabash Cannonball." Some of the sports, or loafers, who hung around in front of the drug store thought they were as rakish as Richard Harding Davis when they whistled, very loudly, "My Little Gray Home In The West," when Miss Opal's girls were passing along the street or going in and out the drug store. But they never whistled anything, not even the "Bonnie Blue Flag," when P. A. Duncan breezed along, after they made the "Little Gray Home In The West" mistake with her once.

She turned upon the boys with a rattling speech about man's exploitation of women. There were three girls at Miss Opal's: Jessie Lee, Sula Mae, and Maude Rose. (Maude Rose was the one who walked the street, away after dark, when Mr. Tatum had gone home.) Anyway, P. A. said Jessie Lee, Sula Mae, and Maude Rose were three floor mats for the idle young rich of Oxford. She said the three girls were in bondage to male lust. She said they had been sold as slaves down into a 20th century Egypt. She even compared Miss Opal to some sort of Pharoah in a corset.

Dr. Henley came up and heard this screed. He told P. A. it was fine for her to defend her sex, but that she ought to have enough sense to respect Miss Opal's age and station in life.

The house was gray, but it took a spy-glass to tell what color it had if you looked at Miss Opal's place from the

244

sidewalk that ran along in front.

The hedge in front was so high I used to imagine that its long green fingers scratched the bellies of low flying clouds. This privet, as high as the top of the one-story bungalow, hadn't been pruned in a long time. It not only obscured the front of the whorehouse. It ran down each side of the house.

The house was big, with eight rooms on the first floor. At one time, long before I was born, it had been the Manse. The old Presbyterian church had been in the field next to it. The old church burned to the ground, in 1890, when the fire fighting equipment was nothing but one hand-pulled reel and buckets. All the water came from wells and cisterns.

Apparently, the Manse was badly run down. After the new Presbyterian church was built, in Oxford proper, a new Manse was built, too. I think Miss Opal bought the Manse about 1918.

Papa said the elders thought they had hornswoggled Miss Opal. She paid $1200.00 for the lot and the bungalow. Papa said $600.00 was a top price. Later on, the elders said they understood that Miss Opal was a seamstress. Sometimes they said they understood she was going to give music lessons.

Miss Opal told Papa the elders were so glad to get her money they never asked her a word about what she did for a living, what she was going to do with the old Manse.

By my day, when Miss Opal was "not in the profession actively, but merely a supervisor," as Papa put it, the old issue about the desecration of the Manse was almost forgotten. Albeit, occasionally some old-timer said something about "gathering moss from the old Manse." About once a month Just Plain Snake Imboden, soused on his own stuff, would stumble down the path toward Miss Opal's place. He always sang "Bringing In The Sheaves," and he emitted little apostrophes, to trees and birds, about "Susanah and the Elders."

245

But Miss Opal never let Just Plain Snake Imboden in the front door. He entered through the back. And Miss Opal made him pay the spot cash, (I think it was $2.00) everytime he came to pleasure himself. Miss Opal never let Just Plain Snake put any pleasuring on a tab, on the wall, as they said, the way she let Ramsay Davis and some others "write it down" until the first of the month. She never let Just Plain Snake Imboden carry a bill over until the early fall, when the tobacco market opened, the way she did with Hughie and Hector Scott, identical twins, who farmed and kept batch out in Sassafras Fork, ten miles from town.

As I understand it, there had always been whores in Oxford, but our ladies stayed at home in the old days. They weren't in political activities and social reformations. Indeed, the solid old phrase, "Up in Mabel's Room," indicates the continuity of soiled doves. Too, Judge Robert W. Winston, in his book of memoirs, "It's A Far Cry" (Henry Holt and Co., 1937) says, in the 1870's, that there were more churches in Oxford, according to population, than in any town in the state, that there were twice as many saloons as churches and twice as many bordellos as saloons.

In my time Mrs. Opal's place was the whole shooting match. Of course, whores were about as rootless and homeless as poker chips. But at the time I am writing about there were the three girls whom I called by name, Jessie Lee, Sula Mae, and Maude Rose. It is my honest opinion that these three are accurate examples of the type found in Oxford, in that era, or in almost any small, sleepy Southern town.

I knew them pretty well, if never intimately, if never physically. Miss Opal used to order candy, magazines, and other oddments from the "Ivanhoe," and Mr. Hasbrook and Mr. Matson let me deliver the packages. I always backtracked, through Mr. Ed Settle's lovely woods. When I brought the package to the back door, Miss Opal always inquired about Papa, and she always gave me some refreshment.

Each girl had a separate tale, or history. I heard these stories many times, as I sat on the back porch, eating a piece of gingerbread or sipping a big dipper of root beer. Miss Opal usually had a barrel of pickled pigs' feet and a barrel of salted herring on the back porch. I loved them and she handed the pigs' feet and the salted herring to me with both of her fat hands.

Later on, if someone said he smelled "whorehouse" on me, where I wiped my hands on my britches, he wasn't referring to any "inside the whorehouse" odors, whatever they were.

I almost forgot that Miss Opal subscribed to *Grit* and to the *Southern Planter*. I delivered these, to the front door, from the "Ivanhoe," because I delivered all the other *Grits* and *Southern Planters* to the front doors in town.

I suppose I was "King of the Mountain" in the curious eyes of my friends. They asked me a lot of questions, especially if any man was inside the place "a-doing of it" with one of the gals. Actually, I never saw or heard anything. When I delivered *Grit* and the *Southern Planter*, Miss Opal always met me at the front door.

She was cordial and she asked about the news downtown, but she never asked me to come in and take a chair, or anything like that.

If Papa knew about my errands — and surely he must have known — he never said a word, not to me. However, a few years later, I'm sure it happened after Miss Opal passed away, Papa saw me coming from the pool room: "I'd rather see you walking from a whorehouse than a stinking pool room," he told me. "So would I," I answered him, "but on my allowance I can't afford it."

He must have laughed later on, even if I was a smart-aleck, because I knew that "Brer" Thompson and Dr. Henley knew about our exchange.

Alas, my mother found out my errands. From the way Mother carried on one might have thought I owned a harem. I am sure she thought I had gonorrhea, or "the gonorrhea," as we called it (an article was placed before virtually every malady, "the pneumonia," "the typhoid fever") just from knocking on Miss Opal's front door.

If she had known about the gingerbread there is no question a stomach pump would have been applied to my belly, but by "Brer" Thompson rather than by Dr. Henley.

The important thing, to me, though, was I got to know all about the "din of sin."

Jessie Lee couldn't have been much more than twenty. She was the youngest of the three girls. When I saw her on the back porch, when she didn't have on all of her heavy-dating paints and that perfume I could smell thirty yards away, she looked like a farm girl who was waiting to milk the cow or gather the eggs.

She was friendly but sort of withdrawn, and she reminded me a lot of the farm girl, Maude Muller, in Whittier's poem. Several times when I delivered stuff from the "Ivanhoe," she was sitting in the back yard drying her hair.

Her hair was yellow and it fell all the way to her shoulders. It reminded me of a yellow daisy-chain. I guess she washed it a lot. When it was dry and she started combing and brushing it, I thought of small yellow rose buds on a trellis. I know she was just another whore. But I remember a verse Ramsay Davis used to say about every yellow-haired girl he knew, from Jessie Lee to P. A. Duncan. Ramsay Davis said he wrote the verse. If so, the muse struck but once:

St. Paul swore, and St. Peter said,
And all the saints alive or dead,
Vowed she had the sweetest head
Of yellow, yellow hair.

The other girls evidently resented the verse. I heard Sula Mae and Maude Rose sing the song about "Mary Ann," substituting "Jessie Lee," somewhat unevenly:

Pull your shades down, Jessie Lee,
Last night in the pale moonlight,
I saw her, I saw her,
She was combing her golden hair,
It was on a rocking-chair.

Jessie Lee'd give her hair a yank to let me know it wasn't a wig.

I didn't know much about bosoms except some were big and some weren't. If the word "falsie" wasn't used back then, the two others accused Jessie Lee of wearing "gay deceivers."

Of course, I had sense enough to know how she made her living but when she sat there in the back yard, her face free of everything but a few freckles, I wouldn't have been surprised to hear her mother call her in to learn her piano piece for the recital.

Dr. Henley said she was a "little light for the traffic," but "Struttin' Bud" Davenport said Rabbit Maranville, the short-stop, didn't weigh more than 125 pounds, wringing wet. Just Plain Snake Imboden said Jessie Lee could close one eye and pass for a needle. He said when she drank a little cherry smash she looked like a thermometer.

Maybe, that was why I heard grown men say that Jessie

Lee wouldn't sell Just Plain Snake a glass of lemonade in the bad place.

Jessie Lee said she came from "up the country." The place never was specific. However, some men said they knew her folks. Sometimes her folks lived on a farm two counties away. Again, the place was seventy miles from Oxford.

She went into this business solely to help her family out of a financial jam. The wilt got the tobacco crop, or the boll weevil got the cotton. (This varied). But Jessie Lee's folks were straight-forward, all right from the ground up. They had voted three times for Bryan. They were such good Christians they wouldn't allow an Ingersoll watch on the place. But the bank failed, or the "time" store got the whole crop, or her Papa had "the T and the B's" in both lungs, and the landlord ran them off the farm.

Jessie Lee was doing her family duty. That was all. In fact, some people thought she was the girl Mr. Matson was protecting with his stick each night, the girl in the city, with the brother named Jack.

Frankly, I never thought she came from any farm. I say this because one day, in the back yard, we were talking about Hughie and Hector Scott. She liked both of them, and she couldn't tell one from the other. Anyway, she said they'd be in to see her as soon as they "kilt theer hogs and skint 'em."

I never heard of anyone's skinning a hog, except in one of John Ehle's novels.

I suppose a psychologist would say that in exonerating Jessie Lee the local sportsters exonerated themselves. What they did with Jessie Lee was the same as playing a crooked faro wheel at a church benefit. The money went for a fine cause.

After she left our community, the alumni told Horatio

Alger stories about Jessie Lee. She moved to a big city, to some place like Danville or Norfolk. It was better to have the state-line drawn in the mind. She had bailed out her family. She had saved enough for a business course. She learned to write on a typewriting machine. She got a job working for a brilliant young lawyer. Now, Jessie Lee and the lawyer had two fine sons. It was reported that her husband would go to Congress soon.

So, all of the local blades felt the same pride men feel today when they contribute to some educational foundation that really pays off tangibly in human dividends.

Sula Mae said she was from a big city, but she never did say precisely which one. She talked a lot about riding the trolley. The big city might have been Richmond, Baltimore, or St. Louis. It must not have been New York since she never mentioned the subway.

She, too, was a victim of circumstances, a creature of life's hard storms. She had been seduced, under promise of marriage, by this rich sport who took her to elegant cafes where the meals cost as much as $1.50, without counting the champagne, or "com-pag-na," as Sula Mae called the wine.

Her beau really loved her, but his parents tricked him off to France or Europe. The hateful parents wouldn't give Sula Mae a street car token back up town when she told them she was with their son's child. Then she was thrown out, always on an inclement day, by her own stern, Christian parents. She asked for shelter, and they shouted back the commandment about adultery. ("Brer" Thompson told Papa he had in mind a sermon, "Let Him Without Stones Throw the First Sin," but I don't know if "Brer" Thompson knew Sula Mae's story.)

The baby, now a little girl, as bright as sunshine and as smart as Frances Perkins, was in an orphanage. Sula Mae was hustling just to keep her child in the orphange. She had to send money to the orphanage once a month. Hughie and Hector Scott said they had contributed so much to the child's education they were going to be sure to attend her graduation.

However, Sula Mae's real objective was to save enough, at Miss Opal's, to take the little girl out of the orphanage. Then the two would go out west, as far as Memphis, maybe, and get a fresh start together.

If Sula Mae never made positive identification of the mythical swell who supposedly got her pregnant, her eyes and facial expressions cast innuendoes everytime she looked at the rotogravure section of the Baltimore *Sunday American*. (Ramsay Davis said Sula Mae used her eyes and facial twitches the way those characters in James Fenimore Cooper's Indian novels dropped bits of clothing in the forests for trail-blazers.)

She would see a picture of some polo player or yachtsman and she would jerk the rotogravure section tightly to her bosom. Then she would run from the room, biting her lip hard. Whenever this happened Jessie Lee and Maude Rose figured, or they figured that Sula Mae figured that they figured, that Sula Mae was looking straight at the picture of the alleged father of her alleged child.

In the reflective days after the departure of the whorehouse, the news came to Oxford occasionally that this child was a nurse who worked twenty-four hours a day among the sick in some big city's slum.

Again, it was reported that this nebulous child had become a movie star. Some of the alumni assumed that Sula Mae was living in "Hollywoods" with her daughter-star. For a fact, someone said he saw Sula Mae in a news picture of a swanky Hollywood swimming pool party. Once Ramsay Davis said he had heard that the daughter-star was a good friend of the silent screen queen, Mary Miles Minter, whom my local people confused with a brand of chewing gum.

There was in town a sign-painter named Baldy Moore. Actually, he was named for Major Archibald Harris, popularly called "Major Baldy." But, Baldy Moore's folks didn't mess with "Archibald." Everyone called him "Baldy Mo." Once or twice each year he got tired of Oxford, and he'd hobo around the country painting signs, barns, street numbers, or doing odd jobs for spending money. It was Baldy who said he saw Sula Mae in Hollywood.

Some folks didn't believe Baldy because he said Sula Mae's daughter had some orange trees in her back yard, and he'd pull an orange, straight from the tree, and eat one whenever it pleased him.

Somebody said, most casually: "When was this, Baldy?"

"Why it wuz lass spring, it wuz. I got back here fore George Green and Jacob Fuller come to town."

People nudged each other. They knew it was a damned lie because, as they said, who in the hell ever saw an orange except at Christmastime?

When people in town wanted Baldy Moore, they yelled out: "Baldy Mo. Where is Baldy Mo?"

He'd come running. "My name ain't no no damn town. My name is 'Baldy Mo,' dammit, not any 'Baldy Mo'."

Sula Mae must have been about twenty-five. I am sure she was younger than Maude Rose and older than Jessie Lee. She wasn't bad looking at all. She would never let out that she knew a man, if she saw him in public. She didn't get maudlin drunk more than two or three times a year. But she did chew Blackjack Gum. I delivered many packages of it from the "Ivanhoe."

Ramsay Davis said he just couldn't imagine a lady's chewing gum, especially in somebody's damned ear. But again, as the Scott twins pointed out, and I reckon they knew, Sula Mae never ate any parched peanuts when she was pleasuring a man, not the way that Maude Rose did.

At the time, I considered Maude Rose quite mercenary. I contrasted her to Jessie Lee and Sula Mae as I contrasted the Hessians to the legions of Nathaniel Green.

If her family had been victimized by economics, she said nothing about it. Nor did she mention anything about being violated by a rich, blue-blood. Indeed, from the way I got it, if she said anything about being mistreated it was about some sailor who roughed her up in Norfolk, or how some hick cop "taken it" away from her in a cell, how he gave her "boudacious" laughter in lieu of currency of the realm.

However, she did introduce the town to the X–Ray, to what Dr. Henley called the "Roentgen machine." As I said, she was the one who did the strolling, and some of the gentlemen said Maude Rose could tell a buck from a five dollar bill on a moonless night, under the depot platform.

She may have been dull if all work and no lollygagging makes one dull. As Ramsay Davis said: "Maude Rose is short on social amenities. You have to show her spot-cash before she even says 'howdy.' " The way I got it, Maude Rose worked with the bloodless efficiency of one of the new adding machines. Ramsay Davis said: "Her mind is a cash-drawer."

I always heard that even when she got tree-top drunk she wouldn't give you a biscuit if she owned the whole Pillsbury factory. But liquor loosened her tongue, if not her favors. To hear Maude Rose tell it, she knew all the fighters from Willard to Sharkey. She had a picture of the late Kid McCoy, and she claimed to be one of his innumerable wives. She had lain on silken pillows with the cattle barons in the west and she had been on the special Pullman

254

palaces of some of the big railroad tycoons.

I saw her eat, a few times, on the back porch, in hot weather, and she held her fork as if she were milking a cow. And Miss Opal was always calling her down for saying "barnyard" words. Just the same she had been intimate with plushy sports all the way from Saratoga to Palm Beach.

I guess her trouble was she had traveled too far. She had known too many intimacies. Anyway, Hector Scott said he and Hughie figured out that Maude Rose would have to be at least 216 to have done half of the things she said she had done.

Maude Rose was about thirty, I suppose. I think "blowsy" is the word for her. Some years later when I read Somerset Maugham's short story, "Miss Thompson," and then saw the movie version, called *Rain*, I really wondered if Somerset Maugham had run across Maude Rose somewhere in his travels.

When she left Oxford, she was hardly ever mentioned. Occasionally, someone might say: "What was the name of that big-mouthed whore that was here towards Miss Opal's last days?"

When I was big enough to know Miss Opal, eye-ball to eye-ball, she must have been around sixty. She reminded me of one of those fat, kind looking old ladies that Copley painted.

She never came down town unless the trip was necessary. But when she came down town to go to the bank or to see Papa on some legal business, she dressed up, fit to kill, but she didn't rouge her face. She wore large picture hats, blue and red ones. She carried a gold-headed cane, really more of a staff than a walking-stick. It had no handle. It was the same kind that I saw in pictures when a British bailiff, or whatever he was, led the procession to announce that court had opened or that Parliament had convened.

She carried a lorgnette downtown. She could thread a needle without any sort of spectacles. Papa said the lorgnette was to stare down any pious sisters who gave her uppity looks.

Insofar as public recognition was concerned, Papa and Dr. Henley and the other gentlemen were total strangers, if she met them on the street. She always came down town in the public hack, or the taxi, operated by Lee Fuller. (Lee was a wall-paperer, too, and both sides of the hack — it was first a surry, and then the taxi — were hung with samples of various kinds of wall-paper, the big sheets that came in large rolls.)

Lee would park around the corner from wherever it was Miss Opal had business. When her business was done, she came back around the corner and left for her place.

I never heard of but one unseemly confrontation. That was the day Just Plain Snake Imboden was "dillified" and slapped Miss Opal on the back, in front of the courthouse, where she had been to list her taxes. Just Plain Snake slapped her behind and said, in a loud voice: "Howz bidness, Mist Opal, old gal?"

Sheriff Venable ran out from the courthouse. He threw Just Plain Snake in the old cement horse-trough that used to be in front of the courthouse, and then he locked him up until the next day. The Sheriff said he soaked Just Plain Snake in the horse-trough and locked him up because he was drunk and talking out of his fool head.

As I said, the front and the sides of the house were virtually obscured by the enormously tall growth of the privets. The screened-in front porch was almost obliterated by clematis and nandina. This grew as a jungle in summer. Of course, the clematis played out in winter, but no one sat on the porch in cold weather. And, the nandina, with its jolly, red berries was a Christmas scene straight from Dickens, who, Papa said, was really responsible for rescuing the secular joy of the Yuletide from old Cromwell and our Puritans.

The front porch was not for any "hoe-hoppers," to use Mr. Matson's ribald phrase. It was reserved exclusively by Miss Opal for a type of foregathering that was surreptitious but not clandestine. (If I seem to split hairs, I still think the distinction is valid.)

A few gentlemen of our town met here regularly, but still spasmodically, never by rote, to pass the compliments of a star-struck evening with Miss Opal and with one another.

It was a sort of club, a home away from home. I guess it was a place for men who didn't get enough attention at home or who got too much attention.

Men such as Papa, Dr. Henley, and Sheriff Venable sat there on the cool, shrouded porch, with no lights save the stars and moon. They sat and told their favorite stories. They didn't have their stories interrupted by their wives, who always seemed to think they could tell the stories better, and they didn't have to edit anything or do any pantomine for the benefit of the children.

As they talked, or as they sat in cool quiet, with silence doing the talking, they drank juleps made from local corn, well water, mint, and powdered sugar.

The gentlemen and Miss Opal never kicked up any racket anyone on the dirt sidewalk could hear. Still the place was a kind of open-secret in town. People didn't talk about the porch club for the same reason they didn't talk about their demented relatives. Everyone in town had some kind of open-secret, I guess.

None of the whores was ever allowed on the front porch

while Miss Opal's male contemporaries were there. She never called one to bring a pitcher of lemonade, even. No, she got whatever was needed, herself.

Of course, there was usually some implied threat to the continuation of the porch club. But this related to the whorehouse, to "Sodom and Gomorrah," itself.

The Ladies' Society, abetted by the missionary circles, said Miss Opal's place was an affront to all decent people. Usually, the desire to purge Miss Opal came when there was a serious drought or when a terrific hailstorm had damaged the tobacco crop. I remember two public meetings in the courthouse. One was during a summer when wilt almost wrecked the tobacco crop. The other one came in the middle of a local epidemic of dysentery, which some ascribed to bad drinking water.

Albeit, the "Ladies" were seriously handicapped. They talked behind their fans, pretty much, because the subject matter was so shocking. And even without a fan, none had the temerity to say the word "whorehouse" loudly and clearly. (Everyone in town knew that no one abided more closely to the exact letter of the Sunday blue-laws than Miss Opal. As Mr. Matson said: "There are no bed-springs a-creakin' on the Sabbath at Miss Opal's and who else can say the same?")

Naturally, P. A. Duncan would say "whorehouse," or anything else. But although she lambasted men for exploiting the soiled doves, she saw the reform movements as the persecution of women by other women.

On both occasions, Sheriff Venable said it wouldn't do at all to give Oxford a black-eye all over the state by really blowing up the issue about Miss Opal. He didn't say so, but the women got the drift that the names of some of the patrons might slip out. There might be some surprises.

"This has to be handled with delicacy," the Sheriff said

at both public meetings. He went on to say that although he was bowed down with innumerable pressing matters, he'd just step down to the place in question and have a word with the party concerned.

But, ere long, Miss Opal's menacing shadow was purged by a badly needed rain, or attention was diverted by some newer sin. Nonetheless, Miss Opal was Oxford's emotional ace-in-the-hole, even during the times when her den of sin was not an overt issue. The self-righteous used her for a community scape-goat, if not precisely the same way Aaron used one in the Book of Leviticus.

Several times Papa quoted a ballad from W. S. Gilbert's "Gentle Alice Brown" in relationship to the attitude of the righteous to Miss Opal. I learned this ballad by heart from Papa's maliciously delicious quotings of it:

'I have helped Mama to steal a little kiddy from its dad,
I've assisted dear papa in cutting up a little lad;
I've planned a little burglary and forged a little check,
And slain a little baby for the coral on its neck.'
The worthy pastor heaved a sigh, and dropped a silent tear
—
And said 'You musn't judge yourself too heavily, my dear
—
It's wrong to murder babies, little corals for to fleece;
But sins like these one expatiates at half-a-crown apiece'.

In my greasy-bread days Miss Opal was an old whore for whom time was running up the white flag. She ran the whorehouse the same way a big league star might take a job managing a bush league team when his active playing days ended.

While I've never been sure, I think the Sheriff knew Miss Opal when she was still active in the trade, in some city.

259

He and Papa referred to her occasionally, and always privately, as a "former lobbyist-at-large for the best interests of the people."

Apparently, Miss Opal had been pressed into service, in her active days, when it was important that some legislator had to be persuaded to vote for a certain important bill. Again, she prevented negative votes against important legislation by entertaining some recalcitrant solon so lavishly he missed the roll-call.

The regular coterie visited the front porch during warm weather, but Dr. Henley came by the year round. He always brought his bag. Actually, he treated Miss Opal and the girls when they were sick, and he examined the girls regularly for venereal diseseas.

Sometimes Papa brought the circuit judge or an out-of-town lawyer to the porch for a cool drink and a long conversation. The Sheriff brought special guests, too. One of these was a United States Marshall. The Marshall was a tremendous man. The Sheriff said he was too big to be human and not quite big enough to be a horse. Papa said the Marshall used a whole julep to chase a whopping drink of straight whiskey.

I talked with the Marshall several times, but not at Miss Opal's. I was astonished to learn that Bat Masterson, the celebrated western law man, whom I would encounter later on in a TV series, spent most of his life as a reporter. Masterson was a reporter for the Washington *Evening Star* when he died in 1924. He died at his typewriter, and the last words he wrote were these: "There is an equal distribution in nature. Take ice. In summer the rich get all they want and in winter the poor get more than they want."

The other gentlemen sauntered along and sort of slipped up on the blind side of the place. Dr. Henley, who had the first "machine" in town, always parked his Oldsmobile right

260

in front. Generally, during the spring and summer, he came by when his nightly rounds were done. His car was there, in plain view, if someone needed his services. He came by so he could drink a whole mint julep without having to let the ice melt while he went on call and back. He dropped in so he could smoke a whole cigar without having it go out forty times. He visited Miss Opal for the same surcease that his present equivalent finds at the country club or in watching the big board at the stock exchange.

People said Dr. Henley was "stout," or he "carried some flesh." He was fat. At Miss Opal's he took off his collar, put a handkerchief around his neck, let his suspenders drop until his belly hung down like a boulder over a cliff, and he kicked off his shoes and rubbed one aching foot against the other one.

Many times, late at night, after his rounds, he and Miss Opal sat alone. (Invariably, Dr. Henley sat in an over-stuffed chair, the very same kind that Scattergood Baines sat in, in the short stories by Clarence Buddington Kelland.) No one else ever sat in his chair. Miss Opal called it "the Doctor's place."

He had a lot to tell her and she had a lot to tell him. Most of the by-play was inside stuff. During the day Dr. Henley had been everywhere. He had seen it all.

Miss Opal was a combination gossip columnist, sports editor, and society writer. The back-chat between the two was a good deal similar to the Huntley-Brinkley Reports. But there was never any of this insufferable Rotary Club "David" and "Chet," or "Joe" and "Opal" business.

I remember old Dr. Henley as being as out-going as the receding tide. I always see him as a chunky Samaritan toting a black satchel.

Papa was there, with his feet on the railing. He tended books and poems the way other men tended growing plants. I think, and I thought, of him as the laureate of Miss Opal's front porch. He recited poems, without having to answer the telephone or to stop and hand something to Mother.

(And I knew something the others may not have known: Papa was always writing down his thoughts. Frequently, these thoughts came out as bits of verse, as poems. When he quoted one of his poems on the porch he said it was something he had read in some paper or magazine. He couldn't remember just which paper or magazine it was.

(Papa loved the night. The sky was an old post road. The moon was a coach rumbling across it. Here and there a star was a lantern hanging at an inn.

He wrote a poem in which he compared thunder to barrels rolling across an old wooden bridge. Another one had the wind playing power lines for a 'cello. There was another poem about hot weather. Papa wrote about weather as if he were discussing the personality of a cherished friend. I remember the conclusion to the one about hot weather, even if I didn't get the analogy at that time:

From the nimble way the sparrow pirouettes
On one toe, you'd think he's a ballet dancer,
If you didn't know his antipathy for Tschaikovsky.

The Sheriff was a bachelor. He was said to be a real hand with the ladies, but he didn't run around in Oxford. People said he had lady-friends in the cities, whom he visited, when he needed to visit a lady. He never fooled with any local women, to my knowledge, but his presence there on the porch had a wholesome influence on the activities inside.

The Sheriff must have been at least fifty, but he was trim. You could see the muscles rippling through his sleeves, and against his pants in the calves of his legs. He was red-headed. There was all over him an almost incredible redness.

His hair was naturally curly. It seemed to be on fire with crackling flames. But no one ever called him "Red." Ordinary people had too much respect for the Sheriff to use a nickname. Too, red was still a hoo-do color at this time.

The image of complete cruel neglect was "a red-headed step-child," and if someone was "red-headed" he could be arrogant or he could have been sandbagged, caught for a cedar-bird, in some card game or business deal.

"Brer" Thompson said red was jinx because the earliest sins were scarlet. He said the artists usually gave Cain and Judas red heads. However, I don't think I saw any paintings of the two.

Dr. Henley said physicians at one time had tried to diagnose illness by a patient's color, and a red complexion was considered a symptom of terrible humor and sick blood.

Papa said the superstitions about red hair had historic roots. (He came to a boil when I accused him of making a pun.) He said the British were terrified of their red-headed Danish enemies, that the symbol for terror remained after the Danes went into the pastry business.

I don't know how generally these legends were known around home, but no one ever called the Sheriff "Red."

He was the political "boss," if we had one at home. He did favors for people, got them jobs and small loans, and they voted for him. Just the same, Papa said the Sheriff's honesty was impeccable.

Papa and Dr. Henley and "Brer" Thompson kidded him a little, on the side, when on one else was around. They referred to him as the "generalissimo". They called him the

"Kingfish," long before anyone ever heard of Huey Long. Papa called him "Mr. Murphy," after Charles F. Murphy, the head sachem at Tammany Hall.

Sometimes on the porch, but never anywhere else, the coterie sang "Tammany," Gus Edwards' old song.

Tam-ma-ny, Tam-ma-ny,
Big Chief sits in his tep-ee
Cheering braves to vic-to-ry.

"Struttin' Bud" Davenport came by infrequently. He was a nice fellow. He didn't get in just because of his wealth. While his main contribution was pitching he could do the multiplication table up to 24 times 24. (That may seem something today. It's really a trick, though.) He knew, by heart, the time-tables of virtually every railroad in the nation.

Papa and the other hard-working gentlemen hardly ever had any real vacations, not in their whole lives, except the ones they took on "Struttin' Bud's" high-balling trains. He knew where to change and which trains had deluxe diners and how many tunnels there were through any big mountain in the country.

They would sit on the porch, sip their juleps, and take leisurely train trips. While "Struttin' Bud" didn't love engineers as much as he loved ball players, he knew a lot of them. In fact he was the only man in town who called Casey Jones "John Luther" Jones, his proper name. He said, too, that "Casey" was a mess-up. It was really "Cayce," from the Kentucky town in which John Luther Jones lived until he got himself killed, driving the "Cannonball," at Vaughan, Mississippi, in April, 1906.

"Struttin' Bud" was in a hurry, all of the time, it seemed to me, and he might drop by the porch just to pay the compliments of the evening and to pitch, for both teams, the post-season game between the Giants and Cubs that decided the National League pennant in 1908.

If he got too upset about "Bonehead" Merkle's failure to run on to second base, Dr. Henley would switch him off to Young Babe Adams, winning three games in the 1909 series.

There was a pianola in what the coterie called the "physical enthusiasm" portion of Miss Opal's place. When the gentlemen weren't on the porch, the music was a little louder.

A couple of pals and I used to lie on the edge of Mr. Ed Settle's beautiful woods and listen. The pianola didn't play "The Joyous Farmer," "March Militaire," or "I'll Sing Thee Songs of Araby."

The music was low-down as a wiggling snake yet it was saturated with comet's hair. Instead of "The Rosary," it played "Bill Bailey," "Salty Dog," and "O, You Beautiful Doll," and "I Wish That I Could Shimmy Like My Sister Kate."

I would lie there in the sharp sweetness of pine litter while the music took off with the wild magic of Santa Claus's sleigh. As I lay there I imagined that the piano keys were horses shod with lyrical lightning.

The titillating music, and the proximity of the whorehouse, perhaps, induced a flood of sensual speculations. I was aflame with an itch that defied all scratchings. Of course, I didn't believe in the stork but that sensuous music stripped the world of all winged creatures, for an interlude, and it not only routed the cabbage patch but vanquished the world of horticulture, for a spell.

In common with most small-town boys of our section and generation, I was invested, certainly obliquely, with grandiose notions about the purity of Southern womanhood. I had many recurring day-dreams wherein I, at deadly peril, saved the purity of some noblewoman, albeit, the immaculate, high-born lady was always as lovely and as fetching as P. A. Duncan and Dovey Simpson.

But the music and the knowledge of what occurred in the back rooms at Miss Opal's took the edge off the blade which I inherited for the protection of imperiled purity. As I lay there in the pine litter my long, long thoughts were ones that Mother would certainly label as carnal.

And I had some practical speculations also. In that era before the pill, before sexual liberation, I wondered if whores ever became pregnant? I never heard of any whore's becoming pregnant. I wondered if whores had some special protective powers, some sort of sacrosanct goober-dust, perhaps?

Then one day at the "Ivanhoe" I put all of my brass and guts in my throat and asked Mr. Matson if whores ever had babies.

He was sweeping the rental library with the feather-duster. Without looking my way or without pausing for deliberation, the old Indian scout thundered: "Hell, yeah, boy. Where do you think all the cot ding bill collectors and bank presidents come from, anyhow."

As I wondered about sex I wondered equally as much about growing up and getting good sense and taking my place on the porch. If sex was one of the privileges of maturity, liberation from the niggling world of school report cards, of eating at the second or the third table at big family dinners was just as rapturous to contemplate.

I was curious, not curious yellow, but green, if curiosity has to have a color. What I call curiosity is a desire to know, to know why and how. Surely, this is a lust of mind, a perseverance of delight in the indefatigable pursuit of knowledge. This sort of curiosity may be sensual or even lascivious, but it exceeds in scope and intensity the brief vehemence of anything that Mother would have called carnal pleasure.

Well, all that was another world, and one world at a time is more than enough. Yet I go back sometimes when the wind whistles old ragtime tunes in the tree-tops, when the moon is a fat, happy man, like Mr. Ed Settle, overlooking his bountiful, sacred domain.

On fall nights I am likely to be seized by a sort of inverted wanderlust, inexplicably, and I walk out where the whorehouse used to be. I tell my folks I want to stretch my legs. Perhaps, I am trying to stretch my heart, a formidable chore.

On these wine-heady, perfumed fall nights I don't see the drive-in bank or the shopping center that flares its neon signs where Mr. Ed Settle's lovely woods used to dance in the moonlight. I never see the new housing development because I always see those marvelous fire horses, Bertha and Matt.

Miss Opal's yonder in the old cemetery. Papa was her executor, and I think he and the Sheriff put up the stone that says:

Here Lies Miss Opal Galehouse
A Friend To Mankind And To Men

(I never knew she had a last name until I saw the stone.)

But on these exquisite fall nights the whorehouse is back behind the scented jungle, and Papa, Dr. Henley, Miss Opal and the others are on the porch. A phantom pianola is knocking out "O, You Beautiful Doll" and "I Wish That I Could Shimmy Like My Sister Kate."

When the phantom music stops, I almost agree with Henry Miller that chaos is the score upon which reality is

267

written. For, there's no Kate in town anymore. Nor a Katie, either. Her name is "Kathryn" today, and the society reporter for the local newspaper better make damned sure it is spelled that way.

Oxford, January 24, 1968

There is a record-bar in Oxford today, as there is in virtually every small town. Sales are limited, generally, to recordings and to sundry tapes. The music played and sold is rock, hard-rock, and acid-rock, and country music. ("Country," if not a complete misnomer, must be ambiguous; for, try as hard as I can, I am unable to determine just what country it is that is responsible for this type of music.)

The customers are youngsters, predominantly. Pop heroes come and go like tribes of ants at picnics. Each hero has a cult, and the aficionados stand around the record-bar and snap their fingers and shake their shoulders and hips in a sacrosanct, if not downright, occult manner.

It must be difficult to stay "in," to keep track of the demise of the deposed demi-gods and the coronations of the new sovereigns. One of the blessings of advancing age is that one is spared the necessity of keeping up with all of the latest folk-heroes, or, in many cases, the anti-hero-heroes.

It's wonderfully refreshing to be able to say, "I don't know," even if one is diplomatic and restrained and does not append, "or give a damn, either."

While I have not orchestrated my life to dictums and to aphorisms, I make it a loose rule never to expand my circle of acquaintance and never to read any book on the best-seller list. Obviously, one misses out on many charming people and on many amusing books. Just as obviously, one misses legions of consummate bores and stacks of fifth-rate books.

268

For a long time an Oxford man, I. G. Hutchins, operat-
a music store. Apparently, "I. G." were initials, solely. "I.
G." didn't stand for any given names. If someone asked an
Oxonian what "I. G." stood for, the answer was "Izzard
Gizzard," which didn't mean a damned thing, either.

Actually, everyone in Oxford referred to Mr. Hutchins as
"Piano." Adults said, "Good-morning, Piano." His wife was
always referred to as "Mrs. Piano Hutchins," to distinguish
her from "Mrs. Meat Market Hutchins," whose husband was
the local butcher.

Unlike today's record-bar, Mr. Hutchins sold few recordings. He sold sheet-music and an infinite variety of musical
instruments. Prospective customers could try out a piano or
a parlor organ, if their hands were clean, and a pianola
usually ground out some snappy tune to attract patrons.

But there was no simulated dancing inside the store. Mr.
Hutchins never smiled, whistled, or snapped his fingers. He
tipped around the store as gingerly as an undertaker who is
afraid any extraneous sounds might blow a three thousand
dollar funeral.

He wore dark suits the year around, topped off with a
gray derby and pearl-gray spats. (Mr. Matson said "Piany
wears them spats to save on socks.") He was so thin people
said he could pass through a keyhole fully dressed. I still
remember him as a mobile cadaver, half-embalmed, tripping
about the music store with the silent ease of an elongated
cow. I still have the distinct feeling that Mr. Hutchins was
weaned on green persimmons and dill pickles.

Whenever the possessive was added, as in Hutchins's,
which is still correct, and which used to be used consistent-
ly, the name contained an additional syllable and it was
invariably pronounced — "Hut-chins-es," — the very same
as "the Court of St. James's" was spelled and pronounced
by the British until fairly recently.

The music store, as I have noted previously, was located next to the bank. There was an outside loud-speaker, and some sort of music enveloped the sidewalk from eight in the morning until nine at night, six days a week.

Two large show windows were cornucopias of assorted musical instruments. On the left window, as one faced the store from the street, were these words, in gold letters, three inches high:

"Hutchins's Musical Conservatory
Oxford's House of Culture"

and on the right hand window the words said:

"Pianos, Pianolas, Organs, Sheet Music
Talking-Machines and Musical Instruments"

Floating around the words was a host of musical notes, sharps and flats, like misshapen golden cherubs flying forever in a circle to nowhere.

The only emotion Mr. Hutchins ever showed came when a fly bashed itself on one of the floating notes or on one of the gold notes or when a bird made a mess.

Mr. Hutchins's eyesight was up to Hawkeye's. He could spot a squshed fly from the back end of the store. He'd run out with a bucket of soapy water and a sponge. When he scoured the window thoroughly he polished the letters and the musical notes with a piece of chamois.

Papa said Mr. Hutchins's eyesight was so powerful that the *Titanic* would still be sailing if "Old Piano" had been the look-out. When he went to Hill's for his morning and afternoon grape juice, some wag would say a fly or a bird had just messed up a letter or a note. Mr. Hutchins came tearing back as if the devil had a blow-torch at his coattail.

"Talking-machine" was anachronistic when I was a boy, but Mr. Hutchins never altered his signs from the day they

270

were painted. But, for all of that, many local people continued to say "talking machine," as well as "dead-wagon" for hearse, "velocipede" for tricycle, "machine" for automobile, "pressing-club" for dry cleaners, "flying-machine" for airplane, and "tooth doctor" for dentist.

Mr. Hutchins had an endless supply of specially-made advertizing cards. Although everybody in town knew the contents of the cards almost verbatim, he handed them out at all public gatherings.

One side of the card said: "Visit Hutchins's Music Store And Recapture Those Halcyon Days of Tranquility, Peace, and Culture You Knew Long Ago."

This bit of elucidation appeared on the reverse side (I am looking at one of the ancient cards at the moment): "Halcyon days, meaning a time of tranquility and peace, comes to us from Greek mythology. When Ceyx was drowned, his wife, Halcyon (or Alycone) threw herself into the sea. However, compassionate gods turned the dead bodies into birds known as halcyons, generally identified as a species of kingfisher. The ancient Greeks believed this bird spent seven of the coldest days of the winter building on the sea a floating nest made of fishbones. Seven days more were required for brooding. Under normal conditions such a nest could not survive the shock of waves and wind. Hence, the gods calmed waves and winds. Thus the period of seven days before, and the seven days after, the winter solstice was called the 'the halcyon days.' Later it was supposed, even if we know better, that the halcyon or the kingfisher, itself, had magic powers to charm the sea and the wind."

Indeed, provincial Americans said if a kingfisher was hung up, its beak became a weather-wave, always pointing in the direction of winds and storms.

Additionally, Mr. Hutchins had an inexhaustible supply

271

of cardboard fans, with plywood handles, the type people used at church. On the front side was a picture of Jesus receiving the little children. On the back side this little essay appeared: "Where is the geographical center of the United States? According to the U. S. Geodetic Survey, the approximate geographic center of the United States, proper, is the Eastern part of Smith County, Kansas, at latitude 39 degrees, 50 minutes, and longitude 98 degrees, 35 minutes. The town nearest to this point is Lebanon. Anybody can find the geographic center if he will take a good outline map of the United States, proper, and balance it on the point of a needle. The point should be in the northern part of Kansas.

"Hutchins's Musical Conservatory is the Cultural Center of our community. Your artistic needle always points to our refined establishment."

Papa told me that Mr. Hutchins obtained the information about "halcyon" and the geographical center of the nation from "Governor Poly." I always understood that Mr. Hutchins's interest had fastened to a couple of conversations "the Guv" had on the street, perhaps, with "Struttin' Bud" Davenport. Evidently, the allusions to "halcyon" and to Smith County, Kansas had appealed to Mr. Hutchins and he had asked "Governor Poly" to write the information on paper.

"Governor Poly" and Mr. Hutchins can't be blamed if the geographical center has changed since the admission of Alaska and Hawaii. But I survived countless funerals, wakes, and weddings by twirling a fan as I tried to imagine Smith County, Kansas, and the town called Lebanon.

Many times, as I sat in church, I created Smith County, from my own yearnings, much as William Faulkner created Yoknapatawpha County. The place became so real to me I almost expected to get some mail posted from Lebanon.

272

Today, I admit, unblushingly, to being a devotee of "Gunsmoke." And, ever so often, I hope that Marshall Dillion's job will take him to Smith County.

In the early days of the music store, Mr. Entwhistle had bought the first local talking-machine. Someone asked Dr. Henley: "Have you heard Mr. Entwhistle's talking-machine?" "Yup," the doctor replied, "I see her just about everyday."

If Mr. Hutchins hadn't bothered to change his sign, "talking-machine" had already run the gamut from graphophone, to gramaphone, to victrola. And recordings had run the gamut from various cylinders and discs, to heavy records, with the music on one side, only, to records with music, or recitations, on both sides.

We had a "cabinet" victrola at home. We arranged our family concerts to suit everybody. Mother loved "The End of a Perfect Day" and "Just A-Wearying For You." Sister cried over "Paradise" and "Three Little Words." Papa and I went for "Bill Bailey" and "Pretty Baby."

One of our records was a recitation by Nat Wills, called "No News, Or What Killed the Dog." It was continued from one side of the platter to the other. I mention this because in the past twelve months I have heard several T. V. comics, including Allen King and Flip Wilson, give the same story verbatim, in the guise of brand new material.

I had an instrument, called "The Autoharp," which I bought at the music store. The instructions said: "The Musical Wonder of the Age — the Instrument that Plays Itself With Just a Little Assistance from the Musician." I was never extremely proficient, but I could produce something that sounded close to "Flow Gently Sweet Afton," when Mother was listening, and something that vaguely resembled "Poontang Ramble," when Mother wasn't listening.

As I recall, I paid, or Papa paid, Mr. Hutchins six bucks for "The Autoharp." But Ramsay Davis, who fancied himself a shopping guide, or a protector of the unwary, said he could get the same instrument from Sears and Roebuck for $1.95.

Ramsay always had a copy of each current issue of the Sears, Roebuck Catalogue. There must have been other copies in Oxford, but from the way Ramsay Davis talked many people assumed his copy was the only one extant. Hence, he had all the inside information that was supposed to make "Old Piano" look bad, even infamous.

Mr. Hutchins hated Ramsay's guts. He said Ramsay was a "cheap opportunist, a pimp trying to get elected to something or to get up some law clients." Ramsay said he was merely protecting us from "this local mercantile Count Dracula." I didn't know what Ramsay meant, not at the time. But, come to think of it now, Mr. Hutchins was a tall, skinnier version of Bella Lugosi who played the bad lead in all the "Dracula" talking movies.

Today, when I think of Ramsay Davis' exclusive rights to the Sears Catalogue, I remember Mr. Turby, our dairyman. Mr. Turby named all of his children from characters in the *Arabian Nights*. He had a son, my age, named Aladdin's Lamp Turby.

There were eight children. When Mr. Turby assumed his last child had been born, and his assumption was correct, he threw his copy of the *Arabian Nights* into the fireplace so no one else could duplicate the names.

As I foot-note I might add that Aladdin's Lamp Turby was a whizz at math. When he went off to college, under his own steam, he got Papa to change his name, legally, to 'Ladd L." Turby. ("L." was just a letter. It didn't mean anything. It was like putting "Hon." in front of a legislator's name.")

Mr. Hutchins also sold "The Zither-Harp," advertized as a "New Overstrung Instrument of Extraordinary Beauty and Elegance, Producing A Tone Which For Sweetness, Purity, and Resonance Far Exceeds Any And All Instruments of Its Class." This marvel, sold for $3.00, I think.

The "Guitar Zither" cost about $2.00, and two instruments that cost a dollar, each, were extremely popular with school boys and girls. These were the "Combination Pipe Organ and Brass Band," and the "Clarion Brass Band Harmonica."

These instruments made school children individual strolling orchestras. Both instruments, small enough to tote in your hand, were built along the same lines: A harmonica was fitted with tuned bells, in the latter model, and in the first a tiny keyboard had an arrangement of two tuned bells.

I guess half the children who went to grammar school played, or played at, "The Clarion Brass Band Harmonica" going and coming. We had to check the·instruments with the principal, along with our sling-shots, bats, Barlow knives, and marbles, the same way some western saloons made cowboys check their guns.

Once or twice a year "Struttin' Bud" Davenport would stand in the doorway of the music store and hand out brass band harmonicas and jews'-harps to every kid who passed. The adults cussed him and said he was in league with Mr. Hill, the druggist, who sold a special brand of headache medicine, a powdery potion called "Surcease" which he and Tom Day made in the back end of the drug store.

There were always several kinds of pianos in stock at Mr. Hutchins's. I remember, distinctly, two models, both of which were popular in Oxford. One was the Beckwith Home Favorite and the other was the Beckwith Acme Cabinet Grand Concert Piano.

The Home Favorite retailed for about $175.00, and the Grand Concert sold for about $400.00. Ramsay Davis swore he could order the very same pianos from Sears and Roebuck for $69.00 and $166.00 each.

Mr. Hutchins said that was an infernal lie. He added: "A man who'd lie about a piano would lie about his mother." And he pointed out that even if what Ramsay Davis said was true, Sears and Roebuck didn't sell stuff on time, not even false teeth to folks who were half-dead from malnutrition.

He was right. Most local people bought pianos, and other expensive items, on time. The interest rate was always six percent, but the carrying charges varied. Whatever it was people bought, they usually paid double the list-price, or more, when they made their last "time" payment.

We had a Beckwith Home Favorite. Papa and I hated it, out loud, and I don't think Mother loved the piano, even if she smiled while Sister practiced her various "concert pieces" for Miss Birdie's various "graduation programs."

I don't know how long Sister took music under Miss Birdie; but if she ever got beyond "The Joyous Farmer" and "Narcissus," I can't remember. Sister would tune up, generally, right after supper when Papa was reading the paper. In a few minutes his hands shook so much he got the whole newspaper all scrambled up.

He'd sling the crumpled paper down and stomp out, saying over his shoulder: "The elephant that died to furnish those ivory keys really made the supreme sacrifice, and all in vain, by God."

Women, especially from out in the county, were always coming to the music store to try out the various organs. Some wanted organs for home use, but others were appointed to learn the organ so that a country church could have one for its various services.

I used to fool around the music store a lot, taking care not to over-stay my leave, and I remember the Golden Parlor Organ. It cost about $60.00, or $19.00 at Sears and Roebuck, according to Ramsay Davis. But one of Mr. Hutchins's organs was really awesome. This was "The Imperial Grand Organ, Action D, Six Octaves," and it cost about $200.00.

I never knew what all that meant, particularly the "Action D, Six Octaves" part, but I learned it by heart, and I used to say it, "The Imperial Grand Organ, Action D, Six Octaves," over and over whenever I was having a tooth filled. I don't know if our dentist, Dr. Ambrose, thought novocaine was sissy, or whether he just didn't have any.

"Folding organs" were sold for use in school rooms, homes, and to evangelists. I think the folding organ was a real asset to the itinerant preacher, especially if he had a girl to play it. If a "floating" preacher started bellowing on a street corner, with no music except a tambourine, he never attracted what Papa called the "sophisticated red-necks." But if an organ was whumping away, a street corner evangelist not only lured a standing crowd. People leaned out of second-story windows to hear the music. The preacher might crack himself up as a "po, feeble servunt of de Lawd's," but the way many caught change tossed from second-story windows made me think the preacher was Tris Speaker, without spikes.

Those folding organs weighed about 30 pounds, and they sold for around $40.00. Ramsay Davis said, for once, "Piano" Hutchins's price wasn't much above Sears and Roebuck, but the difference was that the mail-order house threw in the stool and you had to buy the stool at the music store.

When Ramsay Davis talked about the difference in Sears'

price and local price, people assumed he was getting ready to run for the state legislature. People were sure of his intentions when he made a stir about the organ stools. He explained that the stools were supposed to go with the organs the same way a merchant gave a nice tie when you bought a new suit, the way stores gave shoe-strings to regular customers, and the way the hide went with the meat when you bought a steer.

When Ramsay Davis announced formally, for the General Assembly, he bought a folding organ and a stool. But I think the purchase was made through Hughie and Hector Scott. I don't think Mr. Hutchins would have sold Ramsay a folding organ, for fear he'd aid Ramsay's campaign.

Ramsay put the organ on the back of a truck when he went around holding rallies. The identical Scott twins took turns dancing and playing the organ. They were great clog-dancers, but neither ever mastered the organ, although you could tell "Didn't He Ramble" from "Wait Till the Sun-shines Nellie."

Some of the rallies were first-rate. Ramsay Davis would push one of the Scott twins off the stool and explain that was how he would dethrone Squire Moorefield, our long-time incumbent legislator.

The whole campaign blew up one day, though, at a rally out at Sassafras Fork. Mr. Hutchins came with Sheriff Matt Venable and claim and delivery papers to get the organ, and the stool, too.

Ramsay Davis hollered "foul" all over the rally. He swore he had given one of the Scott twins the full amount for the folding organ, and two or three dollars for the stool, whatever it cost. But Mr. Hutchins had his books and a copy of a receipt that showed only $18.00 had been paid. Mr. Hutchins and the Sheriff got to the rally at a terrible time. Shortly before this rally had commenced, Just Plain Snake Imboden had come by with a two-horse wagon load of "A-Number-One Corn Whiskey," in mason jars. When Mr. Hutchins and the Sheriff arrived, everyone was singing, dancing, and whooping it up.

Mr. Hutchins and the Sheriff were in a devil of a row of mean stumps. The Sheriff didn't want to seize the organ and make the voters mad. Mr. Hutchins didn't want to offend any customers, but he couldn't afford to let Ramsay Davis abuse him and get away with larceny, too.

About this time, Mr. Ed Settle came along in his tremendous buggy. He said he heard the music and singing a mile away. So, he paid off the balance owed to Mr. Hutchins.

The rally, as a political rally, ended, and so did Ramsay Davis's campaign for high office, but the fun went on until after dark.

That same night Mr. Ed Settle made a present of the organ to a young lady by the name of Hazel Fremont, who had taken piano lessons in Oxford under Miss Birdie.

She took the folding organ to her father's home, which was next to a grist mill he ran on the Sassafras River. Soon people started coming to hear Hazel play. Sunday afternoon became a regular concert time throughout the community. In pretty weather folks came in wagons, buggies, in cars, and afoot to sit in the yard as Hazel played the folding organ. If the weather was raw, the happy crowd filled the home and the grist mill.

Two or three years later a good bridge was built across the river, at the site of the grist mill, to replace the ford. The road was broadened and improved. Three stores, a post office, a garage, and a grammar school sprang up. By unanimous vote, the new village, the post office, was named "Folding Organ." It was so listed in the postal guide for twenty-five or thirty years, until the post office and the school were consolidated with the slightly bigger ones at Sassafras Fork, proper.

There's nothing left there now but the name. It is a name without any place. But it's hard as hell for me to explain to new people and new tycoons in Oxford all the details that led to the official naming of Folding Organ.

Mr. Hutchins always kept a stock of harmonicas, accordions, trombones, cornets, drums, guitars, mandolins, and banjos. Ukuleles were popular with courting boys, "cake eaters," as such sports were called. I remember young men, in sailor hats, striped jackets and white ducks, playing "Supertone Ukuleles" and "Banjo Ukes" to their lady-loves. Indeed, I grew up to become one of the alumni.

Not many violins were sold. I suppose anything that was hard to master was called "sissy" or "show-off." Nonetheless, a few kids and adults had violins, usually Mr. Hutchins's "Our Stradivarius Model." It cost about $8.50. You could get "Benjamin's Illustrated Violin Method," a booklet of instructions, for 75 cents.

Boot Ransome and P. A. Duncan were the best violinists in town, but neither ever played at the "Musicales" staged intermittently, always for some good cause, at the Opera House.

P. A. played the violin solely "to loaf and invite her soul," or so she said. Sometimes, in fair weather, I could hear her playing for her mother, Miss Texanna, in the Duncan's parlor. I thought she did a fine job on "The Flight of the Bumblebee," but she usually ended up by sort of making a parody of her own fast playing. She'd quit before the end and switch to Gottchalk's "Bamboula."

Boot did all of his playing in a chair in front of his blacksmith shop after supper. He'd play awhile and water his flowers awhile. I always got the notion he was serenading the flowers. He played by ear ("Main strength and awkwardness" were his phrase for it), but his hands seemed to be free, easy, and comfortable. He never played the fast music P. A. Duncan played.

He played the "Serenade," by Franz Schubert, "To A Wild Rose," and two that Sidney Lanier wrote for the flute, I think. These were "Little Ella" and "Swamp Robins."

If anyone said anything to Mr. Ransome, or requested a tune, he'd put his violin inside the dwelling portion of his forge and start watering his flowers. Sometimes Papa called him "Fritz," after the great Austrian violinist, Fritz Kreisler. Mr. Ransome always smiled, just enough so it could be called smile. Then he'd nod, to let Papa know that he knew, that he was pleased.

Members of the "Silver Cornet Band" came into the music store frequently to see about new instruments. Frequently several would be tooting at one time, but not necessarily the same tune or march. Papa wasn't stuck on the Bible, but he said anyone who didn't believe in the story of the Tower of Babel should stand in front of the music store when seven or eight of the "Silver Cornets" were trying out something inside.

I used to run errands for Mr. Hutchins, when I wasn't playing games or delivering stuff for the "Ivanhoe." His pay was damned poor compared to Mr. Hasbrook's who let me graze freely on the candy in the "Ivanhoe." Mr. Hutchins paid me with stamps. I didn't write many letters. I could sell the stamps to Papa or trade them at some of the local stores. The trouble was the stamps usually got all stuck up. I think five two-cent stamps is the most I ever got for helping Mr. Hutchins.

But I accomplished something, just the same. I learned to play two tunes on the piano pretty well. But I didn't learn these tunes on the piano. No, I learned to play "O, You Beautiful Doll" and "Old Folks at Home" by putting my fingers on the key-board of a self-player. I always "played along" with the pianola standing up, and that's the only way I could translate the tunes to the piano.

I never had the slightest notion of one key or note from another. Mine was purely a mechanical performance. But I liked to sneak in my trick at some party or sociable.

There was an advertisement that said: "They all laughed when I sat down to play the piano." It didn't mean some clown jerked the stool out as one was about to sit down. It meant that the person about to sit had mastered the piano, by mail-order lessons, and no one knew it but him or her. One might say, "They all laughed when I stood up at the piano."

Of course, if no one confused me with Miss Birdie or Paderewski, I could get through "O, You Beautiful Doll" and "Old Folks At Home" without having to skip very much of either.

I can still do that today, and my grown children refer to me as "The coolest vertical piano player extant." Albeit, they are sufficiently thoughtful not to add that my extensive repertoire consists of only two numbers.

As I have suggested, Mr. Hutchins was so thin his body seemed to be a hinge swinging from his head. I always had a notion he subsisted on a diet of green lizards. The biggest thing about him was his Adam's apple. If his throat had been cut there would have been enough seeds to reproduce the apple orchards in the Valley of Virginia.

Mrs. Hutchins was big enough to pick up a piano, but she too was flabby. She had three bellies − distinct ones. Her bellies connected the way Germany, France, and Austria-Hungary were lined up on the old maps of Europe.

Her given name was "Lovelace," and Mr. Hutchins called

her "Love." I suppose they were in their early fifties, at that time. They had no children. As she put it: "The Lord has not seen fit to bless us with a child." Whenever she said these words, she shook her fat head. Her huge jowls made joggling sounds. She cocked one eye towards heaven, as if she were reminding God that He was remiss.

Mr. Matson rejoined: "Gawd, the dog's hind foot. It ain't Him." It's her. Old Piany can't get toe the real place fer them acres a fat wrinkles. I don't think Piany knows it, but you can't get no wrinkle pregnant."

She was the only lady I remember who wore a hat all of the time, and the hat was practically nailed to her hair with long hatpins, and once at a funeral she cut Tom Sampson, the shoe-shop man, so severely on his face Dr. Henley had to put in two stitches. For a petrified fact, that happened, and some other men were really lacerated by hatpins worn by other women.

(The town board passed an ordinance prohibiting the wearing of any hatpin that protruded more than half-an-inch, but I don't think either of the local policemen ever actually measured any protruding hatpins.

(All the women's organizations in town said the hat-pin ordinance was an evil ruse perpetrated to harass and to subjugate their sex. There was a day-long demonstration in front of city hall, although "the town office" was the local phrase at that time.

(P. A. Duncan and Mrs. Ashton-Brown held a big sign, one painted by Baldy Moore, that screamed, in red letters, "Clean Up City Hall." This prompted several local men to ask what had happened to Skid Mayo, the janitor who cleaned and dusted the town office? There was even a report that Skid had been fired. This false rumor produced considerable consternation among his many creditors, of whom Just Plain Snake Imboden was chief.

(There were several tempestuous speeches. In the best, or the most vindicative, P. A. promised there would be a woman candidate for town commissioner in the next city election.

(Papa told Mrs. Ashton-Brown that there were several legal precedents: "Good madame, the whole damned state of New Jersey passed the same hat-pin law in 1913." Mrs. Ashton-Brown replied: "Huh, New Jersey wouldn't have passed that heinous law if Woodrow Wilson had still been governor."

(Papa bowed, in mock defeat. But as we walked on, he assured me that Wilson, of all men, was anti-long-hat-pin. I asked how come, and Papa said I'd know when I learned more about Wilson's private life.

(The hat-pin ordinance was not rescinded. Indeed, it is still on the town books, but no one tried to enforce it. It was a limbo law, the same as Prohibition, and the one that forbade spitting on the sidewalk. Of course, emitting plain saliva was vulgar, but spitting tobacco juice was so tied to local economy it was an act of patriotism, virtually.)

A customer had to go directly to Mrs. Hutchins's chair with whatever it was he had purchased. She took the money and put it in a cash-drawer in a desk beside her large rocking-chair.

Day after day Mrs. Hutchins sat in her rocking-chair listening to "soulful" records, such as "Silver Threads Among the Gold," "When You and I Were Young Maggie," "The Little Lost Child," and "In the Baggage Car Ahead."

As Mrs. Hutchins listened to her daily concerts, she usually read from Eugene Field's book of poems, *With Trumpet and Drum*. (Papa said .this book was published in 1892, but fortunately, not on the same day that Lord Tennyson died and the Daltons got killed in Coffeeville,

Kansas.)

Her lips moved as she read, but the words didn't slip out. Her lips were the saddest I ever saw. They moved as if they were toting graveyards, or mill-stones, anyway. I really think she knew most of the poems by heart. Actually, most of the print, on many pages, had gone with the bloom of the roses that flourished in 1892. Mrs. "Piano" Hutchins's tears, across the years, had washed out whole lines, the way the Johnstown's Flood washed away the dam and the city.

But I could tell when she reached the part in "Little Boy Blue" that said:

Oh! the years are many, the years are long,
But the little toy friends are true!

At this juncture her lips stiffened into a wet sort of lady-like militance, and through her watery eyes I could see the same staunch fidelity that galvanized the local Confederate veterans when someone mentioned the name of Robert E. Lee.

I don't think she ever read "Jess Afore Christmas." Maybe, that poem was too happy, too mischievous. Anyway, no one died in it. I thumbed through her book several times when Mrs. Hutchins was at funerals. The pages with "Jess Afore Christmas" and "Seein' Things" were almost drought-stricken, certainly compared to those poems that were all swamp, except for the absence of alligators and moonshine stills.

Mr. Matson and the "Ivanhoe" crowd were chortling, constantly, over "When Willie Wet the Bed," the poem of Eugene Field's that was circulated around the United States surreptitiously, for so long.

Mr. Hutchins, "Old Piany," as Mr. Matson called him, was horrified at the egregious offense to his wife and to the late poet, Eugene Field. He wanted to institute suit for slander, or libel, perhaps. Papa told him one can't libel a dead man, especially Eugene Field. Papa explained that if this weren't true then people couldn't walk around with immunity and call General Sherman a son-of-a-bitch. If the dead were susceptible to libel, Papa went on, folks couldn't call Mr. Carter, the liver pill man, a gut-busting bastard everytime his hell-fired medicine acted.

Mr. Hutchins consulted every lawyer in town trying vainly to get an injunction, or a writ of mandamus, to shut up old Ollie Matson's evil mouth.

The Ladies' Cultural and Improvement Society joined the fight to save Eugene Field from soul slander, although they were always poised to attack anything connected with the sorry-looking "Ivanhoe." But the women only made bawdy matters worse because Mr. Matson ascribed every smutty ditty he knew to Eugene Field, deceased.

He said Field wrote the old excessively raunchy ballad about the discovery of America. The opening stanza is as benign as a water-lily in comparison to the ensuing stanzas:

In fourteen hundred and ninety-two
A Dago from Italie,
Walked up and down the streets of Spain
Selling 'hot-cha-mallie.'
He walked up to Queen of Spain,
Demanded ships and cargo,
And swore he was a son of a bitch
If he didn't discover Chicago.

(Today on television Flip Wilson has a ludicrous skit about Columbus's coming to America to discover Ray Charles.)

"Brer" Thompson interrupted one anti-Matson protest to

tell how a misplaced comma had changed the entire meaning of one of our oldest, most cherished carols. He said most of us sang, "God rest you, merry gentlemen" with the comma after gentlemen. Obviously, the comma follows "merry." The line means, "God keep you happy, gentlemen."

This diversion caused Mr. Hutchins to call off his dogs. Mr. Matson found others to molest and Mrs. Hutchins cried without harassment.

"Silver Threads Among the Gold" and "When You and I Were Young Maggie" really turned Mrs. Hutchins on, but for the precise mood-music she seemed to attain consummate projection from "Little Lost Child" and "In the Baggage Car Ahead." The "Little Lost Child" is supposed to be the first song ever illustrated by lantern slides. A story-song, it tells, in less than a hundred words, how a big city policeman finds a lost child who turns out to be his very own. Sometimes, Mrs. Hutchins played this record straight through as many as ten times in a row.

But when the happy ending came, in such a tragic manner, she always threw out her enormous chest the way I imagined Bob Fitzsimmons must have done when he knocked out Jim Corbett with the famous "Solar-plexus" punch.

A pass-ing po-lice-man found a little child,
She walked be-side him, dried her tears and smiled —
Said he to her kindly, 'Now you must not cry,
I will find your ma-ma for you bye-bye.

At the sta-tion when he, asked for her name,
And she an-swered 'Jennie,' it made him exclaim:
'At last of your moth-er I have now a trace;
Your lit-tle features bring back her sweet face.

*'Do not fear my lit-tle darling, I will take you
right home;
Come sit down close be-side me, no more from me
to roam.
For you were a babe in arms when your mother left
one day,
Left me at home, de-serted, and took you my child
a-way.'*

"In the Baggage Car Ahead" was as sad as an insolvent
widow, with six children, who has been conned into an
expensive funeral and who has just learned her husband's
life insurance has lapsed. But it did have a herky-jerky gait
to it, a swing that suggested the rocking poetry of a big
train plunging through the night.

Mrs. Hutchins cried throughout the playing of this record, and she laid her book of poems in her ample lap. She
held onto the sides of her chair as if she were seated on the
train and the road was as curvy as a crooked dice game.

*On a dark storm-y night, as the train rattled on,
all the passengers had gone to bed,
Except one young man with a babe in his arms
who sat there with a bowed down head;
The innocent one began crying just then,
as though its heart would break, –
One angry man said, 'Make that child stop its noise,
for it is keeping all us a-wake.'*

*'Put it out,' said another, 'Don't keep it in here,
for we've paid for our berths and want rest.'
But nev-er a word said the man with the child,
as he fondled it to his breast.
'Where is the child's mother? Take it to her.'-
this a lady soft-ly said;*

288

'I wish that I could,' was the man's re-ply,
But she's dead in the coach ahead.

Mr. Hutchins seemed to be almost oblivious of his wife's daily concerts. Normally, he stood in the front of the store, with his thumbs hitched to each side of his vest, his derby hat jammed tightly on his head. People in town swore old "Piano" wore his derby in the bath tub. But I really don't know because I never saw him take a bath.

When a lady-customer came in, he swept the floor with his derby. This was always a grandiose gesture. Mr. Hutchins never fumbled, never flubbed his dub, but he didn't smile or say bright words, and his great sweeping movement always reminded me much more of a wind-up toy than it did of some Chesterfield.

He wore celluloid collars and cuffs. He put on new collars frequently in hot weather. As I recall, these celluloid collars cost a penny a piece, and the cuffs were two for a cent.

(All the drummers who traveled the gritty trains wore celluloid collars and cuffs. When they were dirty, they were thrown away. They were hardly ever washed.)

Mr. Hutchins changed left cuffs fairly often during his busy times, especially on Saturdays. He wrote notes, memos, and assorted business items on his left cuff. And when he was busy, he used his left cuff as a temporary ledger on which to enter a charge account. When a cuff was written up, Mr. Hutchins put it on his desk, in the back of the store.

On a busy Saturday he might write up a dozen cuffs, or more. After closing time he straightened out the cuffs and copied the memos in his account books.

As I said, women from the country came in frequently to try out an organ. There must have been exceptions, but

I remember each one as beginning, always timorously, with "Jesus Loves Me." She played this opening practice hymn as if she were milking a cow with terribly sore teats and didn't want to inflict pain. But she gained agility, if not artistry, with confidence. By the time she got to "Come Thou Fount Of Every Blessing," her fingers hit the keys as if she were douzing for water during an insufferable drought.

She — whoever the country woman was — always hummed along with her own playing, but when she got to "The Little Brown Church In The Wildwood," she sang loudly, with obvious feeling.

A few people along the street joined in, invariably, especially on the part that says: "Oh, come, come, come to the church in the Wild-wood." Within a few minutes other people along the street started singing harmony, almost unconsciously. Some boomed out those clarion "Come, comes," as others, simultaneously, trilled, "Ohoooo, come, to the che-erch in the va-le-ah."

The fence-rattling crescendo was reached with "Leaning On the Ever-Lasting Arms." From the full-throated, open-mouthed way the organist sang this song, it was hard for me to tell if she was playing for her singing, or singing for her playing.

When she reached this dramatic apogee, she indulged in the unbound freedom of a few runs on the keys. She did her runs the way I thought a boy courting a girl might fool until he got down to serious, or highly pleasant, business. Down to "the nitty-gritty" was unknown, but "down to head-taw" conveyed the central idea.

While the embryo organist was getting the feel of the instrument, Mr. Hutchins fooled around with his feather-duster, brushing his furniture and his stock of goods. There were six or eight fly-stickers dangling around, like bespeckled participles, and he gave each one minute scrutiny.

I always had the impression he was counting the dead flies to determine how much space remained to catch still others. These fly-stickers were manufactured, somewhere, by someone named P. G. Gulley. A portion of the center-field fence at the baseball park was painted with a big yellow advertizement sign:

"Last Summer Goose Goslin Caught 478 Flies
P. G. Gulley's Magic Stickers Caught Eleven Million"

Goose Goslin, now in the Hall of Fame, was a great left-fielder for the Senators and then the Tigers. It was easy to total the number of flies he caught, but I was never sure just how the ubiquituous but mysterious Mr. P. G. Gulley went about the matter of counting the dead flies on his stickers.

But when the country lady got to "Leaning On the Ever-Lasting Arms," Mr. Hutchins sidled up to the organ. He took off his derby, put it, crown up, in the crook of his left arm, as the fingers on his right hand reached over to caress the felt crown.

He joined in the singing. His voice, as deep as a well, shot off baby-wakers as his fingers caressed the top of his derby. This caressing gesture always struck me as being almost surreptitious, if not downright clandestine. I got the distinct impression that some wisenheimer was trying to feel up a girl, maybe in church.

People walking along College Street hummed, whistled, and sang along with the country organist and Mr. Hutchins:

What ta fel-low-ship, what ta joy de-vine,
Lean-ing on the ever-last-ting arms.

291

I suppose I thought "Leaning On the Ever-Lasting Arms" was a local hymn. Some years later when I was on a crowded troop-train, during World War II, a boy from California played the song on a concertina. The concertina resembled one of the ones Mr. Hutchins kept in stock, and I was really surprised at how many of the G. I.'s knew the words to the hymn. I looked all around the day-coach, half-expecting to see "Old Piano," half-expecting to see some fly-stickers dangling down. I really wished I were back in Oxford. Nay more, at this safe distance I'll admit I wished I had been born a baby girl.

In pretty weather people might gather around the front of the music store when Mr. Hutchins put old roles such as "Too Much Mustard" or "Waiting For the Robert E. Lee" on an "advertizing" pianola. When the crowd got to as many as eight or ten, Mr. Hutchins continued his "free concert" with "Alexander's Ragtime Band" and "At a Georgia Camp Meeting."

We had several excellent clog dancers in and around Oxford. These clog, or buck dancers, danced, generally, the soft shoe patterns that are associated with Ray Bolger.

If two of our local champions happened along, they were certain to start dancing towards each other. There was never any prompting. This happened the way a spring rain came, when it was needed. Other folks along the sidewalk made a big circle. The folks in the circle egged the dancers on by whistling, by shouting, "Give us some rag," by patting their feet, and by clapping their hands.

This head-to-head dancing was a sort of shoot-out, done with feet, hips, and shoulders in lieu of six guns. The object was for one man to dance the other fellow "down," by dint of stamina, dexterity, ingenuity, and improvisation.

Frequently the contest ended in a glorious draw, by tacit agreement. Often when the pianola played "At a

Georgia Camp-Meeting," the two friendly competitors joined arms to sashshay up and down the sidewalk in a high-spirited, high-kicking cake-walk.

The best dancers I ever saw, as a boy, were Eddie Foy and George Cohan, whom Papa took me to see, our own High Sheriff Matt Venable, and our identical twins, Hughie and Hector Scott. But the Scott twins, as I said, played at farming out in the country, and many times they weren't around for spontaneous dance-outs and sidewalk cake-walks.

Two crackerjack dancers were Lum Beckwith, a house painter, who always wore white overalls, winter and summer, and Tom Sampson, the shoemaker. Sometimes Tom forgot to remove his work apron, and when he started kicking high it almost looked as if a woman were kicking from a skirt shorter than any that had ever been seen in Oxford.

I remember several times when the pianolas were irresistible magnets Tom left customers in his shop in their sock feet. But the customers understood that this music was the same to Tom that the fire bell had been to those splendid horses, Matt and Bertha.

There were times, however, when Tom tossed off his apron as he came running from his shop. It went sailing into the air and people grabbed it the way women grabbed at a bride's bouquet.

I've been lucky enough to travel around, to see many wonders, but I've never seen a sight grander than Lum, Tom, and the High Sheriff dancing the cake-walk along that sidewalk.

I guess the Sheriff was in his fifties, but he was the sort of man who could dance all night and go straight to fox-hunting, to chasing hounds, the whole next day. (We still eschew horses in our local fox-hunting.) The Sheriff could clog, round, and square dance to beat the band. I guess he really wasn't as good as Gene Kelly, but he had the same loose-limbed grace, ease, poise, and confidence.

He wore blue suits the year around, and he sent off to Baltimore for the sort of frilly white shirts he wore each day of the week. as well as on Sunday. He always wore a black shoe-string tie, and a big black John D. Stetson hat with a narrow band. When the dancing started up in from old "Piano" Hutchins's place, the Sheriff tossed his hat in the air. If a boy happened to catch it — and I know that I did, at least twice — why he felt as if Babe Ruth had let him use his bat.

Apparently no one saw anything incongruous when the Sheriff and Lum Beckwith danced together, but they reminded me of a blackbird and a dove flying in unison.

Lum always got drunk on Saturday when he got his money from his house-painting jobs. When the booze really hit him, he always did one of two things: He was all of the Daltons raiding Coffeeville, Kansas, only Coffeeville was the "Ivanhoe." Or, he made water against a tree or a power pole.

So, the Sheriff had to put Lum in jail virtually every Saturday. But this didn't affect their relationship one whit. No, if the Sheriff had other pressing duties, he motioned Lum on towards the jail. Many times I saw Lum Beckwith stumbling on to the jail. He'd flop down on the stone steps, like a fallen omelet, and wait for the Sheriff to come on down to open the big iron door.

If the weather was cold or wet, when the Sheriff was busy, he'd throw the jail keys to Lum. Sometimes, Lum couldn't get the door open, but someone usually came along to help him get inside. I remember once he called me. I didn't slam the big door after Lum Beckwith stumbled inside. He yelled: "You dough know no more bout bein' a damn jailer than Judge Washingtonmachine knew bout a Tin Lizzy." Everytime I saw him for the next six months he'd say: "Boy, you better stiddy fer a 'fession. You'd starve trying to be a jailer."

This wasn't a bad deal for Lum. The jail was warm enough in winter, near the big stove, and Lum always took the cell by the stove, even if he had to run some bona fide prisoner to another place. In summer the jail was the coolest place in town and Lum got to use the county's pump, soap, and towel, for free. And the meals the Sheriff brought from Greeley's cafe were the most sumptuous served this side of Rector's.

I remember a professional hobo called the "Arkansas Traveler." He was sort of Duncan Hines on jails. The *Torchlight* said this man held the world's record for getting locked up, overnight, in the most jails. In one of these pieces on the cuisine and sleeping quarters of American jails, he practically embalmed our hoosegow with accolades. His statement in the *Torchlight* said: "Take it from a proper connoisseur. There isn't a place between Miami and Boston, or between Baltimore and San Francisco, that is as free of bugs and serves such delicious fare as the nifty emporium presided over by my friend, Sheriff Matt Venable, a true gentleman and a scholar, in Oxford."

Singularly enough, old Lum Beckwith is the only person, the only one whom I remember, anyway, who had to be let out of jail for being a public nuisance.

He liked to sing. His piece de resistance was "The Wreck Of Old Number 97." He sang as if his whole body had been stuffed with strips of paper. If the nuance is elusive, many old-time piano players, and even such successful composers as Harry Von Tilzer, used to stuff an upright piano with strips of paper to produce that amazingly tinny effect they wanted in their music.

295

Lum sang the same way. A lot of the members of the Improvement Society said Lum's singing frightened them. At that, it wasn't hard for me to imagine that I was about to be in a terrible train wreck, when I heard Lum sing. He could do the sounds of a train whistle and bell almost precisely, and he gave these sounds an active sense of imminent doom.

He blew the whistle and rang the bell at the end of every line in the song, and he kept on whistling — "woe-woe" — and ringing the bell with tumultous "ding-dongs," for five minutes after he had sung the last line:

He was found in the wreck with his hand on the thro-tle,
And he was scald-ed to death with st-eam.

When the singing frightened, or upset, people, the Sheriff rode Lum out into the country, eight or ten miles. He'd put Lum out and let him whistle and ring his head off on the walk back to town.

It isn't hard for me to conjure up Lum Beckwith and his wild shenanigans today because "The Wreck Of the Old 97" is "in" bigger than a banana in a hummingbird's mouth for those for whom the guitar is a sort of musical Sinai. Indeed, some of the more pollinated flower-children seem to think this is either a brand-new ballad or an old one that was so obscure it is just now getting up a full head of steam.

The lyrics, prompted by the wreck of a mail train near Danville, Virginia, in 1903, never have been credited to any writer. When the tune was put on a record — it was one of Victor's earliest — it sold more than a million discs. At this time, many Virginians claimed authorship of the lyrics, and several went to court, abortively.

The thing that amuses me is this: Virginians have always

296

thought of "The Wreck Of the Old 97" as "our song." Papa told me, when I was a boy, that the words were put to the music of an old ballad by Henry Clay Work, one called "The Ship That Never Returned." Apparently, the Virginians still don't know what their tune was written by an abolitionist. Papa said Work was imprisoned in 1845 for helping slaves to escape. His peculiar piety was expressed in the amazingly popular song, "We Are Coming Sister Mary," which had a ribald parody in Oxford among the devotees of the sporting-house of Miss Opal's place.

Too, Work celebrated Sherman's junket to the sea with a ditty called "Marching Through Georgia." If the Virginians have never known this, it must be poetic restitution that "The Wreck Of the Old 97" is now sung by youthful liberators who never heard of Henry Clay Work, either.

Oxford, October 10, 1970

There is considerable talk in Oxford today relative to building a mall. Indeed, mall-talk and mall-plans have become a sort of benign epidemic all around.

Perhaps, it took the obiquituous doom of the H-Bomb and the horrors of pollution to instill within us a desire to sit and to stare, to loaf and to invite the soul, to commune with nature while nature is still with us.

Actually, we had a Town Commons in Oxford for about 160 years. The Commons grew to weeds during the Great Depression. By the time some semblance of financial stability returned, newer entertainments and diversions pointed away from the old Commons.

The Commons, itself, may have been a specific geographical fact before Oxford arose around it. Many old accounts tell of stopovers before Oxford sprang up in 1764.

William Byrd must have camped on the spot when he was surveying the boundary line between North Carolina and Virginia in 1729. Prior to the formation of Oxford there was a settlement called Bentonburg, or "Baynyton-burg," which consisted of a crude courthouse, St. George's Chapel, a Glebe house, a goal, a still-house, and ten or twelve shops and dwellings.

When Oxford took shape, the Commons was reserved for a picnic ground, a place for revivals, for dancing reels, and for holding the May Court. When I was a boy, it was still used as a place for genteel loafers, for sparkers, for band concerts, and for political meetings.

The Commons took in a fraction more than nine acres, most of which, up until the late 1920's, was grass, lovely and sparkling grass. There were five springs within the Commons, and all were set in good stones. (There was a legend that Spring No. 3 had aphrodisiac qualities. Some attributed this to limestone, but I suppose any sensual qualities really related to the location of Spring No. 3. It was located amid a magnificent boulevard of oak trees. Wild roses grew in profusion, and it was the favorite spot on the Commons for courting couples. Nonetheless, men drank copiously from Spring No. 3, walking past Spring No. 1 and Spring 2 to get to it. Indeed, several men in town took demijohns of water from Spring No. 3 to their homes, regularly.)

Here and there on the Commons were benches, picnic tables, tree swings, posts for horseshoes, and poles for ring-men, the game played with marbles that were almost as big as billiard balls. At the east end there was an acre or more on which the military and fire companies held their drills, and upon which kids played leap-frog, fox-in-the-wall, football, and baseball.

The biggest holly tree I ever saw in my life was at Spring No. 4, or "Miss Lucy's Looking-Glass." The name derived from Miss Lucy Cavendish, a beautiful young girl —

a sprite, a nymph — who came to the spring to look into the clear water to comb her long hair. My grandmother, who was born in 1855, told me that Miss Lucy was the prettiest girl she ever saw. Miss Lucy died when my grandmother was a small girl.

Today, the land once occupied by the old Commons is a new housing development, Foley Forest. Foley was the builder. I find "Forest" somewhat incongruous since the entire boulevard of oaks, and most of the other trees, were cut down to make room for the new houses.

Each of these houses looks precisely like the ones on either side of it. Each has the same kind of garage and driveway, and every TV antenna seems to be on the same place on every roof. I hope the thoughts of the occupants of these homes are not so uniform as the architecture, but I wouldn't take any bets.

Just this: In 1947 I was in Richmond, and I ran out of money. At that time credit-cards hadn't invaded Oxford. I went into a bank to try to get a check cashed. I told the gentleman who waited on me that he could call my bank in Oxford for verification.

He looked hard at me: "You're from Oxford?" I acknowledged the fact. "Where was the Commons?" I replied, "Along both sides of what is now Cooper Street, down what is now Belle Street, all of the high school football field . . ."

Here he interrupted me with a flourish of his hand: "How much money do you want, boy?"

The other day I mentioned Mrs. Piano Hutchins's addiction to funerals and to sad weddings, those weddings at which people counted on their fingers furtively but could not get from one to nine.

The return of Mrs. Hutchins from a rural funeral, late one afternoon, triggered, inadvertently, the biggest dance-

299

down I ever saw, as well as one of the biggest nights that ever occurred on the old Town Commons.

Although Mrs. Hutchins was not personally acquainted with the deceased, she had armed herself with copious handkerchiefs and she had ridden out to the funeral in the front seat of Mr. Thorne's hearse. Mr. Thorne always drove the Buick limousine in which the bereaved family traveled. (Mr. Thorne was the first man in Oxford to have a regular weekly program on the local radio station. Each Sunday "Thorne's Home for Exclusive Funerals" had a program from one o'clock to one-thirty. Recordings made by Guy Lombardo's orchestra were played continuously. At the outset the announcer said "Thorne's Home For Exclusive Funerals brings you Guy Lombardo and the 'Sweetest Music This Side of Heaven'.")

The hearse was always driven by Mr. Thorne's assistant, P. L. Carson, who was known as "Parlor Lizzard." A "parlor lizzard" was said to be handy with a girl on a settee in a parlor.

En route to Oxford, after this particular funeral, the hearse broke down. P. L. Carson couldn't get the hearse to budge. Finally, a farmer came along and saw an opportunity to be a Samaritan, or to pick up a couple of bucks.

He hitched a team of mules to the hearse, and the mules hauled the hearse, P. L. Carson, and Mrs. Hutchins back to Oxford. The farmer, who had to walk the whole distance, about seven miles, holding the lines, stopped his team in front of Hill's to get something to slake his thirst. About this time Mr. Sim Stickney, owner of our horse and mule business, the "Old Reliable Livery Stable," came along the street. Mr. Stickney explained later that he had an over-due mortgage on the two mules. When he saw the mules and the farmer, he ran across the street to the Sheriff's Office to get claim-and-delivery papers on the mules.

Mrs. Hutchins was subject to the vapors and to the dropsies, and she fainted, beside the hearse, when Mr. Stickney and Sheriff Mat Venable came running up. Three men were playing mumblety-peg on the courthouse lawn, and Old Man Rufe Duncan was kibitzing the game. When this group saw Mr. Stickney and the Sheriff running to the hearse, they ran to the hearse, too; and one man had in his hand the open knife with which the game of mumblety-peg was being played.

Miss Bertha Hornbuckle heard and saw all of the commotion from her perch on the third floor of Bengough's, in the central's office. By this time Mrs. Hutchins was flat on the street, with her head in the Sheriff's lap, and Mr. Hill was working on her with smelling salts. Miss Bertha saw all this, and she also saw a host of other people running towards the hearse. By this time Old Man Rufe was yelling: "Fire. Riot. Hell's a-popping."

Miss Bertha, puzzled, but not indecisive, called the fire company. (There was no 'phone in the armory, and no one was ever there except on drill nights.) Pete Wood sounded the alarm bell, started the American-LaFrance, and drove to the center of activity. He slowed the truck and started yelling: "Where's the fire? Where's the fire?"

No one answered, but Old Man Rufe pointed, vaguely, down Main Street. So Pete drove the fire truck down Main Street, and around the entire block, slowing down every fifteen or twenty yards to holler: "Does anyone know where the damn fire is at?"

Mrs. Ashton-Brown was crossing Main Street, at the post office, when Pete slowed there to inquire about the fire. Mrs. Ashton-Brown stationed herself in front of the fire truck, and, using her parasol for a pointer, lectured Pete on the gross inefficiency of the city government: "For the fire marshall not to know the location of a confragration is as puerile as a mother demanding someone tell her the identity of her only child."

But by this time several of the volunteer firemen had caught the truck. Some had put on their hats and raincoats, and the ax-men had taken their tools from the cases on the sides of the truck.

Around the corner from Hill's, the "Ivanhoe" crowd heard the noise and Old Man Rufe's shouts of "Riot, fire, and hell's a-popping." With perceptible cheer and optimism Mr. Matson asked his friends: "Do you spose somebody's robbed the bank?"

As Mr. Matson continued his gleeful speculation, he mentioned a previous daring day-light bank-robbery, the one attempted by the Daltons at Coffeeville, Kansas.

Ramsay Davis heard someone ask, "How much did the bank-robbers steal?" The President had gone home for the day, and Ramsay ran all the way to Spottswood Street to tell him about the "robbery."

In a few minutes the President came charging up Main Street in his Oldsmobile, although there was nothing merry about it or him at the moment. Ramsay was standing on the running-board as if he were riding shot-gun, or as if he were a Secret Service agent guarding the President in Washington.

I guess the President was relieved to learn that the bank hadn't been robbed, but he really glared at Ramsay Davis. Tom Sampson looked at Ramsay. Tom shook his head and said: "That boy's interest rate just went up to twenty per cent."

The President stood, with his hands on his hips, glaring at Ramsey as if the aborted hero were a zoo. The President looked at Ramsay as if he were visiting the penitentiary, the state lunatic asylum, or the state legislature.

Poor Ramsay looked as if he had discovered America in 1493 or as if he had set a new hop-Scotch record the same day Lindbergh soloed to Paris.

I am reasonably sure that virtually all the "through" passengers on the "foah somep'n train" — the one that was due at four-fifteen, but you knew the hour was past five when you heard it bonging at the depot — got off to see what was going on in Oxford.

I saw Captain Elrod, the conductor, Jim Dean, the engineer, Sim Bullock, the fireman, and one of the brakeman up town.

It was summer when this happened, and some folks were getting ready to eat supper. Some housewives were cooking supper, if few people ate supper at home that afternoon; but several came running to the center of the excitement eating corn-on-the-cob, peach flapjacks, chicken legs, or pieces of fried fish.

Many mothers chased their children up town, and a few children chased after their mothers. Some fathers carried small children on their shoulders, and several women took seats on the iron benches in front of the courthouse, or on the wooden benches in front of some of the stores, to breast-feed infants.

Of course, Mrs. Hutchins had revived by the time the excitement galvanized and preempted the town. She was back at the music store in her huge rocking-chair reading Eugene Field, still wearing her big hat with the lethal pins.

When there were about two hundred adults and kids in the center of town, Mrs. Hutchins, her face red with tears from her tryst with Eugene Field, ambled out as fast as she could put one fat, flabby leg in front of the other, to see what the commotion was all about.

On those rare occasions when Mrs. Hutchins tried to move rapidly, she reminded me of a she-elephant trying out roller-skates for the very first time. People saw her tears, and they assumed she was integral in some calamity or tragedy.

Pete Wood, finally convinced there was no fire, drove the truck back to the fire house. The volunteer fireman rolled out a charred keg of the confiscated whiskey which Matt Venable provided to keep them from catching pneumonia.

They gave Old Man Rufe a pint on the condition that he would forego making a speech about William Jennings Bryan. In lieu of the eulogy to Bryan, Old Man Rufe denounced pints as a means of measurement. "The clumbsiest, most irritatingest thing the devil ever made. A pint's a leetle toe much fer one drink an ain't enuff fer two drinks."

After a couple of rounds of the white mule, all the volunteer firemen and Old Man Rufe went back up the street. The President had parked his Oldsmobile in front of the bank, but when he returned from investigating inside, he couldn't move his car, for the crowd that had spilled over from Main to College Street.

He honked his horn over and over, as he muttered imprecations about people who would have to renew notes, about smart-alecks who loitered in the street who would be needing money for this or that, by God.

The President's threats put a damper on some folks, for a minute or two, but Mr. Matson, who had pushed out into the middle of College Street, broke the semi-quiet with an "off-hand" statement that was actually a studied question: "Wonder how come they putt the burglar alarm outside the damn bank instid of inside the bank?"

At the apogee of the excitement Sheriff Venable had climbed atop the hearse to holler through his cupped hands: "There's no fire! There's no riot!" Apparently, a great many people heard him say, "There's fire; there's riot; but didn't hear the "no." I suppose they heard what their emotions expected them to hear. Anyway, many folks took Sheriff Venable's announcement as official confirmation of mayhem and disaster.

In consequence of this terrible misunderstanding and the attending consternation, the Sheriff climbed to the highest point in town, to the central's office. On the College Street side there was a tiny piazza, surrounded by Charlestonian grill-work. Sometimes Miss Bertha hung things on the grill-work to dry. The Sheriff stood there and fired his .38 calibre Colt revolver three or four times to get the crowd's attention. Naturally, many people down on the street thought the Sheriff was firing at the bank-robbers.

He loaded his revolver and he fired several shots against the town water tank, which stood in the alley behind the bank. The plinging repercussions got the crowd's attention. When they were quiet, the Sheriff bellowed: "There's no damn fire or robbery or anything. So, go on home. Of course, if you want to stay up town and have a good time, why go ahead, but just don't break anything."

As soon as the Sheriff had spoken, Mr. Hutchins put "By the Sea" on a pianola. The music came pouring through the loud-speaker out onto the street. Then he put on "Rufus Rastus Johnson Brown" ("Whatcha gonna do when the rent comes round?"), and "The Band Played On."

While the Sheriff was coming down from the central's office, the music had the crowd perking like a pot of coffee coming to the boiling point. Some man hollered, "Less have some dainsing." Someone else yelled back, "Yes, less us do have some dainsing."

By the time the Sheriff had climbed down to College Street, the crowd had begun to form a huge circle, the same way the wagons circled up for Indian attacks in the movies. Three or four men formed an impromptu welcoming committee for the Sheriff. They ran over in front of Bengough's to escort the Sheriff into the center of College Street, into the middle of the ring. The circle was at least four folks deep all around. The ones at the front of the circle squatted, hunkered down. The next line sort of sagged. The next line peeped over the shoulders of the sagging line. The fourth line, in some spots it was the fifth or sixth, stood on the curb. Many of the men on the curb held children on their shoulders.

Mr. Ed Settle's enormous buggy was in the middle of the street. A couple of children sat on the horse, and at least half a dozen others were squatting and standing in front and in back of Mr. Settle in the buggy.

Boys and agile young men climbed the oak and elm trees that lined both sides of College Street, and five or six boys climbed on top of the President's Oldsmobile, for a box seat. The President shouted blasphemous threats, but the boys pretended not to hear him.

The escort-committee ushered the Sheriff into the center of the ring. "Bill Bailey" was running up and down the street and through the crowd with the majestic power of Man O' War in his prime. The Sheriff pitched his coat to the crowd, as Lum Beckwith started "dusting him off" with his white painter's cap.

The Sheriff cut a few steps as Lum "dusted him" with his painter's cap. The Sheriff was as light on his feet as moonbeams dancing on a lily-pool, and he had tremendous ingenuity for on-the-spot improvisations, for effervescent embellishments of ordinary time-steps.

After his brief solo, the Sheriff bowed to Lum, stretching his right hand in the gesture that said: "It's your turn now, Lum." While Lum lacked the twinkling toes and scintillating feet of the High Sheriff, he danced with his whole body, from his ears to his toe-nails. Quite literally, his whole body shook wibbled and wobbled, as if it were jelly on a plate. He almost staggered as he danced. He was sober, all right enough, but the way he gyrated made strangers think he was about to topple.

After Lum did a fairly short stint, a sample, cries went up all through the crowd for Tom Sampson, the shoemaker. "Where's Tom? Give us Tom. Let's have it for Tom-Tom."

Tom was hardly able to get out the front door of his shoe shop, for the press of the crowd, but when the cries, the ancient tocsin arose, he was passed over the circle, literally, into the middle of the street. I couldn't count the pairs of hands that held 'Tom aloft and then passed him to yet another pair of hands. It was as if a precious canoe were being hauled gently over-land to be launched in a purling river.

Tom landed on his feet, cat-like, reached into the big pocket of his apron, came out with a small paper sack from which he poured sand onto the street. Someone yelled: "How'd you like your ride, Tom?"

"I feel like the man who was tarred, feathered and ridden out of town on a pole. He said, 'If it weren't for the honor of the thing, I'd just as soon walk'."

So saying, he cut a few steps, soft-shoe, on the sand he had dumped on the street. The sounds were the same contagious sounds a snare-drummer makes with a brush. I suppose Tom got the idea for the sand-dance format from Eddie Foy, the great vaudevillian, who made it famous throughout the nation. But Tom's execution was always effective. There was something almost sensual, almost hypnotic, about the sounds of shoe-leather and grains of sand.

The three men joined, with arms around each other's

backs, to do some spirited cakewalks. Ramsay Davis collected three hats and he held the hats up, one at a time, for each of the three cakewalkers to kick. The hat that Tom kicked was held a little higher than the one Lum kicked, and the one the Sheriff kicked was held a little higher than the one Tom kicked. The Sheriff was the highest, most graceful kicker I ever saw.

Mr. Ed Settle, as he had done on previous occasions, quietly dispatched someone to Bengough's to buy a new sailor straw hat, the hard type, with the colorful bands, worn by Fred Astaire in the movies, and he sent someone else to the bakery for a devil's food cake, with white icing.

Mr. Ed pitched the hat to Papa, and Papa held the hat, at arm's length, and almost head-high. Mr. Hutchins had put on "At A Georgia Camp-Meeting," the immortal cakewalk song. When the trio had sashshayed up and down, smartly executing right and left flank movements in cakewalk music time, the Sheriff smashed the crown of the brand new sailor hat with his right foot. Then Mr. Ed handed Papa the cake, and Papa presented the cake to the Sheriff, with a brief ceremonial speech. Papa quoted one of his favorite passages from Shakespeare, the lines from *The Winter's Tale* that say:

When you do dance, I wish you
A wave of the sea, that you might ever do
Nothing but that.

Papa concluded with a compliment that may not have been original, but I can't recall that I ever heard it before or since: "A good and useful man is as tall as the tape measure says, plus the height of his home community and the admiration of his all-weather friends.

"Ladies and gentlemen, using that measure I find our

friend and benefactor, Matthew Venable, stretches from the Atlantic Ocean to the Blue Ridge Mountains, plus six feet and three ax-handles."

(The late John Tasker Howard, and other musical experts, declared "At A Georgia Camp-Meeting" to be the first bona fide ragtime tune. This tune, by Kerry Mills, was published in 1897, but it endures today, and it has many interpolations and appropriations. Of course, the word "ragtime" derives from the clog-dancing of blacks, often referred to as "ragging." Ragtime music was marked by strong syncopations in the treble — that is, making a strong beat weak, and weak beat strong — while the bass maintained a rigidly even rhythm. A type of syncopation had appeared in earlier tunes, such as Dan Emmett's "Old Dan Tucker," but the application of syncopation against a steady bass rhythm did not appear until Mill's tune of 1897, not insofar as I can ascertain.

(Mill's lyrics visualized a Georgia revival, a camp-meeting, at which the younger worshippers, despite solemn sermons, hired a brass band and put on a contest wherein the best shufflers, the winning couple, got a chocolate cake. The dancing contest mortified the preacher and the austere deacons, but ere the gallivanting music ended, the Sanhedrin was doing the cake-walk, too. Mills (1869-1948) wrote many other hits, among them such perennial dazzlers as "Meet Me In St. Louis, Louis" and "Red Wing."

(The late Rupert Hughes, popular author, biographer of George Washington, and uncle of wealthy Howard Hughes, said in 1899, "If ragtime were called 'tempo di raga' it might win honors more speedily. Ragtime will find its way gradually into the works of some great genius and will thereafter be canonized." Hughes's prophecy found culmination in the symphonic-jazz of men such as George Gershwin.)

Clog dancing, like dry grass catching fire from the sparks of a passing locomotive, erupted all around the vast circle on College Street. The pianola rambled and zoomed full-speed, but much head-to-head clogging was done to the patting of the hands and the stomping of the feet of enthusiastic on-lookers.

The faster the patting and the stomping, the faster was the dance beat. And as always, dancers yelled to their adherents, "Pat me fast" or "Pat me slow," depending upon whether they excelled at tap or soft-shoe rhythms.

Several hats were passed, and some money — I think slightly in excess of $12.00 — was collected as a grand prize for the man who could dance down all other men. The Sheriff didn't compete for the prize, because of his star, his official dignity, and because of his tremendous physical advantage.

One of the leading contestants was a corset salesman from Danville, Virginia. I suppose, by this time, he sold girdles, too, but he was known as "Mr. Madame X," Madame X being the name of a celebrated brand of corset which he had sold to the local dry goods stores for a number of years. While "Mr. Madame X's" personal acquaintanceship was pretty well limited to the merchants of Oxford, virtually everyone in town knew him by sight.

He wore the "city slicker" raiment that attached to drummers of the previous generation: celluloid collars, paper cuffs, a large, gaudy, imitation diamond stick-pin, a coat with the big, bright stripes worn by carnival barkers, peg-leg pants, and high-buttoned yellow-shoes, severely pointed at the toes. And he kept some kind of celluloid tooth-pick in his mouth continuously. He twirled the tooth-pick around with his mouth, teeth, and tongue as dexterously as a drum major handles a baton.

He came to Oxford several times each year, and whenever he alighted from the train he marched up town whistling, loudly, "Has Anybody Here Seen Kelly," "K-E-double-L-Y." And the way "Mr. Madame X" whistled I could always imagine he was actually spelling out, "K-E-double-L-Y."

Merchants could hear "Mr. Madame X" whistling before he ever reached the business section. They knew he was in town, and Mr. Bengough and other dry goods merchants would look to see if they needed anything in the line of "unmentionables."

"Mr. Madame X" was as lean and as wiry as the metal band around a barrel, but his yellow, curly hair was a diadem to him. He kept it smeared copiously with smelly pomades. It was said that Mr. Parsons, our local blind man, tipped his hat to "Mr. Madame X," thinking he was a "lady of pleasure."

He combed his hair everytime he took off his derby, and grease splattered around as if someone were cooking sausage. Papa had a strong, if unnatural, antipathy for "Mr. Madame X." Papa said, "I don't trust any man who combs his hair in public. I wouldn't cash his check for two dollars in Confederate money."

Papa also had an aspersion for men who had nick-names such as Pal, Buddy, Sport, and Kid. In all the years he practiced law I never knew him to let a man sit on a jury if he combed his hair in public or had a "cute" nick-name.

And I admit I share Papa's bias, and I've implemented it a bit. I have few rules of conduct, but I never play cards with a man who is called "Doc." I never eat at any place called "Mom's" or "Pop's." And I have never slept with a woman if I thought her own problems exceeded mine.

When the dance-down contest began, "Mr. Madame X" cut a couple of nimble strides, the way Jimmy Cagney did in the movies. Then he settled down to some soft-shoe stuff, what was known as "cutting the razz-a-ma-tazz."

Tom Sampson was a genuine devotee of class. He didn't go in for endurance; and Lum Beckwith, after the initial didoes, left the street to get a bottle.

After about thirty minutes the contest got down to two, or three to be precise: "Mr. Madame X" and Hughie and Hector Scott, the identical twins. It was told for the truth that their own mother was never positive which boy was which unless they bared their middles. Hughie had a big belly button and Hector had a very small belly button.

"Mr. Madame X" danced over near the "Ivanhoe" and the Scotts were over nearer the music store. "Mr. Madame X" didn't know the twins were spelling each other. One would dance awhile and when he tired, he'd shuffle next to the crowd.. Then he'd fade into the crowd and his brother would dance out into the big ring.

Ever so often, one or the other of the twins would feign near-exhaustion, and "Mr. Madame X," hoping to put his opponent down for the count, would yell, "The ragging's on." This meant a fast beat. Each dancer had to match the most spirited efforts of his competitor.

But, obviously, it was "Mr. Madame X" who began to wilt. He shucked his coat and then his vest. He tossed away his derby and his detachable celluloid collar and tie. The top of his yellow shirt was open and his chest glistened with sweat.

Neither of the Scotts removed any clothing. I remember they wore matching blue serge suits, white shirts, and black string ties. Each wore a hard sailor straw, with a blue and white band. And Hughie had an impish way of cutting-the-buck with both hands on his hips.

On and on it went. Two or three more mouth-organ virtuosos joined the first one, and the patters and stompers who were attending the Scotts increased their tempo.

312

The ultimate result was predictable when "Mr. Madame X" called for "Three O'Clock In The Morning," a waltz, a slow tune. He had to slow down or fall down, but he did well with his soft shoe, even if he didn't cut any wide arcs.

When the harp players were practically blowing with one lip, it seemed to me the Scott twins got their second, or, maybe, their tenth wind. Hughie raised his hand for a faster beat, and he could hardly be seen (or was it Hector) for the dust he was kicking. "Mr. Madame X" fell, kerplunk, in the middle of the street. One minute his feet were in motion. He was cutting a slow caper. Then he stopped, stock-still, as if he were a clock whose hands were at high noon. He leaned a bit, a human Tower of Pisa, held his leaning posture a few seconds, and then went blam, as if a tree had been whacked down.

Mr. Matson told his old friends: "Anybody could tell that fellow's got no gizzum, but what do you expect of some indecent bastard who goes around making a living a selling of ladies' corsets?"

After the Scott twins collected their tainted prize money they carried poor "Mr. Madame X" to one of the benches in front of Bengough's. His yellow shoes looked as if they had been through every briar patch in the county.

He didn't stir one whit while the Scott boys were carrying him. I didn't think he was even breathing, but Dr. Henley finally found his pulse, about the way that I imagine Stanley found Livingstone or Peary found the North Pole.

One of the Scott's made a pillow of his coat, shirt, and vest. His derby hat rested on his motionless belly, and his tie fluttered at the end of the bench, a banner of complete defeat and surrender. While he was lying hors de combat, Mr. Haskins, the depot agent, told the Sheriff that "Mr. Madame X" had a through-ticket to Goldsboro, that he was

313

supposed to catch the "ten somep'n train" that night.

Mr. Haskins sent to the depot for a baggage-truck, and when it got to College Street several men picked up "Mr. Madame X" and placed him on the flat, unclosed truck bed. Two or three others grabbed the enormous wooden tongue, and off they went, to the depot. A couple of the harp blowers got on the back end of the baggage-truck. They rode along, blowing "Didn't He Ramble," as they swung their legs in time to the music. I never knew if this was a tribute to defeated valor, or whether the harmonica virtuosos just got on because they had a chance to ride somewhere.

Just as the baggage-truck was leaving, up drove "King of the Green Snakes" Imboden with a two-horse wagon load of his marvelously succulent watermelons.

As I have said, he was brother to Just Plain Snake Imboden. I think Mr. Matson published Just Plain Snake's unabridged biography one day when he said: "I hope his ma and pa enjoyed it when they got Snake. If they didn't, then it was wasted."

The "King" was altogether different. He smelled, eternally, of the rich, warm soil. All of the poems, songs, and foot-notes of ten thousand suns, winds, and rains were written on his face and hands. His face was beautifully wrinkled, from time and weather, and also from loud laughter and gentle mirth. His face was an open letter of recommendation from the soil that gave him birth. If nature had a million mysterious doors and locks, he had the right key for every one of them, or so we believed steadfastly in Oxford.

His hands were magic trowels that always found the secret pulse of the earth. He predicted the weather more accurately than the *Old Farmer's Almanac*, and everyone knew the *Almanac* was the same as a telegram from St.

314

Peter. He could look at the sky at Easter morning and tell what the weather would be on July 4.

People stopped him to learn what to plant, and how and when to plant it. And he was his own shining testimonial. His tomatoes were as big as Caswell County and as rich as rubies. His corn was sweeter than a river of sorghum. And if melons were grown in heaven, surely, the angels looked at the "King's" patch before they planted their own.

He had a life-long, active, highly intimate love-affair with the good earth, and there was never one tiny lover's quarrel. The "King" never talked for publication, but, ever so often, the thrilling rapture and sweep of his love-affair with the earth spilled from his heart and lips the way sap rises in a tree.

Intermittently he'd strike his hands together in joyous amazement to declare: "The soil's the only really true and beautiful sweetheart there is for me, and I wish I was worthy to be wedded to her." So saying he would smile, look all around, and say, almost with a tremor in his voice: "Merciful God, the earth is just one ever-lasting, sweet-tasting dee-light."

When the "King" drove up with his load of water-melons, some of the volunteer firemen, who were also members of the "Silver Cornet Band," had fetched their instruments. A few had put on their band uniforms, the red coats, with big, brass buttons, and with the golden braid that frolicked around like yellow pansies, the gray britches, with yellow stripes up the sides, and the red caps, with yellow plumes and with long, military visors.

Some were in their working clothes. I remember Boot Ransome, blacksmith and champion chrysanthemum grower, came up in the crumpled stove-pipe hat he always wore in his forge. He was wearing his leather apron. I suppose his shirt was still on its peg in the forge because his wide suspenders were stretched across the heavy underwear he wore winter and summer. As noted previously, Mr. Ransome's instrument was the violin, but he played the brass drum in the "Silver Cornet Band."

Whenever the band marched, Matt Venable made Lum Beckwith carry the big bass drum. The Sheriff strapped the drum to Lum's back, and Boot Ransome walked just behind, swinging his drum-sticks. Sometimes when Lum stumbled to the right or to the left, or when he blundered out of reach of the drum-sticks, Old Boot would give Lum a mild konk on the head, with a drum-stick, to get him back in line.

While some of the band members were standing around tooting or beating somewhat furtively on their instruments, the cry went up: "On to the Commons for the night."

The band struck up "El Capitan," and, headed by the leader, or drum-major, Matt Venable, started marching to the Commons. By this time P. L. Carson had fixed the motor on the hearse. P. L. put the hearse in the marching line, behind the "King's" wagon of watermelons. The hearse was to give extra light at the Commons. There were no electric lights on the Commons, save for two or three street lights — Japanese lanterns were put in trees and on bushes for special occasions.

I am sure as many as two hundred adults and children followed the band to the Commons. I suppose a stranger, seeing the hearse, might have assumed we were having a New Orleans funeral.

By the time the entourage reached the post office, down on Main Street, Pete Wood put the fire truck in the parade. The truck would help the hearse furnish extra lighting on the Commons.

Other band members caught the parade along the line of march. I remember Mr. Crabtree, insurance agent and trom-

316

bone player, still had his supper napkin tucked into his collar when he swung into line, and I remember that Mr. Evans, watchmaker and glockenspiel player, was so excited he ran from his supper table to the marching band without his instrument.

When the procession turned the corner at Spottswood Street there must have been five hundred adults and children, including the musicians, and those on the hearse and the fire truck. I never knew whose idea it was, but the band stopped in front of Miss Texanna's house. The musicians faced the house, and the Sheriff led them in a rousingly poignant, if somewhat uneven, rendition of "Let Me Call You Sweetheart." Miss Texanna and P. A. came out on the front porch. I expected P. A. to construe the serenade as some sort of denigration of womanhood. I was prepared to see her affix her right thumb to her nose and then flag her fingers at the crowd. I was surprised and pleased when she curtsied, prettily, charmingly, and disarmingly.

She took her mother's hand, and both bowed to the musicians and to the crowd. Old Man Rufe was on the wagon seat with the "King of the Green Snakes." He was well into his habitual pre-supper stupor. I don't think he knew where he was. Anyway, he started bellowing "Hurrah for William Jennings Bryan." Then he stood, with the "King's" help, and flailed his rapier, or his walking-stick, at all the imaginary dastards who were trying to do in the "working-girl."

The musicians fell in with Old Man Rufe's nightly charade, and they faced back to the street and marched on towards the Commons blasting away at "Heaven Will Protect the Working-Girl."

Just about everyone who could walk and lived on Spotswood, or in the adjoining area, followed in the procession. Many folks were already at the Commons when the "Silver

Cornets" took their seats in the combination bandstand and summer-house.

The "King" put several armfuls of luscious green snakes in Springs No. 1, 3, and 5. He had picked the melons when drops of dew were silver angels dancing all over the greenery. Then he had buried them in the soil, to keep them cool, until he brought the load to Oxford.

The band gave a short concert while the melons were getting good and cold, while people waited for full darkness for dancing on the luscious grass of the Commons, and while Boot Ransome made the lemonade.

I am sure he had made the lemonade for every Sunday School picnic held by every church in Oxford for thirty years. And the Lord only knows how many incredibly savory gallons of lemonade he made for receptions, cake--cuttings, family reunions, and assorted outings. "Boot Ransome" was unutterably synomous with quality "lemonade" in Oxford, just as much so as Babe Ruth and home runs or Martelle and brandy were hyphenated.

The first two or three dances of the evening were waltzes. I must say Papa and Mother cut a fine, a glowing figure. Both loved to dance, and they seemed to cast a single shadow as they waltzed to the music that night on the Commons. Ever so often one or the other whispered some remark. I suppose the furtive snatches of words had some kind of intimate connotations. Everytime either of them whispered, both smiled as if they shared some rapturous secret light years beyond the ken of other mortals. The obvious contagion of this secret sharing reminded me of a line I learned from Proverbs in Sunday School:

Stolen waters are sweet, and bread eaten in secret is pleasant.

Perhaps Papa was thinking of two lines he liked from old Christopher Marlowe:

My men, like satyrs grazing on the lawns,
Shall with their goat feet dance an antic hay.

("Antic" was the old word in England for ancient, and "hay" was a country dance. Apparently "antic day" was old in Marlowe's time (1564-1593). Of course, Aldous Huxley acquired the title of one of his earliest novels, *Antic Hay*, from Marlowe's poem.)

Papa was fond, too, of a brief passage from "Richard III:"

He campers nimbly in a lady's chamber
To the lascivious pleasing of a lute.

Mother always pretended to be embarrassed, especially by the word "lascivious," but I thought her blushes came more from titillation than from shock.

Most of the courting couples and the younger married couples chatted or sparked around on the sidelines as they waited for the faster music to begin. Before the night was over, we had some of almost every kind of dancing extant — waltzes, reels, square dances, two-stepping, and the "Big Bounce."

There were many skits by various individuals during the short intermissions while the band rested and took light or heavy refreshments. Miss Birdie, our piano and voice teacher, our diva, sang several solos, just as she always did whenever a crowd collected.

She was never prepared to sing, although she always just happened to have her music with her. She reminded me of the old song called "The Preacher and the Bear:"

319

A preacher went a-hunting,
Twas on a Sunday morn,
Although twas agin his religion,
He took his gun along.

Actually, Miss Birdie was one of the most effete, self-effacing people whom I've ever known. Nonetheless, she responded everytime to such arm-twisting as was necessary, or decorous, to get her to sing. In this respect she was a bit like the politician who runs for office when he really doesn't want to make the race. Once, it seemed as if no one would file for mayor of office, at a particular local election. Captain Wade had· an editorial in the *Torchlight* about his alarming situation. When Papa saw Captain Wade on the street, Papa smiled and told him: "Don't fret, Captain. Some patriot is certain to make the sacrifice."

Miss Birdie announced each song just before she sang it: "I will render 'O, Promise Me,' by Reginald De Koven." A few drunks wondered, out loud, just what it was that Miss Birdie was rendering to old Reggie, but the women on the Commons knew the lyrics by heart. Most of them had their handkerchiefs ready before Miss Birdie reached the heart-rending stanza:

See-ing the vis-ion of our para-dise,
Hear-ing God's mess-age while the or-gan rolls
It's might-ty mu-sic to our ver-ry souls;
No less per-fect than a life with thee-ee,
O prom-ise me, Oh, prom-ise me.

Mrs. Piano Hutchins sat in her big, over-stuffed chair — Piano had brought it that night on the music store truck — her tears rolling virtually in time with Miss Birdie's tiny, pear-shaped notes.

All the women knew "When The Robins Nest Again," by someone named Frank Howard, followed "O, Promise Me." Most of the women hardly checked their tears. I suppose this saved them the trouble of tuning up again:

Life seems so bright when in thought I'm with you,
Come love, hast-en, come back to me;
We'll build our nest when the rob-ins nest in spring-time,
Donald re-turn, re-turn, love, to me.

Everyone, or virtually everyone, already knew Donald was lost at sea. When I first heard Miss Birdie sing this song, when I was just a shaver, I tied Donald in with the sinking of the *Titanic*. I thought Donald was Miss Birdie's husband. In my child's mind I had her down as a widow, all because of the song.

When I got to high school and began reading American novels, Papa told me that Theodore Dreiser was booked to sail on the *Titanic*, but the powerful novelist was horsing around with a woman and missed the *Titanic*. Papa said Dreiser caught another ship, the *Kroonland*. Papa who really applauded Dreiser's realism, was delighted he missed the *Titanic*, but when I was in college and waded through all of Dreiser's incredible prolixity, I wasn't so sure:

Last night in a dream I saw Donald's proud ship at sea,
And I felt that my heart's dear love,
Could nev-er, nev-er come back to me.
But spring-time and rob-ins will come,
And with them the brav-est of men,
For his very last words to me were:
Dar-ling I'll meet you, meet you,
When rob-ins nest a-gain.

Miss Birdie always closed her concert with "The Last Rose of Summer," by Tom Moore. And her encore, whether or not there was any demand for an encore, was "Curtsy," by Clara Belle Simmons:

A soft little zephyr came blow-ing,
Just break-ing the morn-ing's re-pose;
The rose made a bow to the lily,
The lily she bowed to the rose.
And then in a faint little whis-per,
As faint as the per-fume that blows:
'You're sweet-er than I,' said the lily,
'You're fair-er than I,' said the rose.

Miss Birdie probably sang at a thousand weddings, funerals, parties, musicales, and cake-cuttings, but she never caught the bride's bouquet. She was invited to everything anyone ever had in Oxford, but she was always far more guest than company.

She was pretty, as I recall her, in a prim, unadorned way, like a daisy that stands to one side while all the other flowers turn somersaults in the warm, southern breeze.

Papa referred to Miss Birdie as "our ungathered rose." She was pretty enough and intelligent enough, as a young girl, but her father found all suitors unworthy. Each time he said they would wait for the right man, the man who really deserved young Miss Birdie. But, like Donald in the song, Lochinvar never made it to Oxford.

Papa liked, maybe loved, Miss Birdie, and he felt sorry for her without being maudlin about his pity. Frequently, he likened Miss Birdie to the dear, unmarried lady in Oliver Wendell Holmes's poem, "My Aunt." There are six or seven long stanzas, and Papa could say the whole poem by heart.

I can't do that. But I remember Papa's jocular sort high-handedness when he said:

My aunt! my dear unmarried aunt!
Long years have o'er her flown;
Yet still she strains the aching clasp
That binds her virgin zone;
I know it hurts her, though she looks
As cheerful as she can;
Her waist is ampler than her life,
For life is but a span.

In the following lines Holmes tells how his aunt was braced against a board, had her feet pinched, her hair singed and screwed with pins. Then when she was completely ravishing, her father got out his gun to keep some rascal from stealing her:

What could this lovely creature do
Against a desperate man?

Papa had to blink back a tear when he said the poem's conclusion:

Alas! no chariot, not barouche,
Not bandit cavalcade,
Tore from the trembling arms
His all-accomplished maid.
For her how happy had it been!
And heaven had spared to me
To see one sad, ungathered rose
On my ancestral tree.

Miss Birdie had the first electric car in town, a Griswold

Phaeton, and she operated it long, long after all of the other early cars were junk. She had to have the battery charged after every fifty miles, but she went around the world in fifty miles, anyway. This car had only one door, and it reminded me of a square plug of black tobacco on four shaky wheels. The body reminded me of the super-structure of the *Merrimac*, in the history book. I couldn't tell the front from the back, but the way Miss Birdie drove, that was hard to do, anyway. On the wall by the door was a vase for flowers, and Miss Birdie kept the vase filled with roses, violets, holly, or whatever was available.

When she turned the corner from Spottswood into Main, raking Mrs. Pettigrew's fence on one side of the street and chipping away at Mr. Bengough's iron fawn on the other side, someone always yelled, "Miss Birdie, Miss Birdie."

Then the shout went up town, the way a baton might be passed. Even the dumbest chicken in Oxford feared to cross the street when the tocsin went up. From the frantic way we cleared Main Street a stranger would assume the Tuscarora were on the war-path.

Yet, she had only two slight accidents, in about forty years of highly dramatic driving and careening. Once she hit a pile of watermelons the "King" had built into a mound on the courthouse lawn. The grass looked as if the "Bloody Angle" at Spotsylvania had been refought, but dozens of people picked up luscious chunks of watermelon, just as the Israelites picked up manna in the wilderness.

Another time, Miss Birdie bumped into Mr. Matson. He was drunk and riding his stick horse. Maybe, he was a snake, charming our thrush. Miss Birdie and the Phaeton made a bee-line for him as he leaned there in front of the "Ivanhoe," with one foot in the gutter and the other on the sidewalk. When she was twenty-five yards away, she started screaming, "Look out, Mr. Matson. Look out, Mr. Matson."

324

Matson."

She screamed her warnings until she bumped him, tail over shoulders, and she continued to yell until she hit the mail-box in front of Bengough's. When the Phaeton bounced off the mail-box, Miss Birdie was still yelling, "Watch out, Mr. Matson." The old man looked up from the gutter and said slowly: "Damit, Miss Birdie, you ain't coming back, are you?"

She smoked Fatima cigarettes. They had a strong Turkish tobacco scent, and the Griswold Electric Phaeton reminded me of some sort of Moorish temple exuding incense. The way she smoked couldn't have hurt her voice. Papa told me Miss Birdie began smoking in the great days of the suffragists, just before World War I. With her, smoking was a blue banner of defiance, a smoky taper for women's liberation. Frequently, some smart-alecky boy, some lout totally bereft of manners, would yell, "Hey, Miss Birdie, your tooth pick's on fire."

She would puff some aromatic blue magic and say, softly, "Sticks and stone. Sticks and stones."

There were many other solo attractions that night. One of the Tulgin kids said "The Boy Stood On the Burning Deck," and Mr. Shelton, the Western Union operator said the alphabet backwards. (The sentence, "The quick brown fox jumped over the lazy dog's back" was used generally back then to check out a typewriter. It contains all of the letters of the alphabet. However, Mr. Shelton came up with a new sentence, one that also contains all of the letters of the alphabet: "A quick movement of the enemy would jeopardize six gunboats." The Lord only knows how many laborious hours Mr. Shelton spent making up this sentence. But Papa said, "Good Lord, Willie. Must you obliterate the rustic, the simple pastoral and bring in rampant militarism, just to test a typewriter?)

About train time, someone — I think it was Sheriff Matt Venable — remembered poor Mr. Madame X, all laid out on that baggage truck. A fairly large contingent went to the depot to see about the drummer. Someone found his sample case of corsets, back up town, and several others lifted him onto the day coach. Someone fixed two buckets of Epsom Salts water for his lacerated feet, and the "King" sliced a melon for him to eat on the train. When the conductor saw all of the junk, he threw a tizzy: "This ain't no damn zoo train. Get all that junk out of here."

The Sheriff gave the conductor the kind a smile a man gives when he checks four aces. "All right, Captain Elwood. We'll do as you say, but if you can't haul our sick visitor and his necessary equipment, I'll just give his ticket to Old Man Rufe Duncan."

Captain Elwood, the conductor, threw both hands into the air, in abject surrender. But Old Man Rufe was already seated, anxiously awaiting his trip to Goldsboro. "All right, Cap'n. Git them damn loafers off'n here so us passengers can continue our journey." Then he reached up and tried to pull the cord, the emergency chain, by which conductors used to signal engineers. There was more difficulty getting Old Man Rufe off than there was putting poor "Mr. Madame X" on the train.

Before the older folks finished their waltzing that night, Boot Ransome had several wooden tubs in a neat line around Spring No. 2. Other folks might use large galvanized iron tubs to make quantities of lemonade, but Boot said that was worse than mixing venerable brandy with ginger ale. He always put a little grapejuice in his lemonade, just enough to give the mixture a royal purple color, just enough to impart the sweet kiss of the grape to the tartness of the lemon.

He squeezed every lemon with his own hands, just as if

he were milking God Almighty's favorite cow and wanted to get every precious drop and still not bruise a single teat. He let the sugar slide into the tubs from his right hand so slowly you could almost count the crystals, and each crystal seemed to be sucked down as if an angel were being claimed by lovely, celestial quick-sand. I always got the distinct impression some secular priest was dropping white rose petals for some special benediction. He went from tub to tub slowly stirring with a long-handled dipper, stirring the loving, meticulous way Titian must have mixed paints. At each tub he took a few, meditative sips. It was almost as if he gargled, soundless, with his sensitive lips. Indeed, he might have been taking communion. His face, furrowed as a field of deep-plowed red clay, was beatific when he announced, quietly: "Fuss-strate. She'll do."

When the mixture didn't suit him, he shook his head the way Newton might have done if the apple had gone up or sideways. But he swallowed manfully, just as Socrates downed the hemlock: "The sours got the big-head," he would say. Or, "Too sweet. Too much bride and not enough groom." Then he measured, poured, added, and subtracted until the batch met his requirements. When the batch was up to his standard, he nodded to his assistants and said, almost inaudibly: "Jine her to the t'other. She graduates."

I never saw Mr. Ransome in terms of Longfellow's barrel-chested smith. I think he was in his late fifties. He was about five ten and he weighed 160 pounds. He never tried to bend any horseshoes with his hands, unlike most of the other blacksmiths, and he never went around bragging about how many times he had been kicked and trampled by horses and mules.

His hair was long and black. Some folks said he put lamp-black on his hair, but Papa didn't believe the rumor.

Unlike today's professional hippie, Mr. Ransome kept his long, black hair combed back. It lay in a great, neat pile on his neck almost at shoulder length, much in the style of the American Indian.

He trimmed his own hair with scissors. I saw him, a few times, trimming a bit from the top and the sides, and I can see him now, in pleasant retrospect, holding a fistful of the long hair on his neck with his left hand, behind his head, as the scissors snipped away, behind his neck, in his right hand.

However, he had no such antipathy for barbers as Old Man Rufe professed. Actually he and "Sir William Osler," or Bill Ricks, were pretty good friends. Papa said Mr. Ransome just couldn't stand the loose, sadistic talk that permeated the barber shop all too often. Anyway, it amuses me, wryly, today when I remember that Oxford's first unvarnished long-hair was the village smithy.

When Mr. Ransome wasn't working in his forge, or tending his flowers, or making lemonade for someone else to drink, he sat in a cane-bottom chair in front of his shop. I remember the chair as being tilted, perpetually, against the wall. The ends of the chair barely touched the wall, and I always expected the chair and Mr. Ransome to fall, the way the Roman Empire fell.

He spent much of his spare time reading the *Idylls of the Kings.* He and Papa talked about Camelot as other men spoke of Durham or Raleigh. He had a yellow dog named "Lance." Everyone, Mr. Ransome included, called this big yellow dog "Lance," but Papa told me a piece of privileged communication: The dog's true Christian name was Lancelot. No one else in Oxford ever knew this, and I have never revealed the fact until this precise moment.

I understood, from Papa, that Mr. Ransome's formal education was almost negligible. An orphaned boy, he was apprenticed to a blacksmith at the age of twelve or thirteen. Apparently, no one guided him in his reading. When I knew him, he must have subscribed to every flower magazine of which he had knowledge.

The novels and narrative poems of Sir Walter Scott compelled many of his leisure hours, and in his sleeping quarters, adjoining the forge, were copies of several dozen books. I remember seeing copies of *Little Women, Ivanhoe, The Hoosier School Master, Meh Ley, Surry of Eagle's Nest, Swallow Barn, Mecaria, Georgia Scenes, The Four Million,* and *Rob Roy.*

In his years as an apprentice, he kept to himself. Indeed, he lacked the money to go anywhere, even if he had desired entertainment and human companionship. And in the thirty-odd years that he was a blacksmith in Oxford, he hardly ever left the forge save for band practice and concerts and when he was asked to make the lemonade for special occasions.

Papa lent him books, as did "Brer" Thompson. Mother sent him her issues of *Better Homes and Gardens*, once she looked at them. I always carried these magazines down to the forge, and I remember, too, carrying him copies of *Kim, Just So Stories,* and *Miss Minerva and William Green Hill.*

One could say, with complete impunity, that Mr. Ransome emerged from his years of semi-isolation a well-read man, comparably speaking, the same as Edmund Dantes, in *The Count of Monte Cristo*, came from twelve years imprisonment as a well-read man. Indeed, Papa lent Mr. Ransome *The Count of Monte Cristo* and several Dumas novels.

Ever so often, when Papa was the host for Sans Souci, he asked Mr. Ransome to be a guest, to partake of the fellowship. The smith was grateful for the compliment

329

implied, but he always made some excuse. His world was populated by animals and flowers. When he was with several people, his eyes reflected the torment of the hunted and haunted hare.

And in all of my life I've ever known anyone who was so painfully shy in the presence of women. It was torture, some kind of nameless terror and infamy. His whole face turned ripe persimmon pink down in the deepest furrows on his neck. He acted as if he were standing on active land-mines.

If there was no possible way to avoid a confrontation, he looked at the ground, as if his neck were broken, while the toes of his Congress gaiters pecked the earth until it looked as if many chickens had scratched for worms.

I was sitting with him, sitting rather than talking, one day when P. A. Duncan rode up to the forge on Big Bill. She thought one of Big Bill's front shoes was loose. She alighted and stood holding the reins as Boot Ransome kneeled on the ground and gently lifted Big Bill's foot. Suddenly, Big Bill emitted a tremendous puddle of steaming water.

Boot wheeled, never looked back, mumbled something completely incoherent, and fled into his sleeping quarters.

P. A. gave Big Bill a wallop with her riding-crop: "You filthy, impolite bastard of a horse. You male miscreant, you."

I knew P. A. wasn't repelled by Big Bill's breach of decorum because she delighted if Big Bill "fed the sparrows" on Spottswood Street when she knew Mrs. Ashton-Brown and the Entwhistles were looking. Everytime this happened P. A. gave Mrs. Ashton-Brown and the Entwhistles a smile so saturated with innocent sweetness it could have been served on every battercake in town.

On hot afternoons, just as soon as the sun began to

strike his red tent, Mr. Ransome walked lightly, reverently, among his flower beds with a large sprinkling can. He reminded me more of a shepherd, or some ineffably vigilant mother, than a wrinkled man with a watering can. I certainly can't swear that he counted the drops he gave each flower, but if he thought one had been slighted he made amends, quickly, almost apologetically.

Some folks say he actually talked to his flowers. I don't know about that, but his lips moved, almost imperceptibly as he walked up and down, slowly, pouring water as if the pot held wet kisses.

I really think he talked to himself, to hear the thoughts of a good and useful man, and, thus, parenthetically, to the flowers. Perhaps, he shared, in little asides and soliloquies, his heart's desires with his precious plants.

His pansies, incredibly glorious explosions of dazzling colors, were the biggest I ever saw anywhere. I really thought the sum of creation's desire for immaculate loveliness had been captured eternally in old Boot's blue, white, and yellow pansies. The way he hovered over them in the filtering rays of twilight always made me think he was hearing the good-night prayers of little girls in Alice blue, or in white lace, or little boys in yellow overalls.

As I have said, he always won the blue ribbon at the annual chrysanthemum show, but he always feigned illness when the grand prize was awarded. Papa, or "Brer" Thompson accepted the blue ribbon for him.

Everytime I saw him water his chrysanthemums, pat the dirt around them, I almost expected him to take off his shoes, the way Moses did when he found himself on holy ground.

This ritual with the flowers occurred just before supper. He took only one meal, supper, away from the forge. He went to the "Inn," to Mrs. Jackson's for this meal. But he gave Lance, his dog, supper before he began the walk to Mrs. Jackson's. Seven evenings to a week, Mr. Ransome cooked a pan of pork-chops for Lance. The dog washed the pork-chops down with a bowl of buttermilk. I don't recall any other dog that drank buttermilk, but Mr. Ransome bought a gallon a week, for Lance, just as he bought pork-chops regularly for his pet.

At Mrs. Jackson's he always sat in the far corner, right by the swinging door that opened to the kitchen. Everyone in Oxford knew that was "Boot Ransome's chair." No particular point was made about the chair, the special place by the kitchen door, after Mr. Ransome left Oxford permanently, but, insofar as I know, not a living soul ever sat in the chair so long as Mrs. Jackson lived and operated the dining room.

Mr. Ransome went to the state penitentiary a couple of years after the big night on the Commons. One night, Just Plain Snake Imboden got crazy drunk and rode a horse through the flowers. Mr. Ransome bashed "Snake's" head with his big hammer. He killed "Snake" instantaneously.

In court, Papa pulled all the stops for old Boot. Papa touched all the bases: "It was justifiable homicide induced with violent and sudden passion, triggered by the heinous outrages of a fiend incarnate."

In asking the judge for mercy, Papa said he was sure Mr. Ransome regretted his rash, if eminently justified, action. But Mr. Ransome arose, placed his big hand on Papa's shoulder gently, and said, softly, but with enormous feeling: "No sir. I knew what I was doing. I'd do it again. I meant to kill him, and I'm glad I killed the no-good son-of-a-bitch."

Then he sat down at the counsel table and cried. I knew he was crying for his poor flowers and not for himself. I knew he was thinking about those wondrous pansies Just

Plain Snake had destroyed.

He got a relatively short sentence, for second degree murder, but he lived only a few more years. Yet, his exile in prison must not have been vastly different from his exile in Oxford. If he wasn't happy in prison, as most of us reckon joy, his days were filled with tasks he liked best and did best: He had charge of all of the flowers on the lawn at the governor's mansion, and when the governor had parties that required lemonade, old Boot made it.

I was about grown when he died, when Papa and "Brer" Thompson, Mr. Ed Settle, and the Sheriff sent for his body. Papa told me he was sure old Boot would want me to help carry the coffin.

He didn't belong to any church and we held the service at the cemetery. I never saw as many fresh flowers at a funeral in my life, and I don't think there was a single design from the local florist. During the service "The King of the Green Snakes" Imboden stood off alone at one side of the crowd, as if, in some incomprehensible manner, his last name tied him to all of Mr. Ransome's troubles. But I think every man at the cemetery shook the "King's" hand after the service, and several, including Papa, "Brer" Thompson, and Mr. Ed Settle, hugged his old neck.

Boot lies over there, now, in that portion of the old cemetery with others whom life is supposed to have rejected. Miss Opal is just a few feet away, and Lum Beckwith, the dancing, singing housepainter, lies just below Mr. Ransome and Miss Opal. These graves are on a hill. From the hill, as one looks back toward Oxford, Old Man Rufe's "mossy-lee" looms in the mists like a truncated Grecian temple. They are all mourned by the same April rains and the same lonely January winds that grieve for all of the proper Christians, and for Mr. S. Blatz, too.

My mother, who is now in her eighty-fifth year, always

takes the first of her lustrous pansies to Mr. Ransome's grave. And she always has some fresh flowers, on this perennial visit, for Lum and for Miss Opal, too. I guess Mother never really held with whores and madames, but everytime she puts flowers on Miss Opal's grave she smiles and says to me, "I think your Papa would approve."

There's an element of danger in my going to that wind-swept hill in the old cemetery: A year or so ago when I looked down at Old Man Rufe's "mossy-lee" I twirled my hat in the air, and, almost inexplicably, hollered, "Hurrah for William Jennings Bryan."

If that happens again, and if I am detected, someone will swear I'm off my rocker.